To Johnston
"Bob" Johnston
with my compliments
and best wishes.

THROUGH
THE OVERCAST

ASSEN JORDANOFF

THROUGH THE OVERCAST

THE ART OF INSTRUMENT FLYING

By

ASSEN JORDANOFF

ILLUSTRATIONS BY

FRANK L. CARLSON AND FRED L. MEAGHER

FUNK & WAGNALLS COMPANY

NEW YORK AND LONDON

1938

CONTENTS

v

CLOUDY JOE MEETS THE GANG

INTRODUCTION

THE air ocean has been conquered completely and forever by the same type of man as explored and eventually conquered the high seas. Today, when air transportation is becoming more and more an everyday affair, we should not forget that it has been made possible only by years of pioneering effort on the part of the so-called "adventurers" of the air.

For a number of years there was apparently little chance that the airplane would ever become a rival of the older and firmly established agencies of transportation. Yet, while air transportation seems in the eyes of some to have made slow progress, you have only to compare it with developments in other fields to see how rapidly it has advanced. Until about ten years ago even the confirmed optimist thought that the practical application of aviation to travel was still merely a remote possibility. Today, air transportation is an accepted and accomplished fact.

The chief credit for this rapid advance in aviation belongs, not to any change in principle, but to better engineering methods. The general aerodynamic characteristics of the airplane are based upon the same principles that have existed since its inception; but improved design, the use of better materials, and a more extensive research in all branches directly or indirectly allied to aeronautical science have brought the "air carriage" our ancestors dreamed about to its present stage of perfection.

Present-day flying technique is comparatively new, particularly in connection with flights under adverse weather conditions. Such flights, undreamt-of a few years ago, are possible today because we have the tools to work with— an improved plane, a powerful engine, and precision instruments with which to control them. These instruments are based upon known physical laws, although to the uninitiated their operation seems nothing short of magic.

Since flights under adverse weather conditions can be executed only with the help of instruments and radio, it is absolutely essential that every airman become thoroughly familiar with these tools. With knowledge we conquer fear, and with knowledge we can cope more intelligently with the problems of flight as they confront us. And until we know how to fly under poor visibility and through the overcast with the same accuracy and safety that characterize "contact" flying, air transportation—military, scheduled or itinerant —will never be completely practicable.

Learning to control an airplane is a more or less simple matter, for plane, accessories and avigational aids are all man-made. But when you deal with the weather, which is neither man-made nor man-controlled, you are up against an entirely different problem. You cannot overcome the elements, nor reduce their violence, but you can learn the physical laws which govern their behavior. Once you have acquired this knowledge, you will no longer need to stare at the sky and wonder what causes this, that or the other phenomenon, or what effect it will have upon your flight. It is because weather, and a thorough understanding of weather, are so important to you in your flights that I have devoted so large a part of *Through the Overcast* to this subject. Throughout the discussion I have made every effort to reduce the apparently intangible aspects of the weather to pictorial representation.

Before we get into the book itself, I must introduce you to Cloudy Joe, who appears throughout the volume (for the very simple reason that he could not be kept out), and whose counterpart exists in every field of endeavor. His physical appearance is an exaggerated picture of his state of mind. He is enthusiastic and eager to learn, but I am afraid he will never be anything but a blunderer. Yet I am grateful to him, for he has taught me how a number of things ought *not* to be done. I remember following his example once, and spinning in from about 700 feet to hit the earth straight on the nose. It was not the speed with which I struck the ground, but the suddenness with which I stopped, that made everything go to pieces. I climbed out of what was left, but as I walked away from the wreckage there was no discernible difference between Cloudy Joe and me. Then, and many times since, I am afraid, we could have been taken for twins.

In preparing this volume I have been indebted to those listed below for their cooperation, and I wish to take this opportunity to express my gratitude to them. Their assistance has made it possible for me to complete *Through the Overcast* in its present form, and thus, I hope, to promote still further safety in flight.

C. R. Smith, *President*	American Airlines, Inc.,
Ralph S. Damon, *Vice President*	Chicago, Ill.
William Littlewood, *Vice President*	
Charles A. Rheinstrom, *Vice President*	
Karl S. Day	
Wilbur E. Pereira	
Arthur Caperton	
Dean C. Smith	
E. A. Cutrell	
Richard Goldsmith, *President*	B. G. Corporation,
George M. Paulson, *Chief Engineer*	New York, N. Y.
K. S. ("Slim") Lindsay	
R. W. Leedom	
Carl L. Bausch, *Vice President*	Bausch & Lomb Optical Co.,
Carl S. Hallauer, *Vice President*	Rochester, N. Y.
I. L. Nixon	
Gustave J. Husson	
R. H. Kruse, *President*	Cambridge Instrument Company, Inc.,
U. O. Hutton, *Chief Engineer*	New York, N. Y.
B. O. Watkins	
C. W. Campbell	
Captain Ermin L. Ray	New York, N. Y.
Helen Willyoung	Glen Rock, N. J.
Burdette S. Wright, *Vice President and General Manager*	Curtiss Aeroplane Division, Curtiss-Wright Corporation, Buffalo, N. Y.
Don R. Berlin, *Chief Engineer*	
Robert L. Earle	
William Crosswell	
P. H. Schneck	Curtiss Propeller Division, Curtiss-Wright Corporation, Buffalo, N. Y.
John H. Jouett	Hagerstown, Md.
Sherman M. Fairchild	Fairchild Aviation Corporation, New York, N. Y.
Richard H. Depew, Jr.	
Beckwith Havens	

LUCIEN L. FRIEZ, *Division Manager*
RALPH R. CHAPPELL, *Chief Engineer*

Julien P. Friez & Sons,
(Division of Bendix Aviation Corp.),
Baltimore, Md.

C. S. ("CASEY") JONES, *President*
LEE D. WARRENDER, *Vice President*
GEORGE A. VAUGHN, JR., *Treasurer*
RICHARD WHATHAM, *Vice President*

J. V. W. Corporation,
Newark, N. J.

PAUL KOLLSMAN, *President*
V. E. CARBONARA, *Chief Engineer*
CHARLES H. COLVIN
WESLEY C. BONN
ALAN G. BINNIE

Kollsman Instrument Company, Inc.,
Elmhurst, Long Island, N. Y.

EDWIN LINK, JR., *President*

Link Aviation Devices, Inc.,
Binghamton, N. Y.

W. T. PIPER, *President*
THEODORE V. WELD, *Vice President*
W. T. PIPER, JR., *Secretary*

Piper Aircraft Corporation,
Lock Haven, Pa.

DAVID S. LITTLE, *Manager Aviation Section*
S. J. GUSTOF

RCA Manufacturing Company, Inc.,
Camden, N. J.

FRANK E. MULLEN

Radio Corporation of America
New York, N. Y.

REGINALD E. GILLMOR, *President*
PRESTON R. BASSETT, *Vice President*
ROBERT B. LEA, *Vice President*
CYRIL K. WILDMAN
JUSTIN A. FITZ

Sperry Gyroscope Company, Inc.,
Brooklyn, N. Y.

ALBERT I. LODWICK, *President*

Stinson Aircraft Corporation,
Wayne, Mich.

LT.-COMMANDER P. V. H. WEEMS

Weems System of Navigation,
Annapolis, Md.

GEORGE CHAPLINE, *Vice President*
ARTHUR NUTT, *Vice President*
R. E. JOHNSON, *Chief Field Engineer*

Wright Aeronautical Corporation,
Paterson, N. J.

THE AUTHOR

THROUGH
THE OVERCAST

COURTESY of AMERICAN AIRLINES, INC.

CARLSON

CONTROL CABIN

xii

I

SIMPLICITY OF THE MODERN AIRCRAFT

A GLANCE at the control cabin shown on the opposite page will probably make you feel that it is a very complicated affair. But once you understand how it works, you will find that it is actually quite simple. Anything is complicated until you understand it. A typewriter is a bewildering set of gadgets to the novice, but the experienced typist taps out letters at high speed because he knows his machine so well that he no longer has to think about it. "But," you say, "there are one hundred and three gadgets shown in the picture; it *must* be complicated." Well, just look at a violin. It is simple—on the surface. But I wager that you will find learning to operate the control cabin of a plane much easier than learning how to be a virtuoso of the violin. It is not the number of parts that make a thing complicated or simple, but the difficulty or ease with which it can be mastered.

Here is a list of the various gadgets shown in the illustration. You will soon be so familiar with all of them that you can call them by name:

1. Cabin "fasten seat belt" switch
2. Propeller de-icer switch
3. Carburetor de-icer switch
4. Day and night frequency shift
5. Auxiliary receiver
6. Auxiliary receiver tuning knob
7. Transmitter filament switch
8. Local distance-cutting signal-volume switch
9. Frequency-shift warning light
10. Airport and beacon receiver change-over switch
11. Receiver switch
12. Electric panel light
13 & 14. Landing lights
15. Compass and gyro light reostat
16. Instrument panel light reostat
17. Airline receiver volume control
18. Electrical instrument control switch
19. Dial light for auxiliary receiver
20. Starter switch
21. Auxiliary receiver power switch
22. Volt ammeters
23. Lighter
24. Booster switch
25. Starter selection switch
26. Cabin sidelights switch
27. Cabin dome light switch
28. Pitot tube heater switch
29. Warning light switch
30. Running lights
31. Argonne spot lights
32. Instrument spot lights
33. Electric panel lights

34. Compass and gyro lights
35. Instrument light
36. Ignition switch
37. Beacon receiver tuning control
38. Windshield crank
39. Clock
40. Sperry gyropilot rudder control knob
41. Compass
42. Sperry bank and climb gyro
43. Spare light bulbs compartment
44. Gyropilot level-flight knob
45. Cambridge fuel analyzer
46. Window handcrank
47. Fuel pressure gauges
48. Clock
49. Sperry directional gyro
50. Cage knob for bank and climb gyro
51. Vacuum gauge for Sperry gyropilot
52. Gyropilot bank knob
53. Gyropilot climb knob
54. Vertical speed indicator
55. Sperry gyro-horizon
56. Oil pressure gauges
57. Oil and temperature gauges
58. Carburetor and temperature gauges
59. Primer
60. Cambridge exhaust gas analyzer junction box
61. Kollsman sensitive field-pressure altimeter
62. Turn and bank indicator
63. Gyro caging knob
64. Propeller pitch controls
65. Manifold pressure gauge
66. Throttles
67. Air speed indicator
68. Gasoline quantity gauge
69. Cambridge indicator current adjustment

70. Air speed indicator
71. Tachometers
72. Flaps position indicator
73. Gyropilot rudder speed control
74. Gyropilot aileron speed control
75. Manifold pressure gauge
76. Eclipse engine synchronizer
77. Argonne light
78. Gyropilot elevator speed control
79. Rudder tab control
80. Selector valve for manifold pressure gauges
81. Propeller pitch latches
82. Kollsman sensitive barometric altimeter
83. Fuel tank selector valve
84. Elevator tab indicator
85. Carburetor heat controls
86. Free air temperature gauge
87. Auxiliary beacon volume control
88. Local distance switch (auxiliary receiver)
89. Gyropilot servo shut-off valve
90. Parking brakes
91. Beacon receiver volume control
92. Engine fuel selector valve
93. Argonne light
94. Nose vent control
95. Turn and bank vacuum selector valve
96. Gasoline gauge selector switch
97. Aileron tab control
98. Vacuum pump selector valve
99. Cylinder-heads temperature gauges
100. Stewardess light
101. Safety warning lights
102. Stewardess switch
103. Fuel pump selector valve

From now on, the superiority of an airman will be measured, not by the old yardstick, "Courage," but by the new yardstick, "Knowledge" . . . knowledge of the plane itself, of the medium through which it travels, and of all the allied subjects such as dead reckoning, radio, aerodynamics, etc.

And while such knowledge is desirable in peaceful or transport flying (scheduled or itinerant), it will be the deciding factor in warfare flying.

I have said that, besides being familiar with the plane itself, you must understand the medium through which it travels—that is, the air. I cannot emphasize too strongly that weather behavior, air circulation, and all the phenomena arising from the uneven distribution of solar heat are of the utmost importance to you in flying. That is why I have devoted so much space to weather and its effect on flight.

Before we go any further, let me remind you of something you already know. There are several types of people in every field of endeavor: the person who *knows how much he doesn't know;* the person who *does not know he does not know* (Cloudy Joe); the person who *thinks he knows* (Cloudy Joe's brother)—and last, but not least, *the person who knows how much he knows.* It is the way we think that puts us in one category or another. When it comes to flying—particularly through the overcast—there is only one safe category to belong to, and that is the group who *know how much they ought to know.*

The shortest route in present-day flying is not always a bee-line, for you must frequently fly "the weather." Whether or not you fly good or bad weather, you are faced with many problems—how to take advantage of the upper winds, for example, or how to plot your course to avoid rough air and severe storms. As a result, your course may be changed many times before you reach your destination, particularly when the flight is a long stretch and the anticipated weather changes are even more severe than you expected.

Therefore let me introduce you to the weather.

*The difference between the sheriff and
the weather is that sometimes you can
dodge the latter.*

II

HOW TO BECOME A WEATHER DETECTIVE

(Meteorology)

"How is the weather?" Cloudy Joe asked, squinting up at the clouds.

"What weather?" I answered. "Do you mean weather for the farmer, or for outdoor sports?"

"Good" or "bad" weather frequently depends upon who is interested in it. Good weather for crops may be poor weather for sports; and what is "flyable" weather today in many instances would have been impossible weather for the airman of a few years back.

During the early days of flying, "flyable" weather meant "no wind, clear, unlimited visibility." Later, it came to be described in some such words as "cloudy, with some rain, but breaking."

But when you start on a flight today, you have to know far more about the weather than that it's "cloudy, with some rain, but breaking." You have to know what the ceilings are; you have to know visibilities, dewpoints, cloud formations, etc. And today, before you start your flight, the weather man will be able to tell you, from the data which the government's meteorological network is constantly obtaining, just what kind of weather you can expect throughout your flight.

The meteorologist speaks a language of his own—a language which Cloudy Joe has never been able to understand. But once you have mastered the basic principles and their application, as well as the methods of weather analysis, this special vocabulary will present no difficulties to you. With complete meteorological information at hand, you will be able to plan your flight in advance, and throughout its duration to determine, from the general appearance of cloud formations and the elevations over which you are passing, the best direction in which to steer your plane. Forearmed with this knowledge, you will also be able to choose the most suitable altitudes for safety, comfort and engine performance, and to find the upper winds most favorable for speed.

Heat from the Big Stove (The Sun): Its Distribution and Resulting Air Circulation

The whole subject of weather starts with the sun, because it is the sun's rays, heating ocean, earth and air, that cause the phenomena which we call *weather*. If the intensity of the sun's heat were the same throughout the earth and its surrounding atmosphere, we would not have the present meteorological changes; in other words, there would be no "weather," and life would be almost extinct on the earth. Fortunately, the sun heats the earth and atmosphere unevenly, causing winds, clouds, storms, thunder, rain, snow and sleet, and thus permits life to go on.

In other words, the sun is our constant servant and guardian, causing the perpetual transference of water from ocean to land, from land to ocean. It is the heat of the sun that lifts an enormous quantity of water from one portion of the earth and distributes it, through the medium of clouds, to other sections of the world which need to quench their thirst. We have been used to giving most of our praises to the earth, but we should not overlook the fact that it is the clouds, formed by the action of the sun, which are our real life-savers.

Clouds, as you know from your own experience, are often a menace to the airman, particularly when they obstruct visibility close to the ground. But don't forget that a total absence of clouds from our atmosphere would also mean a total absence of airmen—and every other form of life—from the earth. No wonder that the cloud-forming sun was worshiped by the ancients!

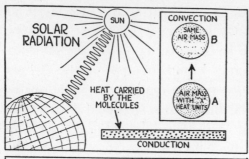

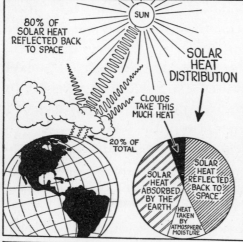

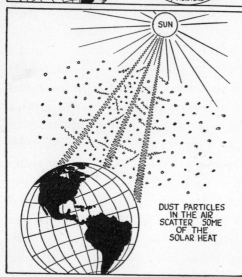

Fig. 1

FIG. 1. The heat from the sun comes to us as radiant energy which penetrates the air. Some of it is absorbed by the air, the ocean and the earth; the rest is reflected back into space. Heat can be transmitted to the air either by conduction, convection, or absorption. The solar heat given directly to the atmosphere represents a smaller portion of the total atmospheric heat than that which is reradiated from the earth—although this reradiated heat also came originally from the sun.

Air is a very poor conductor of heat, so that conduction is unimportant in adding heat to the atmosphere. The two important agents for heat transmission are absorption and convection (vertical air currents). The constant gases of the atmosphere, such as oxygen, nitrogen, argon, etc., are unimportant as heat-absorbing agents. Water vapor, which is always present in the atmosphere because of the constant evaporation from both water and ground surfaces, absorbs a considerable percentage of the solar heat, either directly or as the heat is reradiated from the earth.

Fig. 2

FIG. 2. The amount of solar radiation actually reaching the earth's surface varies considerably from time to time, depending upon the degree of cloudiness. The clouds, which are not

Fig. 3

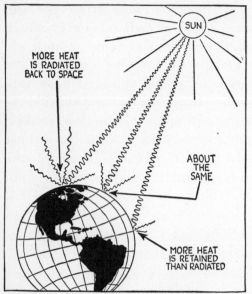

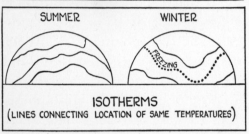

ISOTHERMS
(LINES CONNECTING LOCATION OF SAME TEMPERATURES)

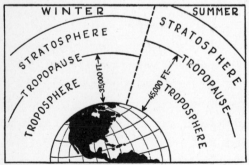

water vapor, but small particles of actual water, act as excellent reflectors. On an overcast day (with the sky completely cloud-covered) only 20 per cent, approximately, of the possible solar heat is received at the surface of the earth, the remaining 80 per cent being reflected back into space by the cloud tops. The average heat distribution throughout the year is divided approximately as shown in the circular graph. On partly cloudy days, however, the solar heat received by the earth may rise to approximately 40 per cent of the total.

FIG. 4

FIG. 3. Owing to the presence of dust particles in the atmosphere, a considerable amount of solar heat is "scattered" and eventually lost in space. As much of the scattered radiation is directed toward the earth as is directed into space, since the scattering is in all directions.

FIG. 5

FIG. 4. The amount of solar heat absorbed by the atmosphere varies over different portions of the earth's surface, as shown in the illustration. At the equatorial region, more heat is absorbed by the earth than is reflected back into space. Around the middle latitudes, the heat reflected back into space is about equal to the amount received. As you near the pole, you find that more heat is radiated back into space than is absorbed. From these facts you can readily see that as long as we have uneven heat distribution, the tendency of the atmos-

FIG. 6

phere will be to try to equalize its heat distribution. This is the secret of air circulation.

Fɪɢ. 5. The lines of equal temperature (isotherms) are bent toward the pole in summer and toward the equator in winter. If the earth's surface were uniform—all land of the same type, or all water—the isotherms would be parallel to the lines of latitude, showing a steady, uniform change between the equator and the poles. However, temperature differences exist at the same latitude because the surface of the earth varies from land to water, with the temperature of the water far more constant than that of the land. In summer the land is warmer than the water, causing the isotherms to bend toward the pole. In winter, the land is colder than the water, causing the opposite effect.

Fɪɢ. 6. In considering vertical heat distribution in the atmosphere, you will find two important layers—the lower layer, or troposphere, in which vertical motions are continually present, and the high-level layer, or stratosphere, where the predominating motions are horizontal. Within the troposphere the temperature decreases steadily with altitude at the rate of about 0.6° Centigrade for each 100 meters. In the stratosphere, the temperature is fairly constant with altitude. The dividing zone between the troposphere and stratosphere is the tropopause. The height of the tropopause varies. In summer it is higher than in winter, because the same mass of air, being warmer than in winter, expands, thus carrying the tropopause region to a higher altitude. Furthermore, the vertical air currents are deeper in summer. For the same reason, the height of the tropopause is greater over the equator than over the poles.

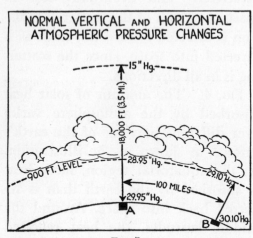

FIG. 7

Fɪɢ. 7. Normally the horizontal pressure difference between two locations on the earth's surface, such as points *A* and *B* in the illustration, is exceedingly small in comparison with the vertical pressure changes you will note with altitude. As an example, the barometric pressure difference between

8

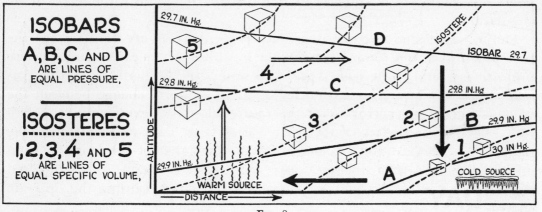

ISOBARS

A,B,C AND D ARE LINES OF EQUAL PRESSURE,

ISOSTERES

1,2,3,4 AND 5 ARE LINES OF EQUAL SPECIFIC VOLUME,

ALTITUDE

DISTANCE

29.7 IN. Hg.   D   ISOSTERE   ISOBAR 29.7

29.8 IN. Hg.   C   29.8 IN.Hg

3   2   B   29.9 IN. Hg.

29.9 IN. Hg.   1   30 IN. Hg.

WARM SOURCE   A   COLD SOURCE

FIG. 8

A and *B* (100 miles apart), as normally observed, is 0.15″ Hg. Now, if you climb vertically from either *A* or *B* to about the 900-foot level, the pressure fall will be 1″ Hg. The measure of difference in pressure between two points on the earth's surface at the same level is the "pressure gradient" or "push," and the greater the pressure change—or steeper the gradient—the more vigorous the air flow will be from the higher pressure to the lower pressure.

AIR CIRCULATION

FIG. 8.   The circulation of the earth's atmosphere follows somewhat well defined trends in accordance with what you would logically expect, taking into consideration the uneven distribution of the solar heat over the earth's surface. The principle of circulation, as shown in the illustration, is for comparatively small areas. However, it can be applied generally, with certain modifications, to larger-scale movements of the atmosphere.

Isobars are lines of equal barometric pressure. This means that the isobaric line passes through locations which have the same barometric pressure. The isobars which you see on a weather map (usually drawn for each .10″ Hg.) are merely lines indicating the edges of "isobaric surfaces" which extend dome-shaped through the atmosphere. Suppose a teacup were placed upside down on a smooth surface. The lip of the teacup in immediate contact with the surface would be analogous to the surface isobar, while the dome body of the cup would be analogous to the isobaric surface. Al-

FIG. 9

though the edge of the isobaric surface may be indicated at one point on the weather map, at another locality it may be necessary to climb into the air to obtain the same pressure reading. Cold air is heavier than warm air; therefore if you climb through cold air, the pressure decrease for, say, the 1000-foot levels will be more rapid than if you climb through warm air. Specific volume is defined as the volume necessary to contain a given weight. For the same weight, the volume of warm air will be greater

FIG. 10

than the volume of cold air. You can readily see that a cubic kilometer (or a cubic mile, if you wish) of cold air will weigh more than a cubic kilometer of warm air.

The circulation principle illustrated in Fig. 8 shows a vertical cross-section of the atmosphere between cold and warm sources of air with lines of equal pressure and of equal specific volume intersecting. The air at the warm source is warmer than the surrounding air, which, of course, being colder, has greater density. Therefore the warm air rises to levels where the pressure gradient, or "push," is from above the warm source to above the cold source. The warm air, as soon as it reaches a point above the cold source, becomes colder and heavier and starts to sink. The rising of the air over the warm source causes a drop of the atmospheric pressure; therefore the gradient or "push" will be from the cold toward the warm source, causing circulation as indicated by the arrows in the diagram.

If we consider the equatorial region as the warm source and the polar region as the cold source, then Fig. 8 shows the circulation between the equator and the pole as it would actually take place if the earth were a perfect sphere with a smooth surface of uniform make-up, and were not rotating.

FIGS. 9 AND 10. These illustrations show local types of air circulation, such as land and sea breezes, as they occur during the day or night. During the day the land becomes warmer than the ocean, heating the air adjacent to the land and causing vertical currents which in turn are replaced by horizontal movements of the cool sea air toward the land, so that the result is just a plain merry-go-round. During the night the situation is reversed: the direction of circulation is the opposite of that which occurs during the day.

FIG. 11. As previously stated, if the earth had a uniformly smooth surface and were not rotating, the flow of the air would be about as shown in Fig. 8. But the actual circulation is about as shown here. The earth's rota-

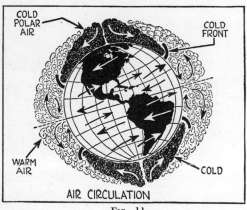

FIG. 11

tion affects the direction of the air circulation, and in the northern hemisphere it constantly deflects the air to the right. At the equator, the earth's surface is farther from the axis of rotation (or hub) than it is at, say, 30° north latitude; therefore the linear velocity is greatest at a point located on the equator, and decreases with increase of latitude. Another factor affecting the direction of air circulation is the friction caused by the earth's surface, which has a noticeable influence on the lower air strata. Roughly, the air circulation parallels the isobars at levels 1500 feet or more above the surface. Below this approximate height, the friction due to the earth's surface is more pronounced and the air has a tendency to flow across the isobars, the angle of flow depending upon the degree of friction and the difference between the high and low pressure sources.

For the time being it will be simpler for you to consider only the northern hemisphere. In addition to all the other factors influencing the equatorial-polar air circulation, there is a *piling up* of air at approximately 30° north latitude; this *air jam* causes a belt of high-pressure areas that encircles the globe. From this high-pressure belt there is an air circulation along the surface toward the equator known as the Northeast Trade Winds—the flow from the high-pressure belt to the low-pressure areas of the equatorial regions.

North from the high-pressure belt to approximately 60° north latitude you will find the Prevailing Westerlies. These winds are mostly southwesterly. The equatorial air moves northward at high levels. *Some of it,* because of the deflecting force of the earth, accumulates at 30° north latitude as shown in the illustration, while some of it continues poleward, causing a piling up of air in the polar region. This results in high pressure with a southward flow of air away from the pole in the lower levels in a general northeast wind. The combination of the Prevailing Westerlies in the lower levels, from 30° north latitude to about 60° north latitude, and the high-level, poleward air flow from the equator causes an accumulation of air in the polar regions not taken care of in a closed polar circulation. This piled-up air invades the middle latitudes through the Prevailing Westerlies as intermittent deep outbreaks of cold air, frequently extending into the Trade Winds. These outbreaks of air from the polar region represent the final effort of the earth's atmosphere to adjust itself to the unequal heat distribution over the earth.

12

III

Figure (Fig. 12)

CENTIGRADE	FAHRENHEIT
100°C—	—212°F
95°—	—203°
90°—	—194°
85°—	—185°
80°—	—176°
75°—	—167°
70°—	—158°
65°—	—149°
60°—	—140°
55°—	—131°
50°—	—122°
45°—	—113°
40°—	—104°
35°—	—95°
30°—	—86°
25°—	—77°
20°—	—68°
15°—	—59°
10°—	—50°
5°—	—41°
0°C—	—32°
-5°—	—23°
-10°—	—14°
-15°—	—5°
-17.777°—	—0°F
-20°—	—-4°
-40°—	—-40°
-50°—	—-58°
-100°C—	—-148°

$$°F = (°C \times 1.8) + 32$$
$$°C = \frac{(°F - 32)}{1.8}$$

Fig. 12

STABILITY AND INSTABILITY
(The Jumpiness of the Air)

Throughout the section devoted to meteorology, the words "stability" and "instability" will be used frequently, and "lapse rates" will be mentioned from time to time. It is of great importance that you understand thoroughly what is meant by these terms.

Fig. 12. Because of its almost universal usage and its convenience, the metric system is employed in the explanations which follow. The temperature scale is given for your convenience.

Fig. 13. In addition to "stability" and "instability," you should also understand the various meanings and values of the term "humidity" as employed in meteorology, and know what is meant by "relative humidity," "absolute humidity," and "specific humidity." Relative humidity is a *percentage* and is expressed as such. The actual moisture content is a certain percentage of the amount of moisture that the air actually will hold when *saturated* at the same temperature. The percentage is the *relative humidity* and is 100 per cent when the air is *saturated*. *Specific humidity* (the most valuable in identifying air masses) is the amount of moisture, expressed in *weight,* compared with the weight of a certain unit of air; for instance, so many grams of water to a kilogram of air. *Absolute humidity* is the *weight* of moisture

13

in a given volume of air. You can readily see that in vertical movements of air (convection) or horizontal circulation, temperature changes will cause changes in the relative humidity (for the warmer the air, the more moisture it can hold; see Fig. 14); will cause changes in absolute humidity (because of volume changes in the air); but will *not* cause changes in the specific humidity unless there is an addition of moisture to the air, or a loss of moisture.

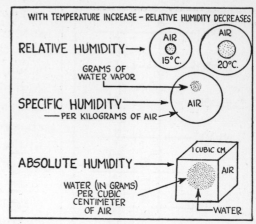

FIG. 13

FIG. 14.   Remember that the higher the temperature of the air, the greater the amount (in weight) of moisture it can hold. As shown in the illustration, air at 70° Fahrenheit can hold more moisture than any cooler air. Imagine that an isolated element of air has been warmed to 70° F. as shown at C, and allowed to absorb all the moisture it can hold at this temperature. When the air cools off, the moisture will start to come out of it, as shown at C¹. The temperature of the air, when it is saturated, is also the "dewpoint" temperature. If the air is not saturated, then the temperature to which the air would have to be cooled to reach saturation is its "dewpoint" temperature. The dewpoint is important, because the difference between the temperature and the dewpoint will be a direct indication of just how much the air will have to be cooled to reach saturation and condensation. The dewpoint is always part of a complete weather report as received by the government weather observers. If the difference between temperature and dewpoint is small, only slight cooling will be required to saturate the air, whereas if the difference between the temperature and dewpoint is great, excessive cooling will be necessary to bring about saturation.

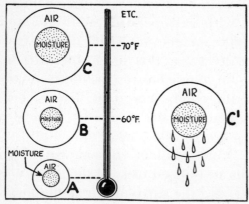

FIG. 14

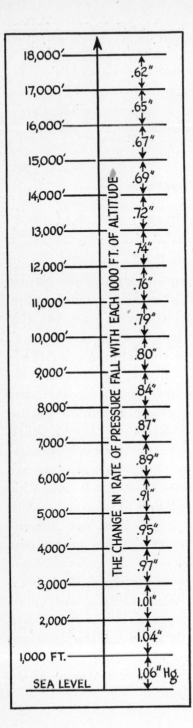

FIG.
15

FIG. 15. If you carried a barograph (pressure-recording instrument) and checked it at each 1000-foot level during your climb, you would find that the actual pressure fall at each step of 1000 feet throughout your climb would decrease. Standard values of actual pressure-changes for each 1000-foot elevation are shown in the illustration. From sea level to 1000 feet, the pressure drop is greatest, and so forth.

FIG. 16. You must climb or descend a greater distance at high altitudes to produce a barometric change of 1" Hg. than would be necessary nearer sea level. (This condition, as explained on page 319, will govern your rate of descent from high altitudes to sea level if you have any regard for your personal comfort.)

To get back to "stability," "instability," "lapse rates," etc.: You must consider the rate at which the temperature changes with *climb into the air*. The decrease in temperature is approximately .6° Centigrade per 100 meters, as an average, but varies from time to time. Suppose you are moving vertically into the atmosphere with equipment to observe temperature change with altitude. If you start, for example, at sea level, with a temperature of 15° C., and climb to 1000 meters, you will find a temperature of 10° C. at this level. In addition, the change in temperature has been steady throughout the climb. The total change of 5° C. for 1000 meters, or 0.5° C. for 100 meters, is the *observed temperature lapse rate*.

FIG. 17. Now, consider the changes which occur within an isolated mass of air when it is *lifted bodily* into the surrounding atmosphere. As the air is lifted, it enters an area of decreased

15

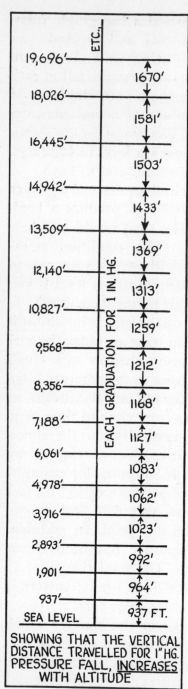

19,696'— ETC.,

←1670'→

18,026'—

←1581'→

16,445'—

←1503'→

14,942'—

←1433'→

13,509'—

←1369'→

12,140'—

EACH GRADUATION FOR 1 IN. HG.

←1313'→

10,827'—

←1259'→

9,568'—

←1212'→

8,356'—

←1168'→

7,188'—

←1127'→

6,061'—

←1083'→

4,978'—

←1062'→

3,916'—

←1023'→

2,893'—

←992'→

1,901'—

←964'→

937'—

SEA LEVEL

←937 FT.→

SHOWING THAT THE VERTICAL
DISTANCE TRAVELLED FOR 1" HG.
PRESSURE FALL, INCREASES
WITH ALTITUDE

Fig.
16

atmospheric pressure, and therefore expands. With expansion, the air cools, this cooling being rather steady because of the steady decrease of pressure. The rate of cooling of isolated bodies of air, when lifted into regions of decreased atmospheric pressure, is called the *adiabatic lapse rate.* This simply means that temperature changes occur within the air mass *without loss of heat* to the surrounding air *or gain of heat* from the surrounding air. This temperature decrease (lapse rate) within the rising body of air is approximately 1° C. for each 100 meters rise. (Actually the rate is 0.98° C.) This temperature lapse rate exists only for unsaturated air, that is, air which at any temperature is capable of holding more moisture than it contains; and the temperature lapse rate is identified, therefore, as the "dry" adiabatic lapse rate. In Fig. 17 you can see what actually happens when an air mass, *A,* is lifted bodily through 300 meters to *B.* The temperature within this isolated body drops 3° C., which is the *adiabatic lapse rate for dry air.* But the observed temperature of the surrounding air at the *B* level happens to be 13.2° C. This means that the surrounding air is warmer and less dense, and that, as a result, the isolated body of air will have a tendency to sink to its original level.

While the lapse rate for unsaturated air is 1° C. for 100 meters, remember—and this is very important—that when saturated air (air at any temperature filled with the maximum amount of moisture it can hold) is lifted, the lapse rate is not 1° C. for 100 meters, but is about half that value.

FIG. 18. You will notice in this illustration that an isolated air mass, moved vertically and with altitude, has expanded and cooled at the dry adiabatic rate. You will also notice that the surrounding air has an observed lapse rate which, coincidentally, is 1° C. for each 100 meters ascent. As a result of equal temperatures between the rising element and the surrounding air, there is no density difference, and therefore vertical motions will neither be induced nor reduced. This state is called *neutral equilibrium* and is sometimes observed in the atmosphere.

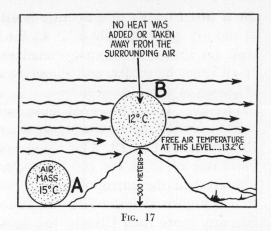

Fig. 17

FIG. 19. The observed lapse rate of air given in this example is only 0.5° C. for 100 meters. This means that if an isolated, unsaturated element of

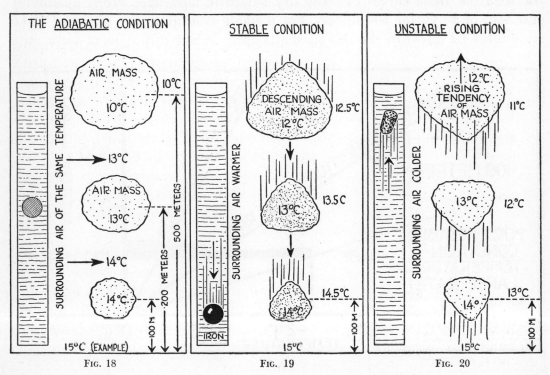

Fig. 18   Fig. 19   Fig. 20

air is lifted bodily in a manner similar to that shown in Fig. 17, it will cool at the *dry adiabatic rate* of 1° C. for 100 meters, and will have a tendency to sink (as shown in an exaggerated manner by the iron ball), since the air will at all times be colder, and therefore denser, than the surrounding air. This is known as a *stable condition*.

Fig. 20. If the observed lapse rate in the free atmosphere, for example, is 2° C. for 100 meters ascent, the situation will be the reverse of the condition illustrated in Fig. 19. The rising body of air will then cool at the dry adiabatic rate of 1° C. for 100 meters, and thus, being constantly warmer and lighter than the surrounding air, will rise, like a cork in water. This condition is known as *instability* (an atmospheric condition which you will not like any more than Cloudy Joe does while in flight).

Fig. 21. Here the usual curves (only Cloudy Joe thinks that such curves cannot be straight lines) are plotted temperature in the abscissae, and altitude in the ordinate. They are shown here as straight lines merely for explanatory purposes: they can actually be either curved or straight. You will notice from these curves that the dry adiabatic lapse rate drops steadily at the rate of 1° C. for 100 meters. For a stable condition, the observed lapse rate must be less than the dry adiabatic rate. When this type of lapse rate

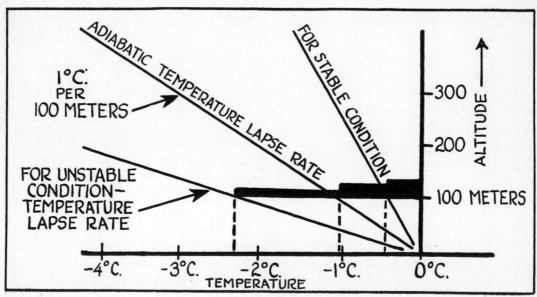

Fig. 21

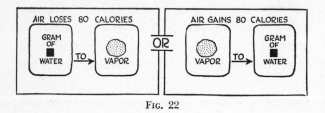

FIG. 22

occurs in the atmosphere, and an isolated body of air, for example, is lifted over a mountain by a sudden horizontal movement, the air sinks again as soon as the lifting force is removed. The curve which represents the unstable condition is the reverse of the curve just described.

FIG. 22. Before we go any further with this subject of weather, I wish to impress upon you the fact that whenever water is evaporated into the air, it takes 80 calories (heat units) to convert each gram of water into vapor. Conversely, when vapor is condensed into water, 80 calories from each gram are released and added to the air.

FIG. 23. Follow me closely now, for you are getting deeper into the subject. You will often observe a temperature lapse rate in the atmosphere which causes a *stable* condition in free air as long as the air is unsaturated. But from our previous discussion you remember that when a rising body of air reaches saturation through adiabatic cooling, the rate of cooling is lessened as explained in Fig. 22, owing to the addition of heat by condensation. That is, the rate becomes approximately half that of the dry adiabatic rate, or

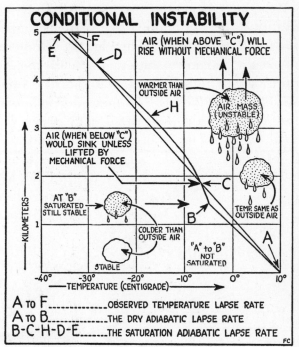

FIG. 23

about 0.5° C. for each 100 meters. This rate of cooling after saturation varies with the moisture content and the temperature of the saturated air. Fig. 14 showed that the higher the temperature of air the greater the amount of moisture (in weight) the air will hold.

19

A to *F* on the graph represents the *observed lapse rate,* which is *less* than the dry adiabatic rate. *A* to *B* represents the dry adiabatic, the rate at which the lifted body of air cools *while unsaturated.* The line *B-C-H-D-E* (the curve of the *saturation adiabatic lapse rate*) indicates the rate at which the lifted body of air cools after saturation.

The rising body of air, as shown in the graph, cools at the dry adiabatic rate (1° C. for 100 meters) until point *B* is reached. From *B* to *C* the rate of cooling is at the saturation adiabatic rate (about 0.5° C. for 100 meters). At *C,* because of the change in the rate of cooling of the lifted body of air, the curves intersect each other. Up to point *C* the lifted air is constantly colder than the surrounding air, so that the air is *stable*—as explained in Fig. 19. From *C* to *D,* the curve showing the rate of cooling of the rising air lies to the right of the curve showing the observed lapse rate of the atmosphere (*A* to *F*), indicating that the rising air is *warmer* than the surrounding air. This state, as you will remember from Fig. 20, is one of *instability.*

As the moisture content becomes less, you will see on the graph that the rate of cooling of the saturated air becomes greater, simply because smaller and smaller amounts of vapor are condensing, and therefore less heat is added to the rising air. The trend of the curve, as the moisture content decreases, will be more and more toward the dry adiabatic, the rate which will again prevail in the rising air after all the moisture has been *condensed.*

Until the air reaches *C,* it must be lifted by a mechanical force, by a mountain peak, or by denser air, since the air is stable—that is, heavier than its surroundings. Above *C,* the air is warmer than its surroundings. From *C* to *D*—the other point of intersection of the curves—the air rises of its own accord because it is *unstable.* Not only that, but its rate of rise will be accelerated up to point *D,* with maximum acceleration at point *H,* as would logically be expected since the two curves are farthest apart at *H,* indicating that the greatest difference in temperature and density between the surrounding and the lifted elements of air exists at this point. When the observed lapse rate in the air lies between that of the dry adiabatic and that of the saturated adiabatic, as shown on the graph, "conditional instability" prevails. Also, as shown, condensation, precipitation and cloudiness form in an air body which is constantly moving upward at an accelerated rate. Later on, when I tell you of the danger of flying in thunderstorms, I will again refer you to this apparent "about-face" from stability to instability. The ability to recognize conditional instability in the air is of great importance in weather forecasting, since it indicates the probability of intense upward currents within clouds, causing severe turbulence.

Before I go any further, let me mention that atmospheric pressure is measured not only in inches of mercury but also in millibars, with 1″ of mercury equal to 33.86 millibars (Mb.) at 0° C. In explaining the following charts, the 1000 Mb. level (29.53″ Hg.) will be used as a reference level. In actual practice, the various values arrived at with reference to the 1000 Mb. level are the values used.

FIG. 24. When air is heated adiabatically, by increasing pressure and decreasing volume, without gain or loss of heat, the temperature rises. But when the air is cooled adiabatically (by decreasing the pressure surrounding the body of air and increasing its volume) the temperature falls. The pressure level used in practical meteorology for determining certain values is the 1000 Mb. level, as I said before.

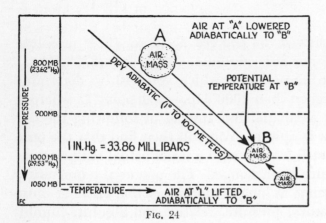

FIG. 24

The adjoining diagram explains the "potential" temperature of an air element at point *A*. Now, go ahead and theoretically increase the temperature at *A*, which is at the 800 Mb. level, along the dry adiabatic temperature curve. (Don't make the mistake, however, of thinking that the air itself slides downhill along a line paralleling the adiabatic curve.) When, while increasing the temperature adiabatically, you reach a pressure of 1000 Mb. at *B*, you will find that the temperature is higher than it was at *A*. This temperature at 1000 Mb., when expressed in the absolute temperature scale, is called the "potential" temperature. For example, let us assume that the temperature at *A* is 10° C. The vertical distance from 800 Mb. to 1000 Mb. is just about 1800 meters. The temperature will increase adiabatically 1° C. for 100 meters descent. This means that the temperature will be 18° higher, or 28° C. (10° C. at *A* + 18° C. = 28° C.) at the 1000 Mb. pressure level.

21

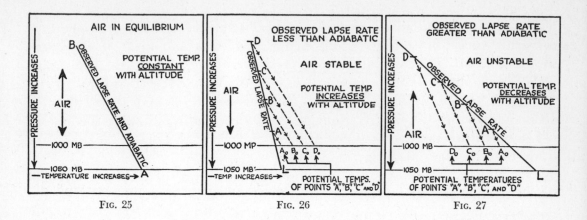

FIG. 25.   FIG. 26.   FIG. 27.

The potential temperature, expressed in degrees absolute (273° absolute = 0° C.) would be 273° plus 28°, or 301° absolute. (0° A. = —273° C.)

If the atmospheric pressure at the point for which you wish to determine the potential temperature is higher than 1000 Mb.—as at point *L,* where it is 1050 Mb.—the process is also adiabatic. But instead of following the dry adiabatic curve downward, follow it upward. You will then find that the temperature has decreased, arriving at *B* from *L* with a lower actual temperature, although the potential temperature is unchanged. The potential temperature of an element of air does not change as long as motions of that element cause dry adiabatic changes. Temperature, pressure, relative and absolute humidity all change during the dry adiabatic process, but the potential temperature does not change. You can see, then, that potential temperature is valuable because it can be used in determining, first, the air mass, and then the important factors of stability and instability.

FIG. 25. You remember Fig. 18, showing the "neutral equilibrium" condition. If on a particular day the observed lapse rate is the same as the dry adiabatic rate, you will find that the potential temperature will remain *constant* with the lifting and lowering of an unsaturated air mass because the temperature will then change adiabatically and will *coincide* at all times with the temperature of the surrounding air. Therefore the air will not induce or reduce vertical movements, and will tend to "stay put." Stop and think for a while, because you are right in the midst of the most important points that I shall explain to you.

FIG. 26. The usual observed temperature lapse rate in the atmosphere is

22

less than the dry adiabatic, and the natural tendency of the atmosphere is toward "peace" or stability. This being true, the potential temperature should normally increase with height. The curve L-D is for stable conditions. (See Fig. 21 also.) If the temperature at A is increased adiabatically to the 1000 Mb. level as at A_0, and the temperatures at B, C and D are also increased adiabatically to B_0, C_0, and D_0, you can readily see that the potential temperature increases with altitude if and when the observed lapse rate is less than the dry adiabatic.

FIG. 27. In this illustration the observed lapse rate in the air is greater than the adiabatic (see also Fig. 21). This, as you already know, is a condition for *instability*. By taking temperatures at points A, B, C and D, and increasing them adiabatically to the 1000 Mb. level, as at A_0, B_0, C_0 and D_0, you will find that the potential temperature *decreases* with altitude. Now, concentrate!

FIG. 28. This graphic illustration represents a theoretical case of convection (vertical movement) and condensation in the atmosphere. It is an extreme condition which I am presenting merely for the purpose of explaining what happens in the atmosphere. This type of convection is called the "reversible" process, or, as we will call it, the "hold-all-moisture" process. The main consideration is that during the lifting and condensation, freezing and sublimation (the change from vapor to ice) all products (water and ice) are retained in the rising body of air. During the so-called "ice" or "hail" stage, the addition of heat given to the air by the freezing water is sufficient to prevent a drop in

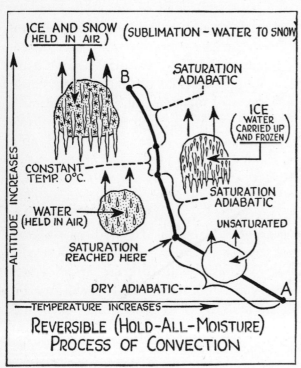

FIG. 28

23

temperature until all the contained water (not vapor) is frozen. During the last stage, the vapor changes directly into ice and snow without passing through the water stage, so that the lapse rate is close to the ordinary saturated adiabatic rate.

Now let's follow the rising air upward along the illustrated curve. At *A* the air is moist, but unsaturated. As it rises, it cools at the dry adiabatic rate to the point where saturation is shown. From this point upward (considering that the point of saturation is at a temperature *above* freezing) the saturated air will cool at the saturated adiabatic rate, holding all the water condensed, as shown at the left-center of the illustration. The steady temperature drop with further lifting will bring the air with its contained water into freezing temperatures. Now, the water in the air must be frozen, so it is assumed that while the water is freezing, the temperature is constant at 0° C. throughout the lifting process, as previously explained and as shown at the right-center of the illustration. After all the contained water is frozen, the temperature begins to fall steadily again at the saturated adiabatic rate until

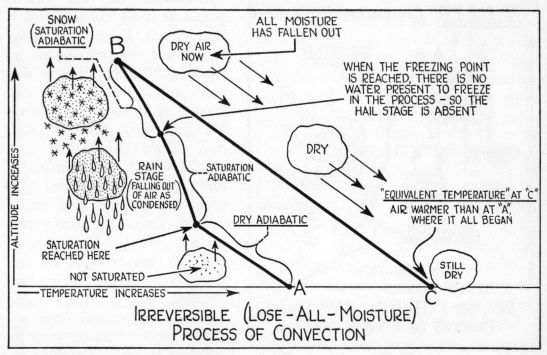

Fig. 29

24

all the contained *water vapor* is condensed at *B*. In this process, you can see, it is possible to reverse each step along the curve *B* to *A,* so that the air element will arrive, theoretically, back at *A* with the same temperature and moisture content as before convection. Such a condition as the one just described does not exist, of course; the discussion is only theoretical. Cloudy Joe is liable to think that elements of air go up and come down with ice cakes in them! But you and I know better.

Fig. 29.   In the other process of convection, called the "irreversible" or "pseudo-adiabatic" process (we shall term it the "lose-all-moisture" process), you will notice that instead of *holding* the condensed moisture during convection, the air element loses all moisture. This is another extreme case given to clarify in your mind the processes of convection and condensation in the atmosphere. Following a body of air from point *A* upward, you will find that while *unsaturated,* its temperature decrease will be at the dry adiabatic rate. After reaching the point of saturation indicated in the illustration, this air continues to rise and to cool at the *saturated* adiabatic rate. (Remember that we are not considering the surrounding air.) During this period, while the temperature of the air is *above* freezing, the water, *as condensed,* will fall from the air, as shown at the left. Therefore, when the temperature reaches freezing, the saturated adiabatic curve is *not broken* by a constant temperature curve for the simple reason that there is now no water left in the air to be frozen, since it has fallen out as condensed. The change is from the water stage into the snow stage, with the precipitation falling out as snow at temperatures *below* freezing, as shown at the upper left. When it reaches point *B,* the air is absolutely dry, containing no water vapor and no products of condensation. Because of this, the air cannot be brought to *A* again along curve *B*. Any lowering of the air will cause dry adiabatic changes because the air is *absolutely dry.*

Take the temperature at *B* and increase it theoretically at the dry adiabatic rate to point *C,* which is on the same level as *A*. The temperature of the air at *C* will be much higher than the temperature it had at *A,* since the temperature was increased at a rate greater than that at which it was decreased during the lift from *A* to *B*. Again, keep in mind that air movement is not downhill or uphill, as you might conclude from the illustration; the arrows are merely illustrative.

The temperature at *C* is called the "equivalent" temperature. The name is probably derived from the fact that this temperature is equal to what it would be if all the latent heat of condensation which is dormant in the air could be applied to increase the air's temperature. In the "lose-all-moisture" process this heat is added to the air because of condensation during convection, and when the air arrives at *B* it is potentially warmer than at *A*. Therefore, if potentially warmer air is brought down adiabatically to the same level, it will naturally have a higher temperature, which in this case would be the *equivalent temperature*. Remember this: the equivalent temperature is the temperature obtained, as explained above, for the original air level, which can be at any atmospheric pressure level.

There is one more important value which must be explained, and that is "equivalent-potential" temperature, or the temperature at which, say, dry air at *B* is brought adiabatically to the 1000 Mb. pressure level. Do you see the point now? While the equivalent temperature could be at *any pressure level*, as long as it is at the original level the equivalent-potential temperature must be at the 1000 Mb. level. If the temperature at *C* were changed adiabatically to the 1000 Mb. level, the resulting temperature, expressed in Degrees Absolute, would be the *equivalent-potential* temperature. The equivalent temperature bears the same relationship to the equivalent-potential temperature as the actual temperature bears to the potential temperature. In other words, in taking the actual temperature adiabatically to the 1000 Mb. level, you obtain the potential temperature. In taking the equivalent temperature adiabatically to the 1000 Mb. level, you obtain the equivalent-potential temperature. You already know that the potential temperature remains unchanged during unsaturated adiabatic changes. You can now see that the *equivalent-potential temperature remains unchanged during saturated as well as unsaturated adiabatic changes.* You don't have to use your imagination very much to see how valuable this latter property is to the meteorologist in identifying various kinds of air, since cold air with a low specific humidity will have *low values* of *equivalent-potential* temperature, and warm air with high specific humidities will have high values of equivalent-potential temperature. Because of this relationship this value can be used as an indication of the kind of air being considered.

I suggest that you go over these points until you thoroughly understand them, for they constitute part of the "meat" of applied meteorology, and you will need to be familiar with them before you go further with the subject.

You already know about the local, small-scale air movements, and the dynamics of lifting and sinking within free air. In large-scale air movements, however, conditions are greatly magnified. Large bodies of air are .frequently lifted and lowered in extensive layers. It is also frequently observed that as long as a layer of air is unsaturated and at rest, it is *stable* (half asleep). The temperature decrease *through the layer* from bottom to top is less than adiabatic. However, if the relative humidity decreases upward through the layer, the lower portions of the layer will become saturated with lifting (owing to expansional cooling) before the upper parts. Upon saturation, the lower levels will cool at a slower rate than that of the dry adiabatic—that is, at the saturation adiabatic lapse rate; while the upper parts, which have not yet become saturated, will continue to cool at the greater dry adiabatic rate until those parts, too, reach saturation.

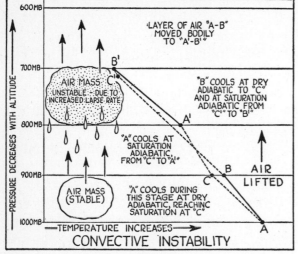

FIG. 30

CONVECTIVE INSTABILITY

FIG. 30. Take a good look at this illustration. A layer of unsaturated air, bounded by the pressure of 1000 Mb. at the bottom and 900 Mb. at the top, has the observed temperature lapse rate, *A-B*. The air is stable, for the lapse rate *A-B* is less than the dry adiabatic. The whole layer is lifted so that the bottom pressure is 800 Mb. and the pressure at the top is 700 Mb. The relative humidity at *A* is higher than at *B*, so that adiabatic cooling will cause saturation of point *A* when it reaches *C*. From *C* to *A'*, the rate of cooling is that of saturated air. The bottom of the layer which was at *A* comes to rest at point *A'*. Now consider *B*. At *B* the lower relative humidity makes it necessary to lift that point a greater distance to bring about a temperature low enough to cause saturation. In the illustration, *C'* is the saturation point. From *C'* to *B'*, the resting place of the air formerly at *B*, the cooling is at the saturated rate. Now notice the temperature lapse rate from *A'* to *B'*. It is

27

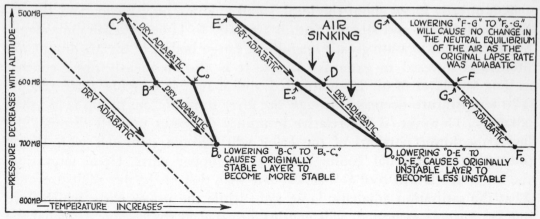

FIG. 31

greater than adiabatic, for the air is saturated and has become unstable. Before lifting, vertical motions (turbulence) were definitely restricted within the layer because it was stable. After lifting, however, the production of instability increases materially the vertical motions within the layer. The ability to recognize this property of "convective instability" as being particularly adapted to *layers,* is extremely important to you and the meteorologist in determining just what kind of weather will result from the large-scale lifting of the air under consideration. The air is lifted in several ways—that is, by terrain and also by different types of interaction with other kinds of air.

Fig. 31. It was shown in Fig. 16 that the actual distance required to cause a given drop in pressure *increases* with altitude. Now, look at Fig. 31. You will readily see that the altitude or "space" between the pressures of 800 Mb. and 700 Mb. is less than the altitude or "space" between the pressures of 600 Mb. and 500 Mb. This has an important bearing on changes occurring within layers of air when they are moved vertically. At the left of the illustration the dry adiabatic lapse rate is indicated as a dotted line. Reading from left to right, consider, first, the air layer between 600 Mb. and 500 Mb. with temperature curve, *B-C.* Imagine that this layer sinks so that the upper pressure becomes 600 Mb. and the lower pressure, 700 Mb. *C* warms adiabatically in sinking to point C_0. *B* warms adiabatically to point B_0. If the distances traveled by the two points coincided, the temperature change would be the same. This is not the case, however, since the distance from the

28

500 Mb. level to the 600 Mb. level is greater than the distance from the 600 Mb. level to the 700 Mb. level. This will cause C to be heated more than B, so that the lapse rate, B-C, which is *stable*, will become more stable after sinking to B_0-C_0.

The second temperature curve, D-E, is for an *unstable* layer. D is lowered adiabatically to D_0, and E is lowered to E_0. As shown before, E travels a greater distance to E_0 than does D to D_0, using the same pressure levels as before. E is heated more than D, so that the resulting curve, D_0-E_0, is for *less unstable* air.

The third temperature curve, F-G, is for neutral equilibrium in unsaturated air (all the layers considered are unsaturated), because the observed temperature lapse rate is the same as the dry adiabatic. Movement from F to F_0 and from G to G_0 will cause no change in the state of the air because both points will warm adiabatically along a curve coincident to the observed lapse rate. Neutral equilibrium will continue.

Bear in mind, from this discussion, that sinking layers of air become more stable. "Inversions," or increases in temperature with altitude will be intensified with sinking.

You may have noticed on some flight where you watched your free-air temperature gauge that instead of decreasing during a climb, the temperature increased with altitude. This condition is called an "inversion." Inversions are very important in weather forecasting, and you should become familiar with how they are formed and maintained.

Fig. 32. Prolonged convectional turbulence (vertical movement) in the air causes the layers affected by that vertical movement to become well-mixed. As has been shown in Fig. 26, the potential temperature normally increases with altitude in the free air. If turbulence is set up in a layer of air, the air moving downward from the top of the turbulence level will arrive at the bottom

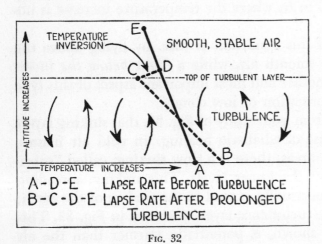

A-D-E LAPSE RATE BEFORE TURBULENCE
B-C-D-E LAPSE RATE AFTER PROLONGED TURBULENCE

FIG. 32

29

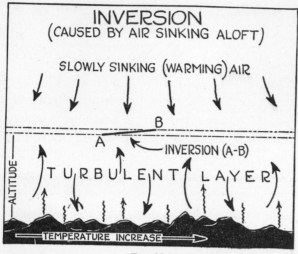

INVERSION
(CAUSED BY AIR SINKING ALOFT)

SLOWLY SINKING (WARMING) AIR

B

A ← INVERSION (A-B)

T U R B U L E N T   L A Y E R

ALTITUDE

←TEMPERATURE INCREASE→

Fig. 33

warmer than the air that was originally at the bottom (such as point D lowered to D_o in Fig. 26). In Fig. 32 the air moving upward from the low levels to the upper portions of the turbulence layer will be cooler than the air which moved downward. You can imagine that continued turbulence will tend to establish an *adiabatic* lapse rate within the turbulence layer. The lapse rate within the turbulence layer (adiabatic) will be greater than the lapse rate within the air immediately above the turbulence layer, so that there will actually be an *increase* in temperature from the top of the turbulence layer into the calmer air above.

In the illustration, the curve *A-E* is the observed lapse rate before turbulence sets in. After continuous exchange of air between the surface and the top of the turbulence layer, the lapse rate changes, as in the curve *B-C,* shown by the dotted line. This lapse rate is adiabatic, or nearly adiabatic. The air above point *C,* not having been affected by the turbulence, maintains its old lapse rate, *D-E.* The area from *C* to *D,* where the temperature increase is noticed, is called an "inversion."

The immediate significance of this condition is that, by flying above the turbulence layer, you will have smooth air, while a flight *below the inversion* would be rather rough. Another and most important aspect of this type of inversion is its effect in the formation of low clouds.

Fig. 33. You already know, from your study of Fig. 31, that sinking layers of air become more stable because of adiabatic heating. In cold air masses, indicated by large high-pressure areas, there is a slow sinking, called "subsidence," of the air, particularly at the upper levels. This sinking, spreading out, and adiabatic heating will not usually extend to the surface of the earth; but it will extend to the top of the turbulence layer, as shown in Fig. 33. This sinking air which, as previously shown, is potentially warmer than the air

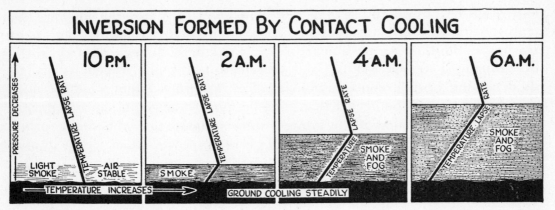

FIG. 34

below, will arrive at the top of the turbulence layer with a much higher temperature than the air within the turbulence layer. Curve *A-B* in the illustration shows the zone of inversion, or increase in temperature from the lower level to the upper. The effects, in so far as flight is concerned, are as explained in the preceding paragraph. The combination of turbulence and sinking (subsidence) in the production of inversions can cause a considerable increase in temperature through the inversion zones. In the winter, it is not unusual to observe a difference of as much as 20° to 25°. Incidentally, while many of the illustrations are somewhat pictorial, they actually represent charts on which values have been plotted.

FIG. 34. The ground cools at night by radiating heat to space. On clear nights, when there are no clouds to reflect the radiation back to earth, the cooling will become augmented. Air in contact with the cooling ground will naturally become cool also. In ground fog conditions, this type of contact cooling occurs in the air adjacent to the earth. As shown in Fig. 34, the lapse rate observed within the air changes as the earth becomes cooler. At 10 P.M. the air is stable, but inversion has not yet developed. Light smoke layers may be observed near the ground. At 2 A.M. cooling of the air in contact with the ground has caused the development of an inversion between the cool air and the comparatively warmer air above. A more pronounced concentration of smoke is observed. The ground becomes cooler by 4 A.M., and still cooler by 6 A.M., with the cooling layer of air becoming deeper, and a ground fog developing, mixed with smoke, and causing a considerable reduction in sur-

31

face visibility. Dewpoint, as you will remember, has been defined as the temperature to which air must be cooled to become saturated; that is, to reach the limit of its possible moisture content. You can easily see, then, that during a night's cooling, air adjacent to the ground can be cooled to its dewpoint, causing condensation into fog. If there is a light wind blowing, the ground fog will be *deeper* than on a perfectly calm night, since a greater amount of cooling air will be brought into circulation by the slight turbulence. On a perfectly calm night, the fog will be very *shallow*. You will find this condition hazardous, not in flight, but in landing. Visibility is often greatly reduced, causing zero visibility conditions at times. After sunrise, when the surface temperature begins to increase, the surface inversion is destroyed, and the ground fog is dissipated.

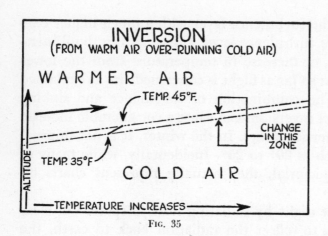

FIG. 35

FIG. 35. You will learn later on, in the discussion of atmospheric fronts, that cold, dense air (the bully!) is constantly underrunning or displacing warm, lighter air. In other words, the cold air acts as a slope over which the light, warm air climbs. As shown in Fig. 35, where warm air is over-riding colder air, a temperature increase with altitude exists between the lower, cold air, and the upper, warm air. In this case, the temperature increase is from 35° F. to 45° F. through the inversion zone. Increases of this amount and more are not uncommon.

The important difference between this type of inversion and the types heretofore discussed is that, where warm air overruns colder air, there is an increase in moisture content (specific humidity) whereas in the previous types there is usually no increase in specific humidity. The significance of this condition with relation to your flight is worthy of the more detailed discussions which will follow later.

FIG. 36. Radiation from air into space, when considered in itself as the cause of inversions, is negligible. This type of radiation is very slight. But,

32

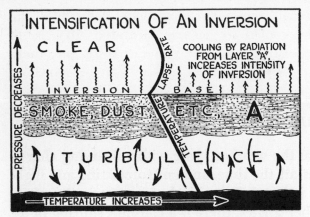

FIG. 36

as shown here, there can easily be an accumulation of foreign particles just below the base of an inversion already formed. These particles (smoke, dust, etc.) are lifted to the base of the inversion by the turbulent air under the inversion, and spread out. Radiation from this layer of foreign particles at *A* can cause *intensification* of an inversion.

An extra ace or two is a good idea . . . . in flying!

33

IV

BIOGRAPHY OF THE AIR MASSES, AND
THEIR IDENTIFICATION

THERE would be little change in the weather if air with unvarying characteristics prevailed over large areas all the time, and our forecasting and flight problems would be considerably reduced. Fortunately for most angles of approach, and unfortunately for other angles, there is a constant shifting of air which has varying characteristics. At times this shifting is helpful; at other times it is a distinct hindrance. The better acquainted you are with the different types of air and the weather associated with each type and with the interaction of different types, the better and safer flight plan you will be able to make.

FIG. 37. You have probably heard a good deal about "air masses" lately, and you may have wondered what was meant. Simply stated, an "air mass" is an extensive body of air which is approximately homogeneous horizontally. In other words, as shown in the adjoining illustration, the value of, say, specific humidity or potential temperature would be approximately the same at *A* as at *B*. (Remember Fig. 24?)

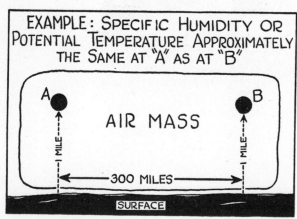

FIG. 37

After having been more or less dormant over large land or water areas, air masses finally assume the characteristics of these areas—just as you would if you sat on a cake of ice for a while. In other words, air over the Arctic regions will become very cold, while air over the Gulf of Mexico, for example, will become very warm and moist. Regions which cause great changes in the overlying

34

air are called "source regions." We cannot truly consider a source region as the *originating* point of the air; it is, instead, an area where air of different origin has moved in and slowly acquired the characteristics of its new environment.

The changes occurring in the air lying over the source for a great length of time are of vital importance in considering the weather which you will find (a) *at the source;* (b) within the air when it *moves away* from the source—gets to "going places"; and (c) between different types of air when they *interact* upon each other. You can readily see that it would be most valuable to have some means of identifying each type of air mass. The first thing to consider is a property or value which will not vary greatly while the air is being modified with movement away from the source. This kind of property or characteristic can be called "conservative," because it tends to remain almost constant.

Actual temperature (the one you read on your temperature gauge or thermometer) changes greatly, and therefore cannot be used as a constant property, although in practical meteorology, with many reports available, temperature is important, particularly when the paths of air masses are watched by means of continuous weather maps.

Relative humidity is extremely variable. Changes in temperature, evaporation and precipitation will cause corresponding changes in the relative humidity.

Absolute humidity varies to a great degree, being influenced by temperature changes, pressure and volume changes, evaporation and precipitation.

Specific humidity, however, is more constant. It changes with addition or loss of moisture in the air. Although specific humidity changes because of evaporation and precipitation, the change is more gradual than with the properties previously mentioned.

Potential temperature and equivalent-potential temperature are fairly constant properties of an air mass. In convection (vertical movement) the potential temperature of an element of air is constant while the air is unsaturated. After saturation is reached, the potential temperature changes constantly because of the ever-changing lapse rate within the rising air. Equivalent-potential temperature of an element of air is constant during convection in the *unsaturated* and the *saturated* stages. With experience, you will become more familiar with the changes which occur within an air mass with horizontal movement away from its source over regions of varying surface characteristics. I can merely introduce you to the main types of modifications which can occur; where and when these changes occur in any specific case you will have to discover for yourself by observing and analyzing not only the air itself but the surface over which it is moving. A definite knowledge of these changes is obtained from an analysis of upper-air soundings of wind, temperature, relative humidity and pressure. From these basic values, the more constant properties—such as specific humidity and equivalent-potential temperature—are computed and made available to you and the meteorologist, and thus the trend of the weather is determined. Always take advantage of meteorological advice when it is available, for the meteorologist has at hand, in comprehensive form, information which it would take you too long to get for yourself.

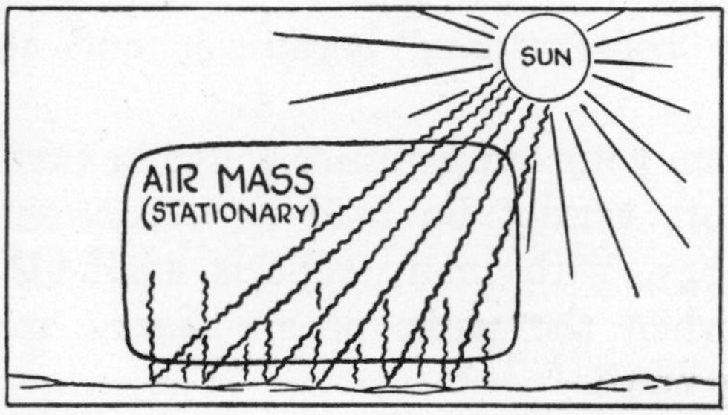

The illustrations which immediately follow present, in a general, preliminary manner and without particular reference to air-mass types, the changes which occur in air after certain modifications. Study these illustrations.

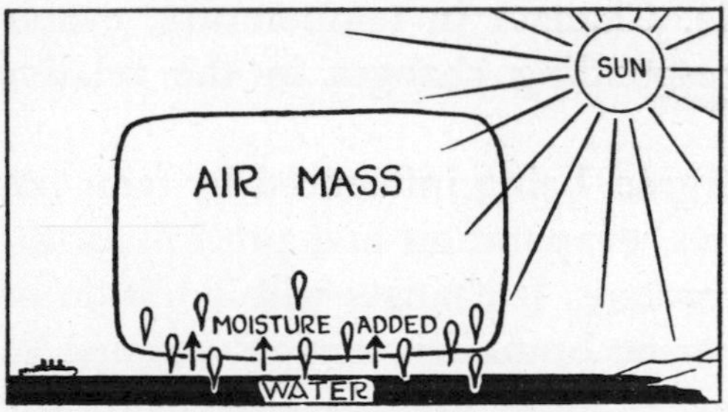

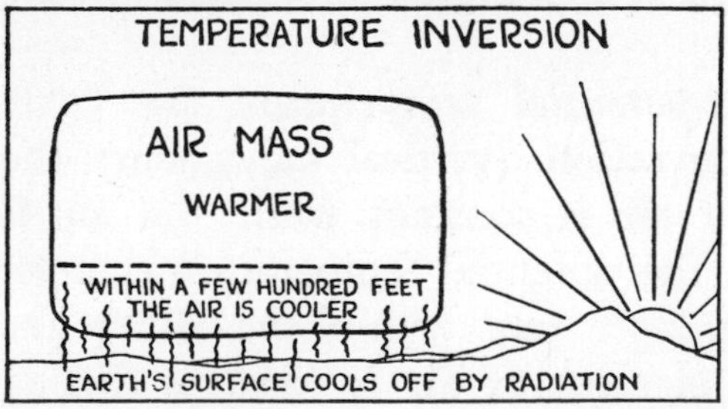

FIG. 38. The air shown here is being heated by solar radiation and by reradiated energy in the form of terrestrial radiation.

FIG. 39. This air mass is being heated; in addition, moisture is being added by evaporation from the water over which the air lies.

FIG. 40. The air is being cooled, after sunset, by contact with the cooling earth, thus developing an inversion as explained in Fig. 34.

Fig. 38

Fig. 39

Fig. 40

36

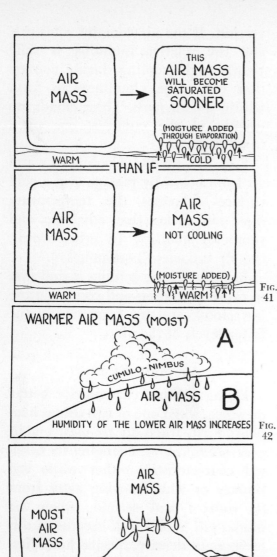

FIG.
41

FIG.
42

FIG.
43

FIG.
44

FIG. 41. The air mass in the upper portion of the illustration has moved from a warm to a cold surface, and is cooling. At the same time, moisture is being added to it through evaporation. This air mass will become saturated before the air mass in the lower portion of the illustration, since the latter is not cooling while moisture evaporates into it. This brings us back to the old temperature-moisture relationship, in which it was shown that the higher the temperature of air, the more moisture it can hold.

FIG. 42. Precipitation from clouds formed in air mass *A* falls into the lower air mass, *B*. Evaporation from this falling precipitation causes an increase in the humidity of the lower air mass.

FIG. 43. Air being lifted over a mountain will cool adiabatically. If it is moist, it will reach saturation, and with further cooling will form clouds and precipitation.

FIGS. 44 AND 45. Cold air moving over a warm surface will be heated from below. Warming of the lower levels causes an increase in the temperature lapse rate. If sufficient heating occurs to increase the lapse rate in excess of the adiabatic, *instability* results, or the air becomes "top-heavy."

FIG. 46. Heating from below, causing instability, also results in con-

37

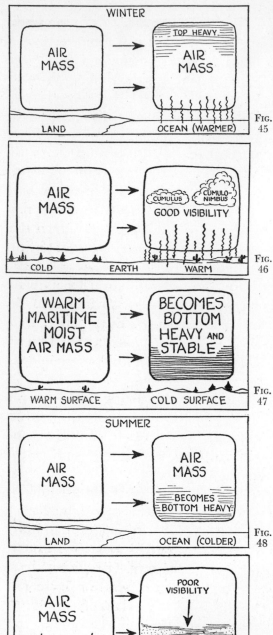

Fig. 45

Fig. 46

Fig. 47

Fig. 48

Fig. 49

vection. If the air contains moisture, and the relative humidity is sufficiently high, cooling during convection can cause cloudiness to form within the air mass. These clouds are usually of the cumulus or "piled wool" type.

FIGS. 47 AND 48. Cooling of warm air from below by passage over a cold surface decreases the temperature lapse rate to less than adiabatic, and promotes *stability*. In other words, the air becomes "bottom-heavy."

FIG. 49. If the cooling is sufficient to cause saturation and condensation, low clouds and fog form within the lower levels of the air.

AIR-MASS FAMILY

Flying weather changes, for better or worse, when one of two things happens: First, when an *air mass undergoes modification,* changing its original characteristics either while stationary or while moving away from its source; and second, when *air masses fail to mix well* because of differences in density, specific humidity, relative humidity, etc.

In these discussions of weather, for the sake of simplicity it will be well to concentrate on the analysis of air masses in and around the North American continent. The principles of weather analysis, however, are the same throughout the entire globe.

Fig. 50

39

FIG. 50. Take a look at this illustration. It is, as you will notice, "spotted" with air masses. Now, if you stop to think, you can readily determine from the "home addresses" (sources) of these air masses what their characteristics ought to be. The illustration itself is self-explanatory, and the terms used, as well as the abbreviations, are standardized in the United States.

Pc (Polar Continental) —Air mass from the northern continental areas
Pp (Polar Pacific) —Air mass from the North Pacific Ocean
Pa (Polar Atlantic) —Air mass from the North Atlantic Ocean
Ta (Tropical Atlantic) —From the Sargasso Sea
Tg (Tropical Gulf) —From the Gulf of Mexico and the Caribbean Sea
Tc (Tropical Continental) —From the southwestern continental area
Tp (Tropical Pacific) —From the trade-wind belt between California and the Hawaiian Islands

You must not conclude that the cyclonic area shown on the illustration is the only place where masses of different characteristics meet and make changeable weather; for cyclonic areas or traveling "lows" may be anywhere at all, over land or water. In this particular case the cyclonic area has been shown as covering the major part of the United States, for the simple reason that this is the territory most suitable for our discussions, and because it will help you to concentrate on the subject.

As air masses move from their sources, they begin to change. Through the middle latitudes (about 30° N. Lat. to 60° N. Lat.) they undergo considerable changes in their original characteristics.

In your study of weather maps, you will find various methods used to "label" air masses. *"Pc"* (Polar Continental), *Pp*, *Tg*, etc., are used in the following explanations.

"NPc," "NTg," etc., used by some meteorologists, simply mean that the air mass is "transitional" or has moved from its source.

Another system of designation indicates the number of days trajectory over land and water surfaces as *"$_1Pc_2$."* This means that after moving from its source, the *Pc* air passed over water for one day, and over land for two days. Such symbols are used so that you and the meteorologist can obtain, in a nutshell, general information pertaining to a particular air mass.

Degrees and types of modification vary considerably with seasons, the state of the surface over which the air travels, etc., snow-covered ground, ice, water, and other factors all having their effect. What you and I may finally

40

conclude about an air mass will be based, first, upon the latest information as to general characteristics of the air mass, and second, upon a study of its behavior and of the modifications it has undergone, not only during the past 24 hours, but frequently during the past several days as well. With actual experience you will, of course, be able to recognize and anticipate changes in air masses, particularly with the additional information available from upper-air soundings (wind, pressure, temperature, relative humidity, equivalent-potential temperature, and specific humidity).

In the United States some of the air masses shown in Fig. 50 enter the country more frequently than others. The most frequent visitors are *Pc* (Polar Continental), *Tg* (Tropical Gulf), *Pp* (Polar Pacific), and *Ta* (Tropical Atlantic). Because of the limited hot areas in the United States, *Tc* (Tropical Continental) is an infrequent visitor and therefore is relatively unimportant. *Pa* (Polar Atlantic) air is also an infrequent visitor, but, on the other hand, is an important one. The air circulation must be from the east or northeast, attending a well marked "low" or cyclonic disturbance, active in the northeast portions of the United States. The movement of this air into the country must, then, be against the prevailing circulation. Winter's more intense "lows" are more apt to invite visits of *Pa* air than are summer's "lows."

COLDER AIR MASSES

Polar Continental Air in Winter. At its source, in winter, *Pc* air is cold and stable. Its specific humidity is low. (Remember that cold air can hold less moisture than warm air.) There are few cloud forms or none at all; those which do exist are mostly fog. There is a *high relative humidity*. This may seem odd at first, but when you consider that *Pc* air can hold only a little moisture, you will realize that what little it does hold is as near the maximum as possible.

As it moves southward, the air is associated with what is commonly called a "cold wave," although the meteorological term is "cold front." With its inflow there are appreciable temperature drops at observation stations over which the "cold wave" passes. Rather high wind velocities are observed in the air, and there is usually turbulence extending to about 3000 feet. The bottom of the cold air mass becomes heated as it moves over a warmer surface, and the air mass itself becomes "top-heavy" within the lower 3000 feet, with turbulence as a natural result. The movement of warmer air from lower to higher levels, and the compensating sinking of the air at high levels, causes a downward movement of potentially warmer air. (See Fig. 32.) This causes an increase in surface temperatures, a condition which in turn decreases the relative humidity. (Remember that warm air holds more moisture than cold air.) The air is usually clear and cold when the air mass does not pass over comparatively warm water surfaces, such as the Great Lakes Region (which will be considered later) or away from zones where it meets other masses of different characteristics.

When an extensive southward, horizontal movement of the cold air takes place, reaching, say, as far as the vicinity of the Gulf of Mexico, you can be absolutely sure that such a mass will undergo considerable change, since the bottom has been warmed up, and additional moisture has crept in.

The addition of moisture and the increase in temperature which occur during fall and early winter when air passes over the Great Lakes before they are frozen, cause continuous snow over the lakes and the adjacent land areas. The higher terrain to the east causes further lifting of the cold air mass, thus intensifying the squalls. When temperatures are below freezing, your plane may be exposed, while in flight, to the icing hazards which prevail through the squalls and the clouds (strato-cumulus) associated with them. I will tell you more about squall characteristics later.

Pc (Polar Continental) occasionally moves southwest over the Rocky Mountains from the vicinity of British Columbia and eventually reaches the Pacific Coast. Lifting the air mass over the east side of the mountains causes snow squalls and a resultant loss of moisture through precipitation. At the mountain tops, the air is less moist than it was originally because of the precipitation which has fallen from it. Sinking of the mass over the west slopes toward the coast causes adiabatic heating of the air, with the final result that the air mass arrives at the coastline much warmer and dryer than it was originally. This condition causes mild winter weather along the Pacific Coast—a much better condition, in fact, than that associated with the flow of air off the Pacific Ocean.

Fig. 51. As a rule, weather in *Pc* air is good for flying when it is free from such radical modifications as those caused by lifting over mountains and warming by water. The air is rather smooth, except for turbulence caused by rough terrain and the slight warming from below. (You see, in winter

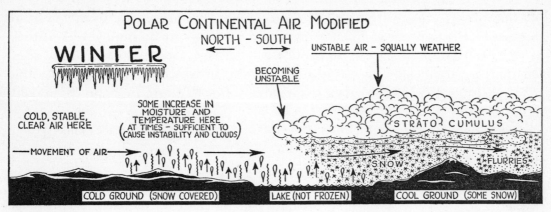

FIG. 51

the greater portion of the United States is snow-covered, so that the *Pc* air is less rapidly modified than in summer when all snow is melted.) East of the Great Lakes low ceilings and visibilities often occur because of snow squalls. The cloud tops through the squalls are usually from 5000 to 8000 feet, making the *optimum flight level* at those altitudes, rather than in or under the clouds. There may be considerable icing in the clouds when temperatures are below freezing. The air is rough in the clouds, but quite smooth above them. Because of higher relative humidities, ceilings are lowest in squalls during the colder part of the year. During the spring, much better ceilings prevail.

If you study Fig. 51 you will be able to see the progressive modification of the air. You will notice that the changes are slight until the air passes over unfrozen water and the bottom is warmed; convection sets in as the air takes a drink in the form of evaporated moisture, clouds form, and snow squalls begin. The turbulence of the squall is intensified as soon as the air is dynamically lifted over the higher terrain away from the lake shore.

FIG. 52. It is important that you understand the nature of a snow squall caused by the passage of cold air over warmer water. The general impression is that squalls observed along the Great Lakes form in the air after the air leaves the lake and enters the land areas to the east and south. Actually, however the squalls are formed over the water as shown in the illustration, and here is how it happens:

The cold air, which is dry and stable, enters the windward side of the lake

43

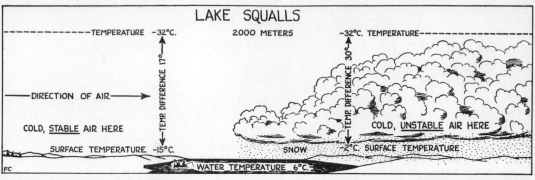

Fig. 52

at the left. Moisture is then added through evaporation from the lake, and the air is heated from below by contact with the warmer water. As you already know, heating from below makes the air unstable, with the result that vertical motions are set up within it. The specific humidity of the air is increased by the addition of moisture, making a larger amount of moisture available for condensation than was available before the air passed over the lake. Instability causes convection (vertical motions) which lifts the air to its "condensation level"—or to the point where sufficient cooling has occurred to cause saturation, condensation of moisture, and its precipitation as snow. All this happens *over the water*. True, lifting of the air mass on the other shore (to the right) will *intensify* the squalls, but such lifting is not the prime cause of the squalls. Notice, by the way, the difference in temperatures shown in the illustration. On the left-hand side you will see that the temperature difference between the surface and the 2000-meter level is 17° C. (Since this is less than adiabatic, it indicates a stable condition.) At the right side of the illustration, the temperature difference between the surface and the 2000-meter level is 30° C., the temperature having been increased by the heat below. This observed lapse rate is greater than the adiabatic, which is 20° C. for 2000 meters. What does this indicate? Instability, of course.

Fig. 53. During the summer, when the winter's snow is melted away and the ground becomes much warmer, *Pc* air undergoes more rapid modification, both at its source and in transit from its source. Because it is heated from below, the air develops very slight instability at its source, but still remains quite clear, as shown at the left of the illustration. *Pc* visits the United States less frequently in summer than in winter since the general circulation

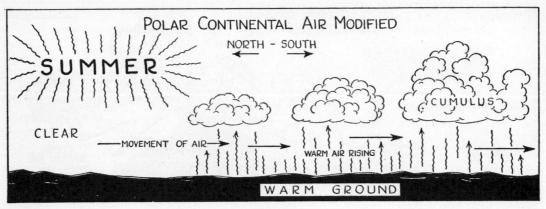

FIG. 53

is less intense. When the air does move southward during the warmer seasons, the moisture content (specific humidity) is much higher than in the winter. Because of convection, induced by heating from below, the moisture content also increases aloft, since the rising air currents carry the surface moisture upward, distributing it more evenly through the air. The temperature of the air is relatively low, but has a wide variation from night to day, due to intense heating during the day and cooling during the night. During the afternoon, sufficient convection is often induced to form small cumulus (wool-pack) clouds, as in the center of the illustration. After longer periods of time, when considerable moisture has been added to the air while stagnant over the southeastern portions of the country, larger cumulus clouds (as shown at the right of the illustration) develop, at times taking the form of local thunderstorms. After sunset, the air becomes stable due to cooling from below. One night's cooling during the summer is often enough to form ground fog in the air. (See Fig. 34.)

Flying through *Pc* air in summer, you will find smooth air outside the clouds—above, of course, the turbulence layer caused by rough terrain. If there are local thunderstorms in the air during the afternoon, flight through the clouds will, of course, be rough, but outside the storm-cloud area smooth air will prevail. The smaller cumulus clouds not built up into thunderstorm size can be topped during the afternoon at from 6000 to 8000 ft.

Polar Pacific Air (Pp) in Winter. Because the North Pacific Ocean narrows toward the north, and the area of water northwest and north-northwest

45

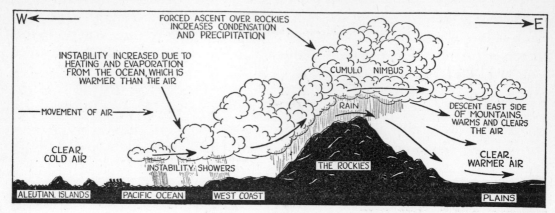

FIG 54

of the United States is smaller than due west or southwest, the air over the North Pacific Ocean in winter is usually of continental origin, modified by a comparatively short stay over water. This modification comes, as would logically be expected, from heating from below, or the creation of instability due to the addition of moisture and heat.

FIG. 54. Over the Aleutian Islands area, the air is quite clear and cold, since it has just left cold continental areas (see left of illustration). Instability caused by heating, and the addition of moisture from below, cause the development of clouds and showers as the air approaches the West Coast. Showers often begin a few hundred miles off the coast, as shown at the left center in the illustration. Showery weather becomes more pronounced when the air approaches the coastline. When the air is lifted over the Rocky Mountains, more precipitation falls from the air, chiefly in the form of rain, because of prevailing, above-freezing temperatures, and sometimes in the form of snow, particularly over the higher ridges. (See right center of illustration.)

Great changes take place within the air after it passes over the mountains and begins to sink into the plains east of the mountains. Most of the moisture contained in the air west of the mountains is lost through precipitation during the passage over the tops. When the air sinks on the east side of the range (as in the right side of the illustration) it is heated adiabatically and arrives over the plains with the temperature much higher than its original temperature, and with its specific humidity greatly lowered. (Remember the "lose-all-moisture" process in Fig. 29.)

46

During its descent east of the mountains, the air becomes clear, warm and very stable. It continues so for a long while after moving eastward. At times, however, there is an exception in this chain of events. This happens when cold *Pc* (Polar Continental) air occupies the area just east of the Rocky Mountains. This dense, cold air mass acts as a "wedge" over which the *Pp* air continues to rise east of the mountains, so that the *Pp* air cannot reach the surface. Naturally, if the air continues to rise, more cloudiness, condensation and precipitation form, and considerable snow falls east of the mountains.

You will experience roughness within the cloudiness of the air mass over the water, on the coast, and when overriding the mountains. The air is "convectively unstable" (see Fig. 30) and becomes turbulent *after saturation*. This means that outside the clouds the air will be much smoother than in the clouds. At times you will encounter icing conditions in the clouds, particularly over the mountains, where below-freezing temperatures are likely to prevail. East of the mountains, where the air becomes warmer and clear, flying is ideal.

Polar Atlantic Air in Winter. During the cold seasons, *Pa* air is an infrequent but important visitor to the United States, affecting the northeast portions of the country and the section east of the Appalachian Mountains. Although, like *Pp* air, *Pa* air is usually a modified continental type, the characteristics of the two polar ocean masses are quite dissimilar. *Pa* air is modified before reaching the United States by passage over the North Atlantic Ocean, which is colder than the Pacific. The colder water of the North Atlantic effects less change in the air mass than does the warmer water of the Pacific. Instability (topheaviness) develops in *Pa* air only in the lower levels, and showers resulting from instability do not usually occur. You will find more precipitation in the form of misting rains and occasional snow from stratiform clouds (well defined layers) in the lower levels of the air mass.

You will also find cloud tops at from 5000 to 8000 feet. This is because the layer of instability is quite shallow. Ceilings are frequently low, especially through the precipitation areas and over the ridges in the northeast portions of the United States, since relative humidities are usually high, allowing comparatively little adiabatic cooling through lifting to bring about saturation and condensation.

Icing hazards through the clouds in *Pa* air become an important consideration in winter. If you should fly through the clouds in *Pa* air for an extended period of time, your plane would become heavily coated with ice. Unless you have definite information about the severity of icing conditions, don't experiment with your own plane! Of course, we know that Cloudy Joe would try to fly his plane under these conditions, but that is his business.

In the lower levels, *Pa* air is turbulent over rough terrain. In the spring, when more heating and a greater amount of instability develop in the air mass, some instability showers will result.

Polar Pacific Air in Summer. In the summer time, instead of being heated from below, thus becoming more unstable, *Pp* air is cooled from below and thus becomes more stable. During the warm seasons, the ocean water is cooler than the air (the reverse of winter conditions). (See Figs. 45 and 48.) You will find large areas of coastal fog on the West Coast of the United States when *Pp* air flows inland in summer. An upwelling of colder ocean water characteristic of the coastal region causes the formation of a belt of comparatively colder water adjacent to the coast than lies farther out. This belt of colder water cools the air still further as it approaches the coastline. Cooling of the air from below (resulting in bottom-heaviness) with high wind velocities prevailing, causes a stratus (well-defined layer) cloud varying considerably in height, but lying always in the lower levels of the air mass. Under slight wind conditions, however, these clouds will be quite low. Because the land surfaces inland from the coast are warmer than the air and thus produce instability, the fogs will extend only a short distance inland. When instability is produced within the air, the fogs and low clouds are dissipated because stability is necessary for their life.

You will find that showers in this type of air mass occur only over the high ridges inland where great lifting of the air takes place. Even then, the clouds will be rather small. If you fly over the top of the low clouds and fog on the West Coast, you will find yourself in smooth air. But be careful in coming down through the cloud layer, for low ceilings and reduced visibility may make landing hazardous. If you notice that the temperature inversion (temperature increase with altitude) above the clouds is at, say, 4000 to 5000 feet, and that there is a brisk wind, you can expect ample ceilings and good visibility. If, on the other hand, the inversion base (beginning of the temperature rise) is low—say, 2500 to 3000 feet—and there is only a light wind, you can expect low ceilings and poor visibility in the air mass below the cloud layer. In other words, the stratus clouds always form under the inversion. Inland the roughness of the air caused by terrain is much in evidence, but this can easily be avoided by flying higher. I hope you will remember all this.

Polar Atlantic Air in Summer. You will find this air mass *(Pa)* characterized by fogs over the North Atlantic Coast, mostly in the form of stratus clouds rather high up, but occasionally very close to the surface. When the inflow of this air in summer is associated with "lows" active over the northeastern states, very low ceilings and visibilities prevail. You see, the difference in temperature between air and water in the oceans is reversed in summer: the ocean surface no longer warms the air, producing instability, as it does in winter. Instead, the water cools the air, causing stability, and resulting in stratus and fog weather types. You can easily see that the hazard to flight in this type of weather comes from low ceilings and poor visibility.

WARMER AIR MASSES

Tropical Continental Air (Tc). This type of air is of comparatively little importance in relation to flight at any season, although it is more important in summer than in winter. This is because the hot, continental areas of the United States and Mexico become more extensive during the warm seasons. The air is hot, and very dry. Although you will, at times, find this type of air quite unstable, it is free from clouds, since the relative humidity is so low that the lift (and cooling) necessary to saturate the air is abnormally high. Flying conditions are usually good, although during the day you will find turbulent air up to high levels.

The description of Tropical Maritime air masses which follows is longer than the discussions of other air-mass types, simply because Tropical Maritime masses, particularly *Tg* (Tropical Gulf) and *Ta* (Tropical Atlantic) are very important.

Tropical Pacific Air in Winter. This type of air originates in the tradewind belt between California and the Hawaiian Islands, an area of high pressure. *Tp* air is important in the western part of the United States during the winter. The ocean water is comparatively cool in this area, and the fact that the air has originated in areas of high pressure tends to have a stabilizing effect on it. (Remember that sinking of air causes increased stability. See Fig. 33.) Some cumulus clouds with showers are observed in the air over the ocean off the Mexican Coast, but these clouds do not reach the size of those observed in the other tropical maritime masses. With movement northward, the air necessarily moves over colder ocean water, with a resultant increase in stability. Because of this change from instability to stability, there is also a change in cloud type. Clouds originally of the cumulus (wool-pack) type are replaced by clouds of the stratus or strato-cumulus (layer) types. Turbulence decreases with the stability brought about by cooling from below. Cloud tops are lowered to between 5000 and 8000 feet. Steady lifting of winter *Tp* air over an underlying wedge of colder, denser air (later identified as "warm front") causes rain over the West Coast of the United States. The air mass and its weather are for the most part important only to the West Coast, but occasionally *Tp* air overrides the Rocky Mountains. If at such times there is a layer of deep, cold *Pc* air occupying the regions just east of the Rocky Mountains, the upward glide of *Tp* air continues over the air east of the mountains, causing snow.

You will find flying conditions quite favorable except when low ceilings and poor visibility are encountered in the precipitation areas because of continued rainfall. Turbulence in the clear and cloudy portions of the air is not severe, because the air is noticeably lacking in convectional instability. (See Fig. 30.)

In summer the normal air flow over the Pacific Ocean is unfavorable to visits of *Tp* to the United States because of the prevailing high-pressure area over the ocean adjacent to the United States.

During the winter, the other Tropical Maritime air masses differ in characteristics from *Tp*. *Tg* (Tropical Gulf) air, originating over the Gulf of Mexico and the Caribbean Sea, and *Ta* (Tropical Atlantic) air, originating over the Sargasso Sea, are extremely important in the United States. At the source, ocean water temperatures are high, as are air temperature and specific humidity, so that the air is characterized by conditional instability. (Remember that in Fig. 23 the air was shown as stable when unsaturated, but that it turned "about face" when saturation occurred?)

Tg air has a very high specific humidity, and because this large amount of moisture almost saturates the air, the relative humidity is also quite high. (Warm air can hold more moisture than cold air, and in this case it holds almost all the moisture it can take.) Because of its high relative humidity, this kind of air does not have to be lifted very high to cause sufficient cool-

50

ing to bring about condensation; therefore this air is characterized by strato-cumulus and stratus (layer type) clouds. *Tg* is slowly lifted when it moves inland over the sloping terrain of the southern United States. This lifting is gradual, and not great enough to release the potential instability of the air. With continued movement over colder land surfaces to the north, northeast and northwest, the air becomes more and more stable, the relative humidity increases, and low clouds and fog form in the lower levels of the air mass over cold ground.

Night and early morning weather within the air mass will be cloudy, with clouds of stratus or strato-cumulus type. After being heated by the sun during the day, the lower clouds often disappear and the air becomes clear. Local thunderstorms do not occur under these conditions. (Local thunderstorms, incidentally, are defined as storms caused by intense local surface heating. This surface heating brings about an instability in the lower levels sufficient to cause a lift which releases the conditional instability of the air.) If, however, the air is lifted by a mountain range or by a wedge of colder, denser air, the lift may be sufficient to release the conditional instability of the air, even in winter, and heavy showers or thundershowers will result. (It will be beneficial if you stretch your imagination in these discussions; visit the air masses at their "home addresses" and travel with them, mentally, as they go places.)

In winter, the *Ta* air mass moving northward from its source region over the Sargasso Sea is cooled from below by the colder ocean water and stability (bottom-heaviness) results. Prolonged cooling of the air mass during its northward travel produces fog over extensive areas. Lifting of the *Ta* air over a wedge of colder, denser air above the northern portions of the Atlantic Ocean and along the Atlantic Coast of the United States produces cloudiness and causes considerable precipitation to fall from the *Ta* air mass. The famous "northeasters" of the northeastern United States—both rain and snow—are the result of the overrunning of colder air by warm, moist *Ta* air.

Your flight through tropical maritime masses in winter will be quite smooth and pleasant, except when the ceilings and visibilities are reduced under very low stratus clouds or in fog areas. There are no icing hazards and no severe turbulence except when sufficient lifting of the air occurs to release its instability. (Refer again to Fig. 23 for an explanation of conditional instability.)

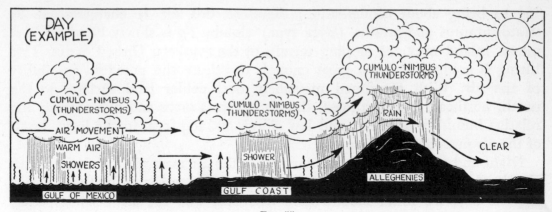

DAY
(EXAMPLE)

CUMULO - NIMBUS
(THUNDERSTORMS)

AIR MOVEMENT

WARM AIR

SHOWERS

GULF OF MEXICO

CUMULO - NIMBUS
THUNDERSTORMS)

SHOWER

GULF COAST

CUMULO - NIMBUS
(THUNDERSTORMS)

RAIN

CLEAR

ALLEGHENIES

Fig. 55

Tg and Ta air are particularly important in the summer. Solar radiation and surface heating over land areas are greatly augmented during the summer, causing low pressure to prevail generally over the continental area of the United States. Over the Atlantic Ocean, where the air is comparatively colder and denser, a semi-permanent "high" prevails. This combination of ocean high pressure and continental low pressure is very favorable for a steady flow of tropical maritime air masses into the United States from "high" to "low." Because the land surfaces are warmer, and the warm maritime air flows far northward into the country, the southern edge of the cold polar air is quite far north, only occasionally reaching the southern portions of the country in intermittent outbreaks of cold air.

Characteristics of Tg and Ta air at the sources in summer are similar in many respects to their winter characteristics. The air is warmer, moister and more convectively unstable to higher levels in summer than in winter, while the amount of lifting required to saturate the air, due to the higher moisture content and higher relative humidity, is less than in winter.

One of the greatest differences between the tropical maritime air masses of summer and those of winter is the modification which occurs with movement over land. *Heating,* rather than *cooling* from below, causes increasing instability. When there is sufficient convection, pronounced instability develops, causing thunderstorms within the air.

Fig. 55. Study this illustration, which shows Tg air moving northward over land from the Gulf of Mexico. At the left you will notice showers and

52

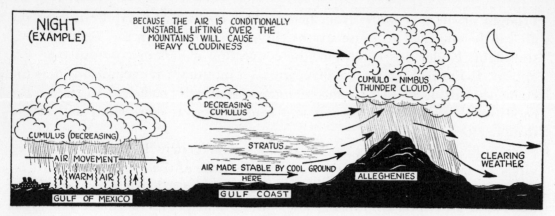

NIGHT (EXAMPLE)

BECAUSE THE AIR IS CONDITIONALLY UNSTABLE LIFTING OVER THE MOUNTAINS WILL CAUSE HEAVY CLOUDINESS

CUMULO - NIMBUS (THUNDER CLOUD)

DECREASING CUMULUS

CUMULUS (DECREASING)

AIR MOVEMENT

STRATUS

AIR MADE STABLE BY COOL GROUND HERE

WARM AIR

CLEARING WEATHER

ALLEGHENIES

GULF OF MEXICO

GULF COAST

FIG. 56

thunderstorms, the result of instability brought about by heating and by the addition of moisture in the lower levels of the air. As the air moves inland, as in the center section of the illustration, you will see that the source of heat from below is still available over the hot ground, although the source of moisture is cut off. Continuation of instability results, with showers and thundershowers continuing in the air. Lifting of the air over a mountain range, as shown to the right in the illustration, will cause more intense convection, heavier precipitation, and more severe thunderstorm activity.

As the air moves farther northward, much of the moisture is lost through precipitation. The specific and relative humidities decrease and the lift required to cause saturation and condensation becomes greater. Air-mass clouds and thunderstorms become less and less frequent the farther north Tg moves from its source. The air, then, is characteristically clear. It still retains that old tropical maritime air characteristic, "conditional instability," however. Any great lifting of the air, as over wedges of colder, denser air, will release the instability and cause thunderstorms at a high level.

Ta characteristics are much the same as those of Tg, except that sea-fogs sometimes result during the night and early morning with the passing of the air over colder ocean water.

FIG. 56. A different type of modification is shown in this illustration. The same Tg air is moving away from its source at night over cooler ground. Cumulus clouds, at the left, tend to decrease overland, due to the stability

53

brought about by cooling from below. This cooling and stabilization of the air can be sufficient to cause stratus clouds to form within the Tg air during the night. Under this condition, the convection clouds of cumulus type disappear. If the path of the air mass crosses a mountain range, as shown at the right, the lifting caused by the mountains is usually sufficient to release the conditional instability of the air and cause vigorous convection and severe thunderstorms.

Your flight through Tg or Ta air in summer may be through varying kinds of weather. In the early morning, because of the cooling of the air by the cool ground adjacent to the Gulf Coast or the Atlantic Coast, extensive low cloud areas prevail, causing low ceilings and poor visibilities, but flight above the clouds will be in clear, smooth air. The sun's heat in later morning, after sunrise, breaks up the lower stratus clouds, while later in the day, convection develops cumulus clouds which at times grow into thunderstorm proportions. You can usually fly around local thunderstorms, avoiding severe turbulence and keeping to the smooth air outside the clouds. Flight through such storms, of course, is hazardous. When thunderstorms are caused in the tropical maritime air masses by extensive lifting of the air along wedges of colder, denser air, the weather becomes hazardous for flying, because, instead of individual storms, you will encounter a line of continuous storm action.

Flying through a wind shift may mean
a good shaking up.

CLOUDS

Once you have learned to identify cloud types and to correlate them with certain atmospheric modifications, you will have taken a long step toward proficiency in practical weather forecasting. Certain cloud types form integral links in the chain of identification of air masses and their interaction with each other. The following description and illustrations of cloud forms are based upon name and probable cause of formation.

FIG. 57

FIG. 57. In the upper background are the thin, wispy clouds known as "cirrus" (*Ci.*). These clouds are indicative of fine weather and are caused by a very high overrunning warmer air. They are composed of small ice crystals.

The lower portions of the picture show "cumulus" clouds (*Cu.*). These resemble piled wool and vary in size with intensity of the vertical currents producing them. They are the convection clouds brought about by insta-

55

Fig. 58

bility within an air mass, and occasionally by lifting of the air over high terrain. Tropical Maritime air masses contain many cumulus clouds. Polar Continental air, when modified during summer movement southward, is characterized by increasing cumulus.

FIG. 58. When the overrunning of cold dense air by warmer, lighter air is widespread, the cirrus clouds thicken into "cirro-stratus" (*Ci.St.*) as shown

56

FIG. 59

in the illustration. The sky appears milky, an effect due to the spreading of the thin, whitish sheet overhead.

This cloud layer will thicken when the level at which overrunning occurs becomes lower, or when the cold air being overrun by the warmer becomes more shallow.

FIG. 59. When the clouds drop lower and form a darker sheet at levels

FIG. 60

lower than cirro-stratus, from which rain or snow often falls, the layer is called "alto-stratus" (*A.St.*). An alto-stratus cloud layer is solid in the lower background, but broken by the wind in the foreground as shown in the illustration.

FIG. 60. Instability in the lower levels of air masses usually causes the formation of a type of cloud characterized by its "roll" appearance. The

58

FIG. 61

darker cloud masses shown in the illustration are typical. The name given to these clouds is "strato-cumulus" *(St.Cu.)*. Stratus *(St.)* is also a low-level cloud type, occurring at strato-cumulus levels or lower. The difference between these cloud types is that whereas strato-cumulus is characterized by a "roll" appearance, the stratus cloud is definitely a sheet cloud. Stability brought about by cooling from below is favorable for the formation of stratus

59

FIG. 62

clouds in warm air masses. During precipitation, addition of moisture to the cooler air through which the precipitation is falling, by evaporation, will cause frequent formation of stratus within the cool air.

FIG. 61. This illustration shows small strato-cumulus clouds decreasing in size and melting away due to sinking after sunset, when the cause of instability (sun's heat) is removed. Frequently during the day the sky will be overcast with strato-cumulus clouds caused by the air's instability, while at night, after instability ceases, the clouds diminish and the sky becomes clear.

Fig. 62.   Cumulus clouds often grow to enormous sizes. Thunderstorm clouds are of the cumulus family, but owing to the size of the cloud and its attendant weather, they are named "cumulo-nimbus" *(Cu.Nb.)*. The cloud with the "boiling" appearance in the illustration has reached thunderstorm proportions, and can be called "cumulo-nimbus." Precipitation from this type of cloud is usually showery. Watch for strong vertical currents within the cloud, as indicated by the continuous action of the sides and top during its growth. Avoid flight through such a cloud; entering it would mean encountering extreme turbulence. Cloudy Joe has flown through this type of cloud on several occasions, and has emerged badly shaken up.

A cloud type caused by convection, but of higher-level character, is the alto-cumulus *(A.Cu.)*, frequently called "mackerel sky." Another, cirro-cumulus *(Ci.Cu.)*, is of the same type, but much higher. Upper-level instability brought about by lifting and cooling of convectively unstable layers of air (see Fig. 30) causes these cloud forms.

A rough general classification of heights at which these various clouds occur follows:

At the very high levels—cirrus, cirro-stratus, and cirro-cumulus *(Ci., Ci.-St.,* and *Ci.Cu.)*

At the intermediate levels (roughly 6000 to 9000 feet)—alto-stratus and alto-cumulus *(A.St.* and *A.Cu.)*

At the lower levels (roughly 6000 feet and below)—strato-cumulus, cumulus, and stratus *(St.Cu., Cu.,* and *St.)*

At the lower levels, but extending into intermediate and higher levels—cumulo-nimbus *(Cu.Nb.)*.

A cloud is like a store sign—it tells you
what to expect inside.

V

WEATHER MAP AND TELETYPE SYMBOLS

CHARTING your course in advance according to weather conditions is the first step in safe flying. That is why the symbols given in this chapter are so important. They are the "a-b-c's" of the weather map, and unless you know how to read and interpret weather maps, you had better let the other fellow do the flying.

FIG. 63.   Here you have the symbols which actually appear on the weather map. The first group of symbols indicates the state of the weather *at the observation station*. Study them carefully. Cloudy Joe never will get the hang of them, but you will need to know them when you come to the illustrations under "Atmospheric Fronts" and "Practical Forecasting for the Airman."

You probably won't have any difficulty in memorizing cloud and pressure tendency symbols; the latter particularly almost speak for themselves. Incidentally, pressure tendency is based on the *net* pressure change, in hundredths of an inch, during the *three hours previous* to the time of observation.

Almost all meteorologists use Admiral Beaufort's scale of wind force. The symbols, you will notice, are straight, slanting lines, or "barbs." These barbs are attached to arrow shafts which "fly with the wind"—that is, point in the direction toward which the wind is blowing—and the arrows touch the edge of the circle marking the observation station on the map.

Turn to Figs. 78, 79, and 80 to see how these various symbols appear in actual use. Each cluster of symbols and figures represents a different observation station.

FIG. 64.   The United States Department of Commerce transmits weather reports by teletype from a vast network of stations throughout the country. These reports are sent according to the following standardized order: Ceiling; sky conditions; visibility; weather; obstructions to vision; temperature;

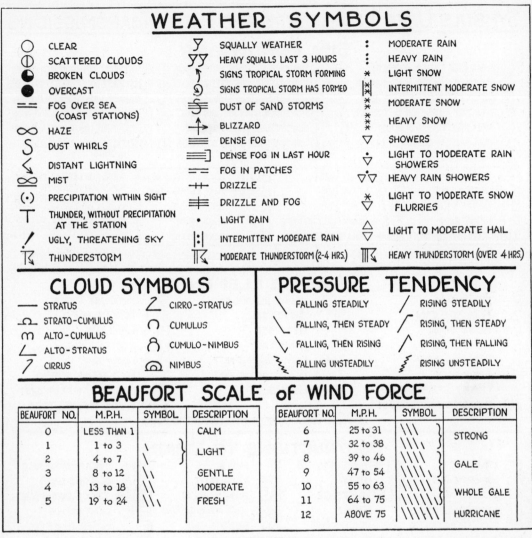

Fig. 63

dewpoint; wind direction; velocity; character of gusts; barometric pressure; field conditions and remarks.

The first factor to be considered in these teletyped reports is ceiling. A ceiling is *unlimited* when the clouds are high (above 9571 feet) or when there are scattered clouds (clouds covering less than 5/10 of the sky) below that level. No report is made on an unlimited ceiling, but a limited ceiling

63

Symbols Used In Teletype and Radio Transmissions

Sky Conditions

- ◯ CLEAR (LESS THAN 1/10 COVERED)
- ◑ SCATTERED CLOUDS (1/10 TO 5/10 COVERED)
- ◍ BROKEN CLOUDS (5/10 TO 9/10 COVERED)
- ⊕ OVERCAST (MORE THAN 9/10 COVERED)
- ◐/HIGH SCATTERED CLOUDS
- ◑/HIGH BROKEN CLOUDS
- ⊕/HIGH OVERCAST

- ⊕/◑ HIGH OVERCAST, LOWER BROKEN CLOUDS
- ⊕/◐ HIGH OVERCAST, LOWER SCATTERED CLOUDS
- ◍/◍ HIGH BROKEN, LOWER BROKEN CLOUDS
- ◍/◐ HIGH BROKEN, LOWER SCATTERED CLOUDS
- ◐/◍ HIGH SCATTERED, LOWER BROKEN CLOUDS
- ◐/◐ HIGH SCATTERED, LOWER SCATTERED CLOUDS

- ⊕◑ OVERCAST, LOWER BROKEN CLOUDS
- ⊕◐ OVERCAST, LOWER SCATTERED CLOUDS
- ◍◍ BROKEN, LOWER BROKEN CLOUDS
- ◍◐ BROKEN, LOWER SCATTERED CLOUDS
- ◐◍ SCATTERED, LOWER BROKEN CLOUDS
- ◐◐ SCATTERED, LOWER SCATTERED CLOUDS

F+	DENSE FOG	SL+	HEAVY SLEET	BD+	THICK BLOWING DUST
IF+	DENSE ICE FOG	HL+	HEAVY HAIL	BSA+	THICK BLOWING SAND
S+	HEAVY SNOW	MI+	HEAVY MIST	K+	THICK SMOKE
R+	HEAVY RAIN	ZMI+	HEAVY FREEZING MIST	H+	THICK HAZE
ZR+	HEAVY FREEZING RAIN	BS+	THICK BLOWING SNOW	D+	THICK DUST

THESE ARE USED AS THE SKY CONDITION WHENEVER THEIR PRESENCE REDUCES THE CEILING TO ZERO, AND/OR THE VISIBILITY TO ONE-FIFTH MILE, OR LESS

NOTE: THE USE OF THE PLUS (+) OR MINUS (−) SIGN PRECEDING THE CLOUDINESS SYMBOLS INDICATES "DARK" & "THIN" RESPECTIVELY

Weather Elements

R−	LIGHT RAIN	ZR+	HEAVY FREEZING RAIN	SL	MODERATE SLEET
R	MODERATE RAIN	SP	SPRINKLING	SL+	HEAVY SLEET
R+	HEAVY RAIN	MI−	LIGHT MIST	HL−	LIGHT HAIL
S−	LIGHT SNOW	MI+	HEAVY MIST	HL	MODERATE HAIL
S	MODERATE SNOW	ZMI−	LIGHT FREEZING MIST	HL+	HEAVY HAIL
S+	HEAVY SNOW	ZMI+	HEAVY FREEZING MIST	T−	MILD THUNDERSTORM
ZR−	LIGHT FREEZING RAIN	SL−	LIGHT SLEET	T	MODERATE THUNDERSTORM
ZR	MODERATE FREEZING RAIN			T+	SEVERE THUNDERSTORM

TORNADO (ALWAYS WRITTEN OUT IN FULL)

Obstructions to Vision

F−	LIGHT FOG	GF+	DENSE GROUND FOG	D	DUSTY	BD+	THICK BLOWING DUST
F	MODERATE FOG	H	HAZY	D+	THICK DUST	BSA	BLOWING SAND
F+	DENSE FOG	H+	THICK HAZE	BS	BLOWING SNOW	BSA+	THICK BLOWING SAND
GF−	LIGHT GROUND FOG	K	SMOKY	BS+	THICK BLOWING SNOW	IF−	LIGHT ICE FOG
GF	MODERATE GROUND FOG	K+	THICK SMOKE	BD	BLOWING DUST	IF	MODERATE ICE FOG
						IF+	DENSE ICE FOG

Wind Direction

- ↓ NORTH
- ↓↙ NORTH-NORTHEAST
- ↙ NORTHEAST
- ←↙ EAST-NORTHEAST
- ← EAST
- ←↖ EAST-SOUTHEAST
- ↖ SOUTHEAST
- ↑↖ SOUTH-SOUTHEAST
- ↑ SOUTH
- ↑↗ SOUTH-SOUTHWEST
- ↗ SOUTHWEST
- →↗ WEST-SOUTHWEST
- → WEST
- →↘ WEST-NORTHWEST
- ↘ NORTHWEST
- ↓↘ NORTH-NORTHWEST

Character of the Wind

- G− FRESH GUSTS
- G STRONG GUSTS
- G+ SEVERE GUSTS
- V VARIABLE

(ABOVE IS INDICATED, WHEN APPROPRIATE, IMMEDIATELY FOLLOWING THE VELOCITY, WITHOUT SPACE OR OBLIQUE)

COURTESY of the U.S. DEPT. of AGRICULTURE, WEATHER BUREAU.

FIG. 64

is always reported, and its height, measured or estimated, is given in hundreds of feet. When the height is estimated, it is preceded by the letter E.

You can readily see how easy it is to combine these various symbols in sending reports. A symbol placed before a diagonal, for instance, refers to high clouds; placed after the diagonal, it refers to low clouds. Plus and minus signs used with sky condition symbols indicate dark and thin clouds, respectively. Used with weather elements and obstructions to vision, the plus and minus signs show intensity. Arrows used to transmit wind direction fly with the wind. Temperature and dewpoint are reported in degrees Fahrenheit, and the velocity of the wind in miles per hour.

How these various symbols appear when they are sent over the teletype is shown in Fig. 67.

*   *   *

One of the most important pieces of information that a meteorologist can give you is the height of the ceiling. He takes this measurement either during the day or at night.

During the day, observation stations generally obtain ceiling measurements by releasing balloons inflated with hydrogen for a predetermined rise per minute. When the ceiling is low, small balloons are used, and the height of the ceiling is obtained by counting the number of minutes between the release of the balloon and its entrance into the cloud base, and multiplying this number by the rate of rise (feet, meters) per minute.

Higher ceilings are measured by larger balloons as they take upper air soundings. These balloons are also inflated for a predetermined rise per minute, and their ascent is carefully observed by means of a theodolite, a sort of surveyor's transit. With the theodolite a reading is obtained both for the elevation angle of the balloon and for its azimuth angle (the number of degrees from true north on the horizontal scale). From these values the distance of the balloon at various levels is computed. When the balloon enters the cloud base during an upper air sounding, its altitude at the moment of entrance is taken as the height of the ceiling. When a large protractor is used in conjunction with the theodolite, the direction and velocity of the balloon at various levels are also computed.

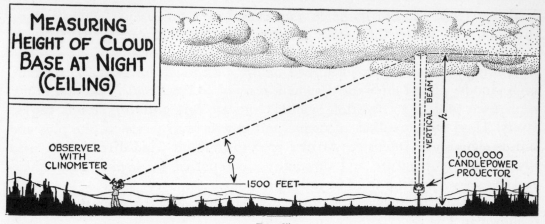

FIG. 65

FIG. 65. Here you have an illustration of how ceilings are measured at night. A vertical light projector throws a spot of light directly above itself on the cloud base. An observer, standing 500 feet or more from the projector, reads the vertical angle of the light spot by means of a clinometer, an instrument for obtaining angular inclination. By means of trigonometric tables, the observer then computes the height of the ceiling according to the formula:

$$H \text{ (ceiling)} = \text{base line} \times \text{Tan. } \Theta$$

Tan. Θ being the tangent of the angle indicated on the clinometer.

The observer in our illustration would compute the distance as "$H = 1500$ Tan. Θ" since he is standing 1500 feet away from the projector. At observation stations the projector and usually the clinometer have fixed locations. In predetermined installations of this kind, the altitude of the cloud base is often obtained by a direct reading from the instrument.

FIG. 66. This map will give you some idea of the number of observation stations throughout the United States which forward regular reports on upper air soundings. The pilot balloon stations obtain data on wind direction and velocity, while the airplane stations obtain a different type of upper air data which will be described in detail later on.

Balloon soundings of the upper wind are forwarded regularly over the teletype system, the wind direction being sent in tens of degrees with true north as the reference, and velocity being sent in miles per hour. Such a teletype

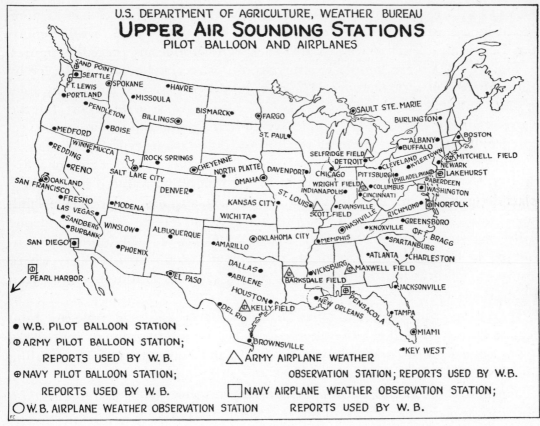

FIG. 66

message would look like this: "WA 17 01818 2033 22138 2240 42343 2444 62446 2350 82354," with each of the larger groups of figures referring to observations at a different level, figured in thousands of feet starting at the surface. Translated, the message becomes:

WA	Washington, D. C.
17	1700 (on the 24-hour clock, or 5:00 P.M., E.S.T.)
01818	Surface level (designated by "0"); wind, 180° true, at 18 miles per hour
2033	Wind at 1000-foot level, 200° at 33 m.p.h.
22138	Wind at 2000-foot level (indicated by the first "2") 210° at 38 m.p.h.
2240	Wind at 3000-foot level, 220° at 40 m.p.h.

and so forth. Reports for the surface and for even thousands of feet are preceded by a figure (0 for surface; 2 for 2000, 4 for 4000, etc.) , while reports for the odd thousands of feet altitude are given without any preceding figures.

Fig. 67. Here are sample weather reports as received over the teletype by the Department of Commerce. These reports are forwarded hourly by each station and, taken in sequence, give a continuous weather report for the various airway routes. The samples given here, as you can see, are not in sequence; I have chosen them at random to show various types of weather.

Notice that some of these reports include a weather class designation—"C" and "I." "X" is also used, though not in the reports reproduced here. These class designations are used by stations located at airports and describe landing conditions. If ceiling and visibility range from zero to 500 feet and one mile, the station reports itself as "Class X." "Class X" conditions are considered below minimum for landing except at certain airline ports where approach facilities are better and for which separate minimums have been established.

If ceiling and visibility range from 500 feet and one mile to 1500 feet and three miles, the station reports as "Class I," and instrument approaches are necessary until conditions change. A "Class C" airport must have ceiling and visibility of better than 1500 feet and three miles.[1]

Stations where clouds are observed include information as to amount, type and direction of movement at the end of their reports.

Fig. 68. Airplane observations (APOBS) are reported by teletype every day from various stations to the Department of Commerce, and include altitude, pressure, temperature, relative humidity, equivalent-potential temperature, and specific humidity for each successive flight level; cloud conditions; turbulence levels, icing levels, and haze levels.

All this information is obtained as a result of special airplane sounding flights, usually made in the morning, weather permitting. An airplane containing an *aerograph* goes aloft in a slow climb to about 17,000 feet. During the ascent, temperature, relative humidity, and pressure values are recorded on the aerograph. From these values other elements are computed which are valuable in determining the type and actual structure of the air mass or

---

[1] These requirements have recently been changed to: *Class C*—ceiling, 800 feet or more (day) ; 1000 feet or more (night) ; visibility, 3 miles or more; *Class N:* (replacing Class I) —ceiling, 500 to 800 feet; visibility, 1 to 3 miles.

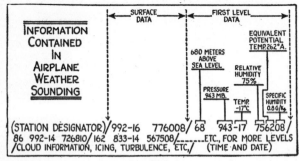

Fig. 68

masses through which the sounding flight is made.

Now look at the "APOBS" report and the explanation that is given in the illustration. No altitude is given for ground level, though for the life of him Cloudy Joe can't see why. Altitude is given for the first level above ground (and for succeeding levels) and is reported in hundreds of meters above sea level, with the last zero omitted—that is, "68" means "680 meters above sea level." The next group reported for the first and succeeding levels is made up of pressure, given in millibars, and temperature in Degrees Centigrade, both of which values are obtained during the sounding flight. The last group for each level includes relative humidity as recorded in flight, and the equivalent-potential temperature, which is computed after flight. This is given in Degrees Absolute (0° C. = 273° A.). But notice this: Only the last two figures of the equivalent-potential temperature value are given; the first one is omitted. In the case of cold air, this omitted figure is generally "2"; in warm air, "3." Specific humidity is given its full value and is expressed as grams and tenths of a gram of moisture per kilogram of air.

Next, the "APOBS" indicates cloud conditions—where they exist—giving type, bases and tops when available for each level. Turbulence, icing, and haze levels are given in tens of meters. For instance, the notation "Tbc. 24-150" in a report translates into: "Turbulence from 240 meters to 1500 meters"; and "10St.Cu./U, 89-200" indicates a cloud level that covers 10/10 of the sky and extends from 890 meters to 2000 meters, with direction of movement unknown (U).

Knowledge can only be passed on—not poured in!

VI

ATMOSPHERIC FRONTS AND CYCLONES

(The Air Bullies)

IF YOU have been talking shop lately with a weather expert, you have probably heard a good deal about "fronts." Well, a front is simply a boundary, or zone of sharp transition, between air masses of different characteristics. The atmosphere puts up a front, so to speak, when air circulation brings air masses of different origin or modification into close proximity with each other. It is very easy to imagine, for example, that if a warm, tropical, maritime air mass meets a cold, polar, continental air mass, a boundary will develop between the two, with the colder, denser air tending to muscle in beneath the lighter, warmer air.

Do you remember that in Fig. 9 I showed you how different values of pressure and specific volume within the atmosphere set up a circulation between masses having density differences? Turn back to that illustration now and notice how the lines of equal pressure and the lines of equal specific volume intersect, with small, closed circulations taking place within the intersection. The crowding of these intersections, or the increase in small "cells" between the two air masses, shows that the density difference between the air masses is increasing and that the lines of equal pressure and equal specific volume are changing more sharply from one mass to the other. Assume that the concentration of these small cells in the atmospheric front is about twenty times the normal distribution within the air mass, and you will get a clearer idea of just what the zone of transition between air masses (that is, the front) is like.

FIG. 69. When enough of these cells have crowded together to form a concentration field of about 10 km. (six miles) in width, we consider that a front has formed between the air masses involved. You know, of course, from a previous definition that potential temperature is constant during unsaturated, adiabatic changes. Isotherms, therefore, are used to show the crowding of two air masses along a front, since increases or decreases in pressure at-

71

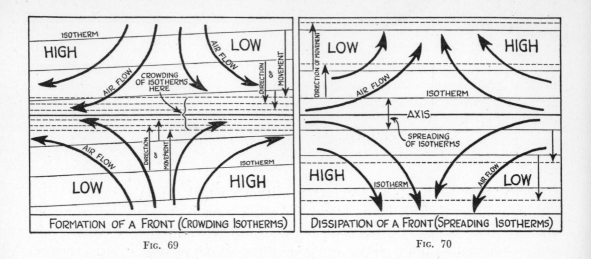

FORMATION OF A FRONT (CROWDING ISOTHERMS)

FIG. 69

DISSIPATION OF A FRONT (SPREADING ISOTHERMS)

FIG. 70

tending the air movement along the surface will not change their potential temperature values.

The illustration shows an air circulation which is favorable to the crowding of isotherms in the air involved. The isotherms in the upper and lower parts of the drawing, for example, tend to crowd at the intersection of the masses because of the resistance offered by the opposing circulation. After crowding, the space between the isotherms will be much smaller that it was in the free circulation, and as a result of all this crowding between the individual circulations, the temperature difference from one mass to the other will become sharper. When this difference in potential temperature becomes greater than 10° C. throughout a zone 10 km. wide or less, a front results—provided the zone of temperature difference extends far enough vertically. Fronts where the temperature difference extends vertically less than three-quarters of a mile or even one mile are not considered important. Lower levels can easily be affected by normal temperature changes from day to night without forming actual fronts.

The ability of the atmosphere to put up a good "front" is important, for, according to the accepted theory, fronts and frontal zones are essential in the development of cyclones. Do you see now why it is important for you and the meteorologist to be able to recognize the existence of fronts and to be able to place them properly on weather maps?

Aside from primary fronts, you will frequently find secondary fronts forming within the forward moving portions of the air. This is particularly true in air of polar origin which is rapidly modified with movement away from its source. Great horizontal temperature differences can develop within the air mass in a short time because of this unequal modification. The curved flow of air into a "low" area tends to bring about a circulation within the air mass that is favorable for crowding the isotherms and developing a front. These secondary fronts are of great importance to you and the forecaster, and have a marked effect upon flying weather.

Fig. 70.   Sometimes air circulates in such a way that the isotherms tend to spread away from the axis. In this case the difference across the transitional zone between the air masses is decreased, the zone or front is dissipated, and air circulation is unfavorable for the formation of another front.

Fig. 71.   Atmospheric fronts are actually sloping surfaces, with the degree of slope varying considerably from time to time. The line indicating a front on a weather map is merely the intersection of this sloping surface with the surface of the earth. Now, if you could take a horizontal cross-section of a

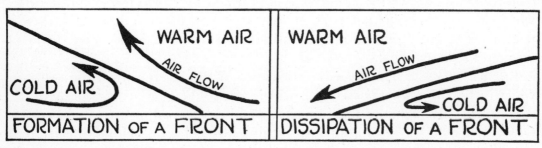

Fig. 71   Fig. 72

front, you would find the circulation of air and the attendant crowding of isotherms as shown in Fig. 69. Here you have a vertical cross-section of the same front. Now, use your head and you will see that the constant movement of air masses toward each other can produce only one result—the continuation and intensification of the front.

Fig. 72.   This vertical cross-section of a front shows a condition which is the reverse of that in the preceding figure. From the way the air is circulating here, you will readily conclude that it won't be long before the movement of the air masses away from each other breaks the whole front up by dissolving the sharp zone lying between them.

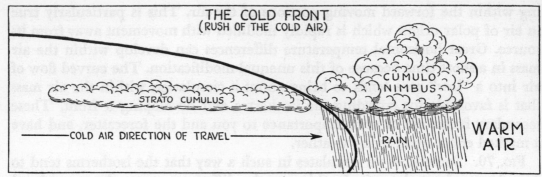

FIG. 73

FIG. 73. A cold front is formed when a mass of cold, heavy air rushes under a light, warm air mass and shoves it up. This pushing up of warm air is just what you would expect, considering the difference in density between the two air masses. As the warm air is shoved up, it cools adiabatically, generally to such an extent that saturation and cloud formation result. These clouds are usually of the cumulus type, formed by convection, or instability within the air mass. (Look back at Fig. 56 if you don't remember how this works.) The precipitation which follows is showery if it takes the form of rain, and squally if it falls as snow.

Because of the instability and turbulence of the layers within the cold air, you will find that clouds continue within the cold air after the passage of the cold front, although the precipitation is either stopped or greatly decreased. Of course, clouds continue to form within the cold air behind the front if precipitation from clouds formed by the lifting of warm air falls through the colder air, saturating certain levels by evaporation.

During warmer portions of the year, when conditions are favorable for the flow of tropical maritime air masses in the path of cold outbreaks, thunderstorms occur along the cold front because of the lifting of the warm air and the release of its potential instability, followed by violent convection (vertical movement) within the clouds.

FIG. 74. A warm front has a much greater slope than a cold front, as you will see from studying this illustration. In the formation of a warm front, the warm air takes a long, steady climb over a wedge of cold air. This slow lifting of the warmer air is attended by the formation of alto-stratus clouds, the logical result of slow lifting and cooling. But there are also other types

74

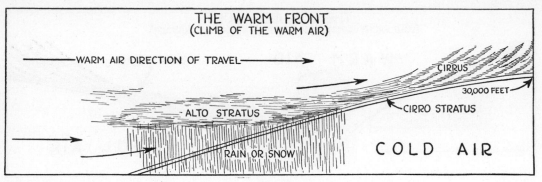

FIG. 74

of cloud which develop with the formation of a warm front. You will find cirrus, for example, far from the intersection of the warm front with the ground, where the cold air over which the warm air climbs is quite thick. These cirrus clouds gradually thicken into cirro-stratus and then into alto-stratus as the surface front comes nearer.

The thickening of the clouds in the alto-stratus area has an important bearing on your flight plan, as condensation in the warm air is at its maximum (since greater quantities of moisture are released) and precipitation falls in the form of rain or snow. What is more, this type of precipitation can extend over very large areas and be quite persistent. The explanation for this lies in the fact that the wedge of cold air over which the warm air climbs is often sluggish and moves only a very little. Consequently the warm air has to keep on climbing for a long time, and a large amount of precipitation continues over the areas affected.

During the warmer portions of the year, when the tropical maritime air is characterized by convective instability, high-level thunderstorms may occur. (Cloudy Joe, of course, has forgotten by this time that we ever talked about convective instability, but you are thoroughly familiar with it from our discussion under Fig. 30.) In this case the high-level thunderstorms are caused when the warm air in its climb aloft releases its potential instability. Normally, if you fly in the clouds above a warm front, you will find that the gentle rising of the air has made the air quite smooth—*except in storm areas,* where the flying will be rough going.

FIG. 75. A cold front, because of its steeper gradient of pressure (stronger push) travels faster than a warm front. With this difference in speed continu-

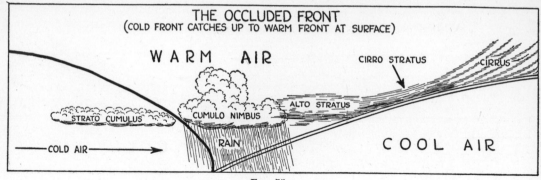

THE OCCLUDED FRONT
(COLD FRONT CATCHES UP TO WARM FRONT AT SURFACE)

WARM AIR — CIRRO STRATUS — CIRRUS

STRATO CUMULUS — CUMULO NIMBUS — ALTO STRATUS

← COLD AIR → — RAIN — COOL AIR

FIG. 75

ing for any length of time, you can readily see that in certain cases the cold front catches up with the warm front, meeting it at the surface of the earth as shown in the illustration. When cold and warm fronts meet in this way, the warm air (warm sector) between them is literally squeezed, and we have an occlusion in the low-pressure crater associated with the fronts.

The weather conditions which attend this development are usually a combination of the warm and cold front types. You will see why this is if you picture both types of weather, as explained under Figs. 73 and 74, as occurring very close to each other without being broken by the area of warm air between them.

Cyclones—in other words, "lows"—occlude rapidly in areas where conditions are favorable for rapid intensification—over large water areas and plains, for example.

FIG. 76. You will find that the air mass over which warm air is rising in a

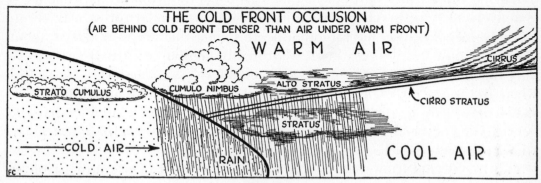

THE COLD FRONT OCCLUSION
(AIR BEHIND COLD FRONT DENSER THAN AIR UNDER WARM FRONT)

WARM AIR — CIRRUS

STRATO CUMULUS — CUMULO NIMBUS — ALTO STRATUS — CIRRO STRATUS

← COLD AIR → — RAIN — STRATUS — COOL AIR

FIG. 76

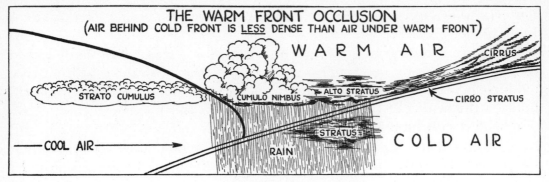

THE WARM FRONT OCCLUSION
(AIR BEHIND COLD FRONT IS LESS DENSE THAN AIR UNDER WARM FRONT)
WARM AIR
CIRRUS
STRATO CUMULUS
CUMULO NIMBUS
ALTO STRATUS
CIRRO STRATUS
COOL AIR
STRATUS
COLD AIR
RAIN

FIG. 77

warm front is seldom of the same temperature and density as the air which underruns the warm air at the cold front. The density difference between the two air masses controls the way in which the occlusion develops.

In a *cold front* occlusion, such as is shown in the illustration, the air behind the cold front is fresher, colder, and therefore denser than the air ahead of the front. As the occlusion progresses, this dense, cold air displaces all the air in the path of the cold front. In a cold front occlusion, therefore, you will find not only a combination of warm and cold front types of weather, but precipitation extending well back into the cold air behind the cold front. Why? Because, while air is being pushed up as in a typical cold front, cooler air just ahead of the cold front is climbing up the slope of the front, thus simulating in part a warm front type of weather.

Precipitation which has already fallen through the air masses in both the cold and warm fronts usually causes a high moisture content through evaporation, while the lifting and additional precipitation brought about by the cold front occlusion (or telescoping) usually cause extensive low cloud formation within the cold air masses.

Keep an eye out for cold front occlusions. In summer they cause fogs, so that you will have low ceilings and visibilities to reckon with. In winter you will have the additional hazard of icing to worry about.

Fig. 77. In a *warm front* occlusion, the air beneath the warm front is colder and therefore denser than the air behind the cold front. Since the cold front then has to climb over the wedge of colder air beneath the warm front, the telescoping of the two types of weather is the reverse of that which takes place in a cold front occlusion. Both in warm and cold front occlusions, however, the warm air originally comprising the warm sector of the low is lifted higher above the ground.

Warm front occlusions are frequent occurrences. Again you usually have a combination of warm and cold front types of weather with the cold front type tending to predominate as the chief cause of precipitation. Often you will notice a thickening of the alto-stratus cloud sheet during a warm front occlusion, with occasional light rains changing suddenly to heavy precipitation, and little or no change in surface wind direction, or temperature. The weather, in fact, is that of the cold front type with only slight surface changes in wind and temperature elements. Take a look at the pressure trend, however, and you will notice a typical change indicating the passage of denser air into an area—that of a fall—with a rising or steadying of the barometer.

Now, then, how does a warm front occlusion affect you in your flights? For one thing, after the passage of the cold front aloft, you are still going to have low ceilings and visibilities. All that saturation by precipitation has caused a low cloud system to form within the cold air under the warm front surface, and it won't disappear until the warm front has passed your observation station at the surface. Of course, you can count on a considerable decrease in precipitation intensity as soon as the cold front passes aloft—in fact, the precipitation may stop entirely—but until after the passage of the warm front you are going to be faced with low ceilings and visibilities.

Fig. 78.   Here you have characteristic surface reports near a cold front in winter, graphically presented by means of the symbols you studied under Figs. 63 and 64. Notice that the air lying east of the cold front is quite warm, the weather is mild, and flying conditions in this section are excellent.

As the cold front approaches, pressure tendencies indicate a steady fall in pressure, and the wind, usually from a direction between W and S, increases in velocity. These are typical reactions to the approach of a cold front. Now study the section over which the cold front has passed. You will find that the wind has shifted to the NW and that there is an overcast sky with moderate snow, caused by the vigorous pushing up of warmer air by the air at the cold front, while the pressure tendency has changed to a steadying or rising barometer.

Ceilings and visibilities are frequently quite low at the front itself, with icing hazards present in winter, as is always the case when the temperatures are below freezing. In areas removed from warm water influences, you will

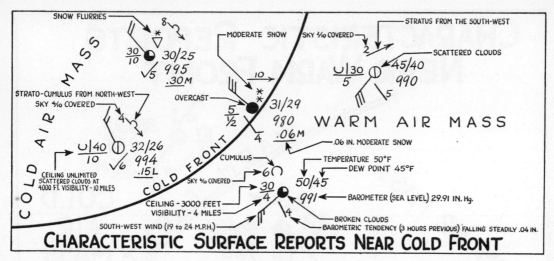

FIG. 78

usually find that the weather improves with the passage of the cold front, since the cloud deck formed in the cold air through turbulence tends to break and, in the case of a rapidly moving cold front, to dissipate into a few scattered clouds or to clear entirely. Under these conditions pressures continue to rise, temperatures remain low, and the wind continues from a direction varying from W to N.

I have said that the cold front conditions shown here are ideal for your flight, but I must qualify this statement in two respects. First, if the cold air trajectory behind the cold front is over warm water, there will be continued clouds and pronounced snow squalls. (Turn back to Fig. 51 and you will see why.) Second, there is a possibility that *secondary* cold fronts will form after the passage of the first.

The first qualification is particularly important when you are dealing with cold air that is moving into the territory of the Great Lakes and the area to the east and southeast. Low ceilings and visibilities, and icing hazards, prevail in the squalls, although in the warm air east of the cold front the weather is usually quite good until the arrival of the cold front. Now, if you follow the progress of this same cold front over areas well to the west and south of the Lakes, you will find only a momentary lowering of ceilings and visibilities, followed by the usual improvement in weather.

As for secondary cold fronts, these often cause a considerable lowering of

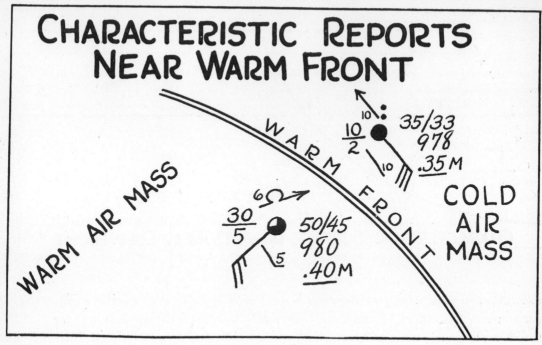

FIG. 79

ceilings and visibilities, a recurrence of snow, and icing hazards. In the case of Lake weather, they also intensify squalliness. With the approach of a secondary cold front, pressure tendency steadies or even falls off a little, and the wind, instead of holding a constant direction, tends to swing back to a more southerly direction. Because of the effect exerted upon wind direction by a secondary front, be careful not to rely too much on wind shifts as a means of locating cold fronts. A shift to NW, for instance, which would normally follow the passage of a cold front, might only be temporary, with the direction veering to W, or even WSW or SW soon after the passage of the first front, because of the influence of the secondary front.

FIG. 79. In studying these characteristic reports near a warm front, notice the ceiling and visibility reports in the cold air mass ahead of the front. They are 1000 feet and 2 miles respectively, and I can hear you asking—"But, isn't the weather supposed to be *alto-stratus?*" So it is, and your question is a logical one. But remember—considerable moisture through evaporation has been added to the colder air in the lower levels by the precipi-

80

tation that has fallen through it. Frequently, in fact, so much moisture is added that low clouds form within the cold air under the alto-stratus cloud system, and reduced ceiling and visibility result. Farther away from the warm front, where the alto-stratus is rather high and where there has been little precipitation, ceiling and visibility are higher, for in this case the alto-stratus does prevail. As a rule the warm front type of weather is much more hazardous in winter than in summer. In summer your problems have to do with low ceilings and visibilities, but in the colder seasons you have to contend with icing hazards as well.

You will observe from the illustration that the change in weather across the warm front, overland, is usually very well marked and is toward much better weather in the warm air. Surface wind, as shown here, is a strong SE. If you could climb into the air above the observation station, you would experience a shift in wind to SW within the warm, overrunning air, and an increase in temperature between the lower, colder air and the upper, warmer air. In winter you can frequently avoid icing hazards by climbing into this warmer air where the temperature may be above freezing.

The change from cold-air weather to warm-air weather that comes with the passage of a warm front at the surface generally brings a rapid improvement in the weather. There is a considerable rise in surface temperatures; the barometer steadies; skies clear over land areas, and the wind shifts to a more S to W direction. But be prepared for weather of quite a different type after passage of a warm front at the surface, if the open warm sector is over a sizable water area. In this case the cooling of warm air by the cold water surface over which it moves causes low stratus or fog to form within the warm air, as already explained under air mass modification. Now, what happens? There is a change in wind direction and pressure tendency, and precipitation, either as rain or snow, stops. But you will still have low ceilings and visibilities because of fog or low stratus formation within the warm air.

Taking a chance may be thrilling—but
flying skilfully is safer!

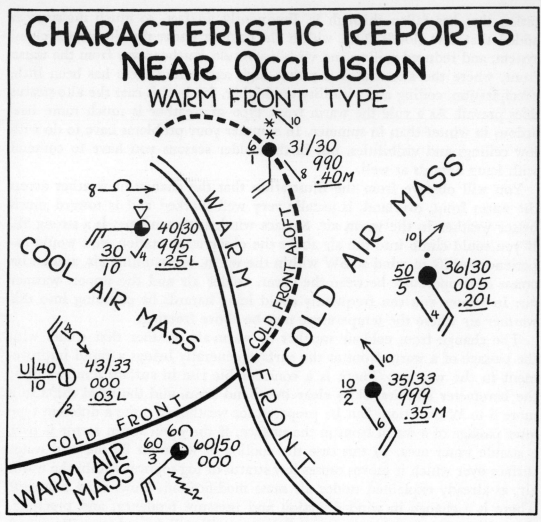

FIG. 80.

FIG. 80. The illustration shows the overtaking of the warm front by the cold front. The open warm sector, or warm air area of the low, is being squeezed downward, as you can see, away from the center. (The center is at the top of the illustration, near the junction of the cold front aloft and the surface warm front.)

In the case illustrated, the air to the right of the warm sector is colder than the air to the left. The density difference between these two air masses

82

causes the air to the left to override the colder air to the right, so that the warm air is lifted, as in Fig. 77, and the original surface of the cold front assumes a position above the ground, over the wedge of colder air to the right.

Study the station report at the right center. Here the weather is typically alto-stratus—overcast at an intermediate altitude with light rain and fair or good visibility. The barometer is falling steadily, and while the surface wind is SE, the alto-stratus clouds aloft are moving from SW, indicating the direction of the warmer current aloft.

Now look at the station report at the lower right of the illustration. Here the weather is characteristic of warm front weather, after enough precipitation has fallen to cause saturation in the lower levels of the air, and the formation of a lower cloud layer under the alto-stratus. Ceiling is 1000 feet; visibility, 2 miles.

Next, study the station reports at the upper center section of the illustration. The passage of the cold front aloft has caused modification in the precipitation. Precipitation is in the form of snow because of the lower temperatures prevailing at the alto-stratus condensation level as well as at the level of condensation within the lifted, cool air. Ceiling and visibility have been lowered to 600 feet and one mile. Just by observing the surface conditions indicated in this report, you know without my telling you that a flight through this area would bring you up against icing hazards. Pressure tendency is falling steadily, though it will steady itself slightly after the cold front has passed. Until the passage of the warm front at the surface, however, you can expect the general falling tendency of the barometer to continue. Here is something worth thinking over and remembering: Even after the passage of the cold front aloft over this station, low ceilings and visibilities will continue until the warmer air to the left behind the warm front enters the station area. Then the weather will correspond with that reported by the station at the upper left, which, being behind the warm front, has already experienced a considerable improvement in the weather.

The next reports to be considered are those at the station in the left center, which is experiencing the typical weather that follows the passage of a cold front. Wind has shifted to a northerly direction, the barometer is rising, and the temperature, with respect to the warm sector, is falling.

The station at the lower left is in the warm sector and the weather is quite good. Wind is SW, the temperature is mild; scattered to broken cumulus clouds prevail at the intermediate level, and the barometer is falling slowly prior to the arrival of the cold front.

CYCLONES

Sometimes you will find that a wave motion develops along a front—a sure sign of trouble. This happens whenever the equilibrium, or normal slope of the front, is disturbed by a vigorous outbreak of cold, deep air along one section while the other sections remain comparatively unchanged, or whenever there is an increase in the overrunning of a warm current at a point along the frontal surface. As the wave or disturbance grows more pronounced, a marked vortex begins to form, with an increase in overrunning of warm air; low pressure develops at the wave, and a cyclone or "low" is formed. These waves form on fronts between air masses which are highly dissimilar; for here, as you can see for yourself, the circulation is favorable for the disturbance of the front's equilibrium. Mountain ranges which alter the flow of air, a comparatively vigorous flow of cold air to the front, or a flow of warm air over the frontal surface all act to form and maintain a wave.

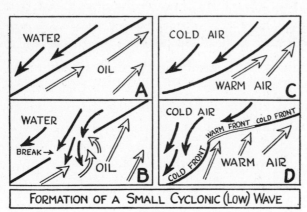

FORMATION OF A SMALL CYCLONIC (LOW) WAVE

FIG. 81

FIG. 81. The adjoining diagrams illustrate the analogy between water and oil, and cold and warm air. In *A* you have a dense fluid, water, separated by a thin partition from a lighter fluid, oil. In *C* you have dense, cold air separated from warmer, lighter air by a boundary. Now suppose the partition between the water and oil is broken, as in *B*. The heavier fluid rushes into the area occupied by the oil, and a roughly circular motion is started as indicated by the arrows. Compare this with *D* and you will see that practically the same thing happens when cold air pushes into warmer air, with an increase in the overrunning of warm air at the front just right of the vortex center.

84

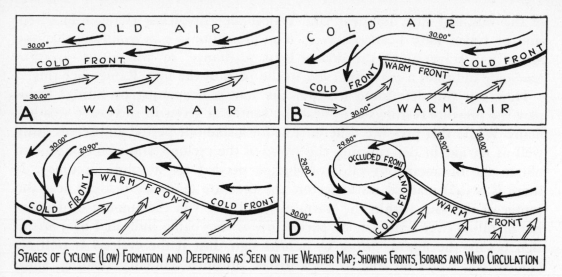

STAGES OF CYCLONE (LOW) FORMATION AND DEEPENING AS SEEN ON THE WEATHER MAP; SHOWING FRONTS, ISOBARS AND WIND CIRCULATION

Fig. 82

(These diagrams have upset Cloudy Joe considerably; he is now convinced that he can find oil in cyclones.)

Fig. 82. Here are the various stages in the formation of a well developed cyclone as they would be shown in successive weather maps. Your first warning that a cyclone is forming is the bulge along the cold front in *A*. In *B* there is a stepping up of circulation and the wave acquires a warm as well as a cold front as it travels eastward. Now study the development shown in *C*, and compare it with *B*. The closed isobars around a definite center of low pressure indicate a still greater intensification of circulation, and a deepening center. In *D* the cold front finally catches up with the warm front, and the cyclone has become occluded. This is a typical development in the formation of a cyclone, with the air in the warm sector being forced farther south from the center of the low. The density of the air behind the cold front and that of the air underlying the warm front determine whether or not the cold front will continue to override the warm front. (Better go back to Figs. 76 and 77 and review cold and warm front types of occlusions.)

In the northern hemisphere the low-pressure area or "cyclone" associated with the wave formation moves usually in a west-to-east direction through areas of active formation. This, of course, is caused by the prevailing circulation of the middle latitudes. There are often variations to the south and north of the west-east line, however, and trajectories involving changes in direction of travel have been observed. You are quite safe in assuming that the center will travel along the line of least resistance, or where the *pressure tendency* indicates a *maximum fall* in the path of the low. Remember this!

How can you determine whether the low is deepening or filling? Compare the pressure readings at or near the center as given in successive weather maps. While this pressure difference is for a six-hour period and serves quite well as an aid in determining the *trend* of the cyclone, you won't be able to obtain the instantaneous value of change needed for absolute accuracy. If there is a well marked warm sector, the pressure tendency reading near the center of the low, within the warm air, will give you the amount of deepening or filling over a three-hour period, *deepening* being indicated by a *minus* sign before the figure, *filling* by a *plus* sign. But if the cyclone is well occluded, you won't be able to get a direct pressure tendency reading, since the warm sector, or open area of warm air at the ground, may be far south of the low center.

Luckily for flight purposes, you can follow the general trend as shown on the weather charts. A point you should keep in mind about cyclones or "lows" is that they are characterized by a decrease in pressure, and a convergent flow or *piling up* of air. The anticyclone or "high," on the other hand, is just the reverse: pressure increases and air flow *diverges*.

If only he knew the "HOW" of it.

VII

FLIGHT SCARES
Fog, Thunderstorms, Icing, Etc.

FOG

ONE of the most insidious enemies you can meet in flying is fog. No matter how fine and smooth your trip may be, no matter how ideal the weather is at flight levels, if your destination and all alternate airports are fogged in, you will be up against it. In time blind landings will be perfected to such an extent that the fog hazard will be decreased, but until then your best defense against it lies in being able to recognize the conditions under which fog is produced.

There are all sorts of ways of classifying fogs, but in the end they all boil down to two main types—advection, caused by a horizontal movement of the air; and radiation, caused by loss of heat to space. Most advection fogs are formed by the movement of *warm* air over a *colder* surface. Occasionally, however, particularly in the Arctic Region, we find fogs known as "frost smoke" produced by the movement of *cold* air over a *warmer* surface. "Frost smoke" is literally nothing but steam rising from the warm surface.

Sea fogs are caused by the movement of warm, moist air *from over a warm water surface* to a colder water surface, where it is cooled. If the movement of the warm air is comparatively slow, the cooling takes place within a layer immediately above the water surface, and we have a low-lying fog. But when the warm air moves rapidly, turbulence is set up within the lower level of the air, causing the formation of an elevated fog. Ocean fogs of this type are frequently both deep and persistent. The sea fogs formed along the New England coast are frequently borne inland with land and sea breezes, or by the general circulation brought about by the pressure gradient (push). Similar conditions exist, during the summer, on the West Coast.

Inland, be on the watch for fog over cool lakes and rivers which are likely to be crossed by warm air. And here is a piece of information that will be valuable to you when you do meet these inland fogs. If the warm air is stagnant, or moves very slightly over the cold area, visibility will be reduced and fog will form at the very lowest levels. But if turbulence is induced by a more vigorous air flow, the fog will lie at a higher level with, in many cases, *fair visibility underneath.*

Another place to look for trouble is where you find tropical air crossing colder land surfaces. This is a frequent occurrence, particularly in the southeastern and southern parts of the United States. If the warm air were not turbulent to some degree, the fog would, of course, form at the surface. But there is generally enough turbulence induced by the terrain to form a stratus cloud deck instead of a surface fog. The ceilings and visibilities that exist under the cloud layer are often so low that you will find it hazardous to fly in the areas affected.

The most usual type of radiation fog—and the one that will give you the most concern when you fly—is the common "ground fog." Ground fog is formed during the course of a night's cooling and causes a considerable reduction in visibility over the area affected. "Burning off" of the fog usually occurs after sunrise with the destruction of the surface inversion produced by the night's cooling. (Remember Fig. 34?)

Ground fogs are often very shallow because, on perfectly calm nights, the condensation brought about by cooling can extend only a short distance into the air. When there is a slight turbulence brought about by a slight wind, cooling extends into the higher levels and causes a deeper fog. The persistence of this fog in the morning hours can cause you a good deal of trouble if you have to land. Ground fogs are most apt to form on cool, clear, practically calm nights when the air is nearly saturated and quite stable; so, before you start out on any night flying, check the temperature and dewpoint difference (a direct indication of the relative humidity). If the difference is small during early night, and the other conditions are favorable for its formation, watch for ground fog!

Of course you know from your own observations that fogs are apt to occur when precipitation falls through the air, thus increasing its moisture content and lifting its dewpoint. You will frequently find fogs ahead of warm fronts when there has been a steady fall of precipitation through the colder air underlying warmer air. A stagnant cold air wedge is more favorable to fog formation than a vigorous circulation. The cold air behind a cold front is also favorable for fog formation when the cold front precipitation saturates the lower levels.

Your main danger from fog is, as I have said before, the possibility that not only your destination but your alternate landing points may be lost in fog. The only safeguard that you can set up for yourself is to study the circulation and general distribution of air over the territory where you are going to fly. If temperatures and dewpoints are rather close together and the air is quite stable near the ground—beware of fog! Remember that precipitation will increase the dewpoint—in some cases to such an extent that fog will develop almost before you know it.

THUNDERSTORMS AND TORNADOES

A thunderstorm is nothing but a cumulus shower grown up, with thunder, lightning, and sometimes hail, added to it. (Cloudy Joe wonders why!) If you have ever flown through one of these storms, you know for yourself that it contains strong vertical currents. These are caused by the vigorous convection present in the storm. If the storm was well-developed, you may have experienced several thousands of feet change in altitude without altering the control surfaces or power of your plane.

Cloudy Joe will never understand the workings of a thunderstorm, for by this time he has forgotten that we ever mentioned such things as conditional and convectional instability—or, as we might have termed them, potential instability or latent power. You, however, will have no difficulty in seeing how these conditions tie in with thunderstorms.

As a phenomenon of vigorous convection, the thunderstorm, for example, predominates in air that has a high degree of potential instability or latent power. Since these qualifications are best met in the United States by tropical maritime masses originating as Tg or Ta, you can readily see that thunderstorms will predominate in this type of air. During the summer time, however, you will find local thunderstorms occurring over the southeast portions of the country in polar air masses which, through modification, have come to contain considerable moisture and a degree of instability.

After the potential instability of the air mass is fully realized, vertical motion of the air is greatly accelerated. This realization of instability comes about when the air mass is lifted either by a front or the terrain, or when there is enough local heating in the lower levels during the day to cause a lapse rate greater than the adiabatic to develop up to the level of condensation. Because of higher temperatures, higher moisture content and a greater degree of potential instability within the air masses, thunderstorms predominate during the warm seasons of the year.

The strong vertical currents set up in the cloud during a thunderstorm are now generally recognized as the cause of lightning. These currents split the raindrops in such a way that the negatively charged portions are carried away, leaving the more positively charged drop centers congregated in certain portions of the clouds. Thus a considerable electrical potential difference is developed between positively and negatively charged portions of the cloud or clouds, or between positively charged portions of cloud and the negatively charged ground. Thunder, as even Cloudy Joe knows, is the noise attending the lightning flash.

FIG. 83. Here you see how hailstones are formed. Raindrops, falling earthward, are seized by strong vertical currents and tossed upward to a below-freezing area. There they are dropped by the current, only to be tossed up again by another current. This keeps up until the now solidly frozen drop, or hailstone, which has been growing steadily during its travels, is heavy enough to fall through the strongest upward current.

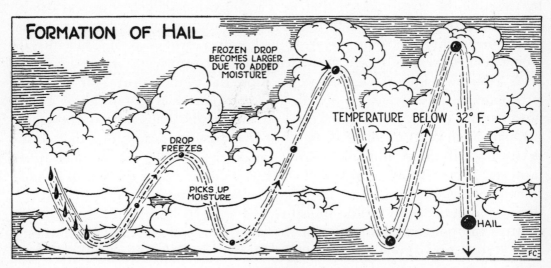

FIG. 83

90

By now, everybody except Cloudy Joe has come to the conclusion that flying through a thunderstorm is dangerous business. In scheduled airline flying, thunderstorms are religiously avoided wherever possible. First, there is the hazard from the rapid and unexpected changes in altitude, for those vertical currents can drop you just about the way they do hailstones, and bring you dangerously close to obstructions on the course. The severe turbulence of the storm not only causes considerable personal discomfort, but places a severe strain upon the aircraft itself. Another of the hazards is from hailstones which strike the moving aircraft with terrific impact.

When it comes to lightning, you will find that cases of dangerous strikes are rare; in fact, it seems logical to assume that the aircraft, instead of inducing a strike, merely happens sometimes to be in a path coincidental to the electrical discharge. But don't minimize the dangers of lightning. When it does strike, there may be some damage. The radio equipment is usually affected first, and other parts of the aircraft can be damaged by fusing or splitting.

I remember being visited by one of these "rare" strikes—a distinction I would just as soon have passed up. The discharge entered the aircraft near the left engine and escaped at the right wing tip. While the charge was in the plane, the engine power was momentarily cut, and the air speed was decreased from 175 m.p.h to 115 m.p.h. And when it was all over, a foot and a half of the wingtip was neatly fused—that is, the metal was melted and joined. In this particular case I was fortunate enough not to have my radio equipment damaged.

TORNADOES

You won't have to worry much about tornadoes as a serious hazard on your flights, since these are of an extremely local nature. However, since tornadoes occur during well-pronounced thunderstorm activity, the general aspect of "tornado weather" is unfavorable.

While we do not know very much about the actual formation of a tornado, it seems logical to assume that there is a "stepping up" in the lapse rate of the air to one much greater than the adiabatic. This change in lapse rate allows a vigorous upward displacement and a resultant inward flow of compensating air, thus causing the intense localized circulation which marks the initial stage of the tornado.

FIG. 84

FIG. 85

FIG. 86

FIG. 84. You will notice that the tornado first appears as a cigar-shaped roll extending from a large cumulo-nimbus cloud of thunderstorm character. The dark mass of the tornado results from an abnormal pressure decrease in the vortex which causes condensation of moisture into cloud.

FIG. 85. A tornado follows an erratic path. Sometimes it strikes and holds to the ground for quite a distance; at other times it merely touches the ground. Wind circulation near the vortex is quite vigorous, as you would expect from the low pressure prevailing at the vortex. It is estimated that pressure of half the normal outside pressure prevails within a tornado.

FIG. 86. Aside from the destruction caused by high wind velocities, there is the "explosion effect" of a tornado to be reckoned with. This is the sudden bursting of an object built to withstand normal atmospheric pressure. The "explosion" occurs when the pressure is rapidly reduced to the abnormally low value present in the center of the tornado.

ICING—AND HOW TO AVOID IT

There are two ways of dealing with an opponent. You can meet him on his own grounds, or you can sidestep. In dealing with icing conditions, however, there is just one method to follow, and that is—to sidestep. I don't need to tell you the damage icing can do to your plane; you know that already if you have talked to Cloudy Joe, who often bumps into this hazard. The important thing for you to learn and remember is when icing is apt to occur.

You can expect to find icing: (1) when you fly your plane through a cloud formation and some forms of precipitation, where temperatures are at or below freezing; (2) when you fly through a cloudless layer of air where the temperature is at or below freezing and into which rain is falling from a warmer stratum above; (3) when you fly from a cold area that has reduced the temperature of your plane to freezing, into a saturated cloud area where the temperature is above freezing. This third case is somewhat unusual, and such icing is generally slight. When temperatures are below freezing, wet snows will sometimes cause icing.

The reason behind icing is this: The sub-zero areas are filled with drops of water. It seems curious that these supercooled drops do not freeze, but the explanation seems to lie in a combination of factors. The surface tension of the drop, its salinity, and above all, the fact that the liquid is undisturbed, all favor the continuation of the drop in liquid form. But once the drop is broken or vigorously disturbed, as it is when it strikes an airplane, it turns to ice. Even with temperatures as low as —15° F. to —20° F., it has been shown from flight experience, water can still exist in the atmosphere in liquid form.

The severity of the icing hazard seems to depend on the size and number of the water drops and the stability of the air which supports them. When the drops are small and supercooled, their surface tension is so great that some rebound as they strike a plane, while others freeze fast to the aircraft. This kind of drop is found in stratus clouds where the vertical motions are restricted. At very low temperatures the small drops tend to freeze as a body, rather than to spread. When freezing of this type occurs the result is generally "rime" ice. Here the ice takes a granular form which can be built up to a considerable extent but which is easily lost through the flow of air around the plane or the vibration of the plane itself. For this reason rime ice is less hazardous than "clear" ice.

Unlike rime, "clear" ice is tenacious, hard and smooth. Although it frequently has a roughened appearance, it is never granular, and air flow around the plane usually has little effect upon it, once it has formed. Under conditions favorable to its formation, clear ice can build up remarkably fast with the worst possible effects upon the plane. If you ever happen to run into ice of this kind, the weight of your plane will be materially increased and the shape of the airfoils will be distorted; control surfaces will become useless, and ice on the propeller will cut down power to a dangerous extent. Enough clear ice to cause sluggish aircraft operation and to make flight hazardous has been known to form on planes in as short a time as *ten minutes*. The best way to avoid trouble is to keep out of all clear icing areas. The illustrations and explanations which follow later will give you an idea of how to do this.

In frontal zones, where cloudiness is denser and vertical currents are more pronounced, you will find that icing hazards are even more severe than in clouds of pure air-mass type. This is particularly true of clouds over mountain ranges where vertical currents help support the large, liquid drops in the air. For example, when temperature and cloud conditions favor icing on the Columbus-Newark Airway, more severe icing is experienced over the Pittsburgh-Buckstown section than anywhere else along the route. In some instances, the icing is obviously connected with cloudiness in air masses of the same type, but there seems to be a greater amount of water available for freezing over the hills. A similar effect has also been noted on flights through cold fronts. So far as icing is concerned, these cold fronts act in the same way as the mountains. It is obvious from all this that the icing hazard is greater if you fly through clouds forming in air subject to strong updrafts than if you fly through clouds that are forming in comparatively stagnant air.

Warm air, you remember, travels upward over a cold wedge of air in a warm front formation. This has an important bearing on your flight plan, since a knowledge of this fact sometimes leads to a way out of icing hazards. The inversion in temperature and change in moisture content between the colder, lower air mass and the warmer, upper air mass sometimes make it possible to escape ice hazards by flying from the colder air into the warmer. But flight to the higher level will not always protect your plane from icing. The temperature of the warmer, overrunning air can be considerably higher than the lower, colder air and still be below freezing. Under such conditions, icing will still be severe through the warm-front, alto-stratus system.

Here is another important point to remember. Icing is sometimes quite severe in both the stratus and the freezing mists which form extensively, during winter months, in polar continental air as it moves southward behind a

94

retarded cold front. Owing to the higher moisture content in the lower levels of the air after movement southward, more moisture is made available for condensation than would ordinarily exist in cloudiness in this type of air. If you were foolish enough to attempt an extensive flight through the stratus and freezing mists with temperatures below freezing, you would let yourself and your plane in for all the perils of a severe icing. This is the kind of scrape Cloudy Joe is apt to get into, but the rest of us simply fly over the top of the stratus, which, fortunately, is quite low in circumstances of this kind.

FIG. 87

FIG. 87. Here you have a plane headed for a cold front. The freezing level of the warmer air to the right of the front is considerably higher than it is behind the front. Notice, however, that the freezing level in the warmer air begins in the cloud formation, quite close to the base, so that any actual cloud flying would result in icing. Under similar circumstances, your best course is to fly under the cloud—provided you know that there is clear weather behind the cold front, and that, while your plane will pass from air above freezing to air below freezing, there will be no cloud formation to encounter after the temperature decrease.

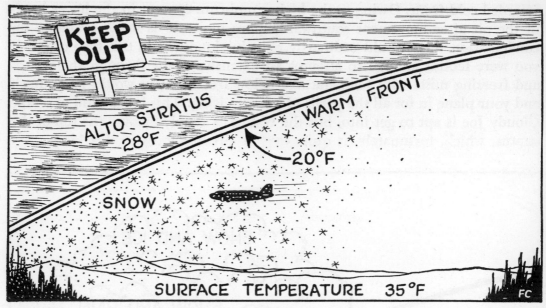

FIG. 88

FIG. 88. This illustration shows a case of warm front precipitation in the form of snow. The air under the warm front slope is quite cold and the snow is well frozen, falling as hard flakes. At the upper part of the cold air, the temperature is 20° F., while the temperature within the warmer air increases at the front slope but continues below freezing. Suppose you have found out from observation that the alto-stratus top is quite high and that you can only reach the top by running the gamut of the icing hazards in the alto-stratus cloud level. Stop and think. Where is your optimum flight level? Under the alto-stratus, where there are no clouds, and right through the snow area. You won't have to worry about icing hazards there, because of low temperatures and the well-frozen nature of the precipitation.

FIG. 89. Almost the same conditions are presented in this as in the preceding illustration, except that precipitation is lacking and a lower cloud layer has formed within the colder air under the alto-stratus. Since there is ample ceiling and good visibility below the lower cloud layer, your optimum flight level is below the layer. You could also fly between the layers, away from frictional surface effects, where the air is smoother, if you were sure that descent through the lower cloud deck would allow contact flight with a

96

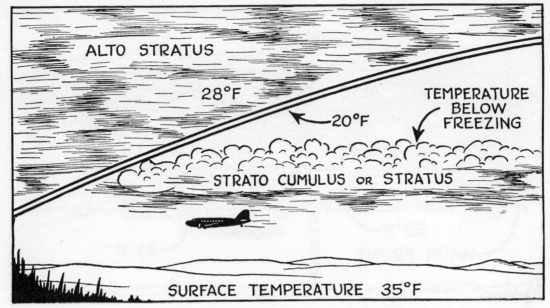

FIG. 89

minimum of cloud flying. Cloud flying, of course, would be dangerous because of the icing hazard present not only in the alto-stratus but in the lower clouds as well.

FIG. 90. Because of the temperature distribution, icing hazards exist in all the clouds shown in the illustration, although there is probably less danger from icing well up in the alto-stratus where very low temperatures prevail. With a ceiling of only 1000 feet, despite good visibility, flight under the lower layer of clouds will be comparatively unsafe, unless over very flat, unobstructed terrain. Under the conditions shown here, it will be equally dangerous to try flying between the layers, since these are apt to merge with the alto-stratus above. Your optimum flight level, then, is either on top of the alto-stratus, or within the upper reaches of the cloud, where, because of extremely low temperatures, you have only a minimum of rime ice to contend with.

FIG. 91. The entire cold air stratus formation shown here, with only 500 feet of ceiling underneath, constitutes an ice hazard. Both within and below the cloud the temperature is below freezing, so that a mist falling from the cloud layer will freeze and offer a second icing hazard in addition to the one

97

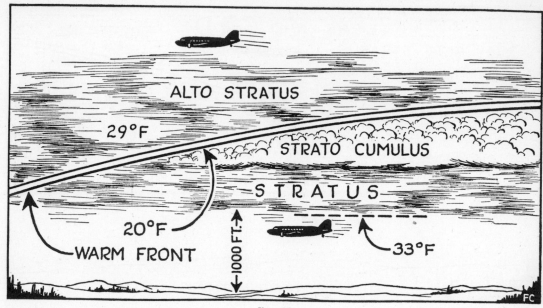

ALTO STRATUS

29°F

STRATO CUMULUS

STRATUS

20°F
WARM FRONT

1000 FT.

33°F

FC

FIG. 90

present in the cloud itself. Fortunately the top of the stratus is low, so that your optimum flight level lies above the top, where the air is somewhat warmer and smoother, and where there is no icing hazard. But be sure that there are enough ceiling and visibility below the low stratus deck to allow quick descent through the lower clouds and a rapid approach to the field.

I pointed out to you that the more severe icing hazards are met in clouds that are subjected to upward currents of air and therefore contain larger water drops for freezing. In the low stratus condition shown in the illustration above, there is an exception to this rule. Although there is a continual gentle uprising of the cold air, it is not sufficient to cause strong updrafts. However, the great number of drops, even though small, provides a considerable amount of moisture for freezing upon impact. The freezing mist obviously presents a great hazard to flight, for this type of precipitation will freeze to any object it touches, unless that object is so warm that it melts the ice right away.

Of course, you may wonder how some flights are carried out through icing areas. The answer to this is that each icing condition must be carefully analyzed, and the airman must determine, *before a flight,* whether or not his

98

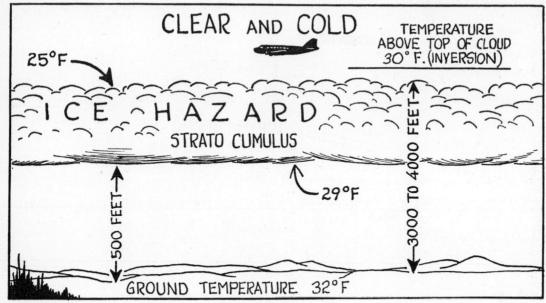

FIG. 91

de-icing equipment will be able to take care of the expected ice. In rime ice, de-icers are usually most effective. In *light* clear icing, when the ice forms only on the leading edges of the wings, de-icers are also effective. When clear ice begins to form *around* the de-icer boot on the leading edges of the airfoils and builds back of the boot along the airfoil surfaces, then it is time to quit depending upon the de-icers, and to escape from the icing zone.

On the way up, observing the free air temperature lapse rate will give you an idea of whether the air you are flying through is of the PHLEGMATIC or TEMPERAMENTAL type.

99

VIII

MAKING THE WEATHER MAP

THE weather map is the main tool of the meteorologist, and, as I have said before, it is also one of your principal aids in charting your air route. These maps are so carefully prepared—the elements involved in their structure are so expertly analyzed—that forecasts based upon weather maps are accurate to a high degree.

You are already familiar with the symbols used in reporting weather and their placement on the map. You have some idea of the number of observation stations throughout the country that supply weather reports. And by the time you have read thus far, you know enough about the weather itself to qualify as an amateur meteorologist! The next thing to find out is how the meteorologist goes about correlating and interpreting his facts and reducing them to the convenient, compact form of a weather map. Imagine that *you* are the map-maker. Where would you begin? Cloudy Joe thinks that you get all the latest reports together and start putting them down on the map, but he's wrong again.

The place to start is with the preceding map. Weather maps reflect a logical sequence of events, and from the latest one you can begin to visualize what may have happened in the interval and to estimate the probable location of fronts and isobars. Their actual location on the map can be determined only from a close comparison and expert interpretation of existing weather conditions as indicated in the latest observation station reports.

Changes in temperature, pressure tendency, and wind direction are all useful in deciding the location of a front. Thus you are justified in *suspecting* the presence of a warm front between two stations if there is an increase in temperature between these two points. Conversely, you are justified in suspecting the presence of a cold front if the temperature decreases between two points, or of an occlusion if the temperature is variable. These deductions should be based on temperatures taken at about the 3000-foot level;

100

below that height, air masses are subject to superficial temperature changes from contact with the surface of the earth. Notice, however, that you are justified only in *suspecting* the formation of fronts, for meteorology is no field in which to leap at conclusions. Before you reach a final decision, you must have plenty of supporting evidence.

Among this supporting evidence are pressure tendencies and wind direction. A pressure tendency change from a rather steady fall to a steady, a slowly rising, or a less rapidly falling barometer indicates the possibility of a warm front. A change from a rapidly falling to a rapidly rising barometer may signify the presence of either a cold or an occluded front. Wind changes at the surface also are significant, if backed by supporting evidence, especially when it comes to locating cold fronts.

You still are not ready, even when all three of these factors point in the same direction, to say, "Here is a front." There are upper air soundings to be carefully studied, as well as the elements obtained in airplane or radio-meteorograph soundings. Values of pressure, temperature, relative and absolute humidities, and equivalent-potential temperatures at various levels must be analyzed. Airplane soundings in particular are invaluable aids when it comes to identifying air masses on a weather chart. How are these soundings used by the professional meteorologist? The answer to that involves a rather lengthy and detailed explanation which will not be particularly valuable to you; but here, briefly, is an example of the use to which a sounding can be put:

Suppose we know from one of these soundings that the temperature in a rather stable layer of air from the ground to about 1500 meters ranges from 2° C. to —3° C., specific humidity from 2.3 Grams/Kilograms to 0.5 G./Kg., and equivalent-potential temperatures from 260° A. to 280° A. At that altitude the temperature increases to 2° C., the specific humidity to about 4.5 G./Kg., and the equivalent-potential temperature to about 315° A.

From all this it is obvious that cold air underlies warmer air, and an analysis of the map will show whether a cold or a warm front exists by disclosing the trajectories of the air masses involved. By showing the point at which inversion and humidity change occur, the sounding also indicates the definite altitude of transition between two air masses.

The average slope of the frontal surface is obtained by comparing the distance (the surface position of the front) with the height (the point at which the front is pierced at the 1500 meter level). Depth of individual air masses, their characteristics with respect to stability and instability, and their probable modification with lifting and sinking are all obtained by comparing soundings from stations throughout an extensive area.

Suppose you have discovered an inversion with levels of high relative humidity within the colder air underlying a warm frontal surface. What inference can you draw? Simply this: Precipitation will fall from the alto-stratus clouds of the warm front; the levels of high relative humidity in the cold air under the inversions will become saturated through evaporation; and a layer of low clouds will form within the colder, underlying air.

When it comes to finding out how an air mass will react to lifting and sinking, the meteorologist uses charts to "experiment" with layers of air, simulating the lifting and sinking as it would actually take place in the atmosphere. In this way he determines the extent and type of clouds, the amount and intensity of precipitation, and the condition of the air with regard to stability and instability.

With a number of factors all pointing to the position of a front, your next step is to sketch the location in lightly on the weather map, and to add the isobars in black pencil. Isobars, as you remember, connect points of equal pressure, and one is drawn for every .10″ Hg. difference in pressure value. You will find that these isobars vary in appearance. Some are comparatively straight; others are circular (as around a high or low) while still others contain a pronounced dip or V. These V's are characteristic of isobars at a front, and their presence on the map is a valuable aid in determining accurate frontal position.

When you have finally decided that a front exists, and where, draw it in more heavily on the map—using blue for a cold front, red for a warm front, purple for an occluded front, and a broken blue line for a cold front aloft, such as exists in a warm front occlusion. Shade in precipitation areas, usually in green, and draw light pencil lines (isallobars) between points of equal pressure change. Isallobars may also be indicated by light, *broken pencil lines*.

With your finished map on hand, you can begin to draw conclusions as to what is going to happen—in other words, to forecast. Drawing accurate conclusions isn't easy, for each set of weather factors is usually a law unto itself. The expert meteorologist, of course, can speed his work by drawing analogies between present and previous cases, but he is too wise in the variable ways of weather to say, "This will happen today because it happened yesterday (or last week or last month) under a similar set of circumstances." He visualizes the intensification or weakening, the deepening or filling of highs and lows, from the evidence before him on the map, from his knowledge of what has happened in the past, and from his long experience; from all these, then, he deduces what is likely to happen in the future. Practice backed by a knowledge of theory increases accuracy in map preparation and forecasting. The experience which goes into the professional weather man's construction and interpretation of a weather map is an important factor in your safety during flight. So is the experience which you will gain from studying and analyzing the weather.

No two fingerprints are ever alike.
Neither are weather maps.

IX

PRACTICAL FORECASTING FOR THE AIRMAN

I AM taking it for granted that everyone—except Cloudy Joe—has come to realize the important part that meteorology plays in the activity of the airman. Before you hop off for a distant flight, always consult a meteorologist if there is one to be found at the airport. What he has to tell you about weather frequently has as much to do with your safety upstairs as the mechanical condition of your plane. Until you have made a flight plan which not only conforms to the Civil Air Regulations, but which also makes full allowance for the weather—stay on the ground!

In making your flight plan, remember this: Keeping up with the weather isn't enough. You have to keep a long way in front of it. On a very short flight, weather conditions often remain constant and the weather that prevails when you take off may still prevail when you come down through. But on longer flights, particularly through areas of cyclonic activity, you will find that the weather is as changeable as Cloudy Joe's girl friend. Whether you are the captain of a cross-country transport, or the skipper of a smaller plane, you have to anticipate changes in the weather and make due allowance for them in your flight plan.

FIG. 92. Study the weather conditions indicated in the illustration. Obviously they are unfavorable for flight between Buffalo and Chicago, although a flight could be completed safely from Newark to Buffalo. But don't be too eager to start! There is a general movement of unfavorable weather from west to east, so that, although the precipitation at Buffalo is shown as snow, the trend is toward a wetter snow and quite likely toward a freezing rain, such as exists in the Detroit area. Your obvious conclusion, therefore, is that conditions are unfavorable to flight over the entire route from Newark to Chicago.

If you started over the Detroit-Chicago section, you should find a favorable flight level over the colder air mass and within the warmer air, where the

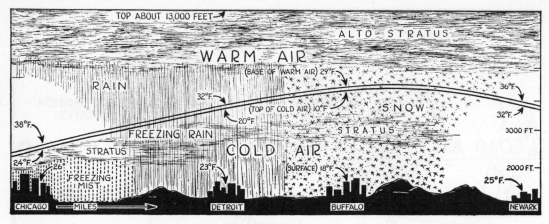

FIG. 92

temperatures are above freezing. But in climbing up to flight altitude out of Detroit and in coming down through at Chicago in an instrument approach, as explained later, you would subject your plane to considerable icing of the clear, hard type, and there would be the additional hazard of reduced visibility over the Chicago area resulting from the thickening of lower stratus clouds and the prevalence of freezing mist and fog under the low cloud layer.

You would, of course, find icing conditions anywhere in the alto-stratus cloud system between the very low temperatures existing high over Buffalo, causing rime ice, and the 32° F. well over Detroit and Chicago. (Clear icing would occur from 32° F. to about 20° F.) Trying to avoid icing hazards by flying between cloud layers would only lead to further trouble. Precipitation would be moderate or even heavy at times, and you could not be certain of your position with respect to the clouds while flying through the heavier precipitation.

*   *   *

In making out your flight plan, be sure to observe the prevailing weather at the flight-originating airport and to inspect all available weather reports along the route and off-course. With the present era of nationwide reports, you will find it comparatively easy to keep an eye on the progress of fronts and the attendant weather phenomena.

105

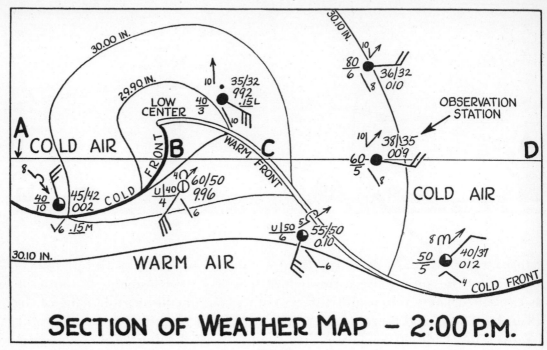

SECTION OF WEATHER MAP — 2:00 P.M.

FIG. 93

FIG. 93. When you are approaching a warm front, observe the cloud sheet, which usually begins as cirrus and gradually thickens into alto-stratus. Points to be considered are these: Will your flight be along the outer boundaries of the cloud system, where there is no precipitation and the warm air overrunning is high? Or will you fly through the thickening portions

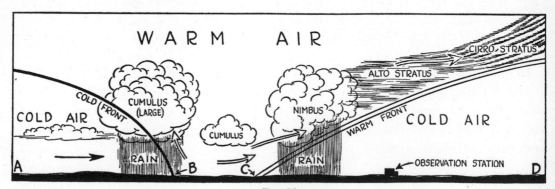

FIG. 94

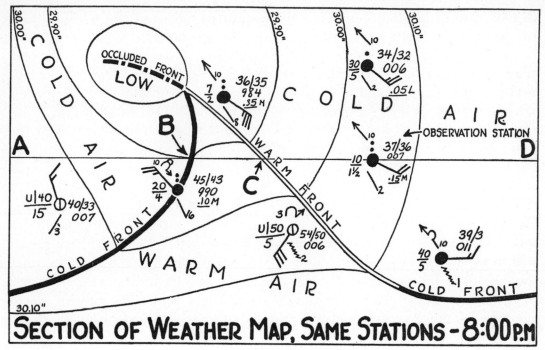

Fig. 95

of the warm front weather system and into the warm air of the warm sector? In the first case, you will find ideal flying conditions. In the second, a number of factors are involved.

Suppose, for example, that you are at the observation station shown to the right in the illustration, and that the weather map for that vicinity shows the

Fig. 96

107

distribution illustrated. There is an alto-stratus overcast at the station allowing a ceiling of 6000 feet. Visibility is rather good. Rain has not actually begun but is expected. Under these circumstances you could probably proceed with ample ceiling and visibilities *except for one thing*. The cold air underlying the alto-stratus has a trick of developing low clouds *within itself* after precipitation begins to fall through it. This is your main hazard in flying through weather of the warm front type. During the warmer seasons of the year, the hazard is confined to low ceilings and visibilities, but during the winter, when precipitation takes the form of snow or freezing rain, icing is an added hazard.

Wherever possible, consult a meteorologist to find out the structure of the air through which precipitation is falling. With temperature and humidity soundings available, he will be able to tell you the level at which low clouds will form. You could, of course, draw your own conclusions if you knew what the sounding indicated. If, for example, the sounding indicates an inversion in the colder air with a steady lapse rate for slight instability existing up to the base of the inversion and a high relative humidity just below the base, conditions are favorable for the formation of low stratus *under the base of the inversion* after precipitation begins. If there is a slight difference between the temperature and the dewpoint at the surface, the probabilities are that a point of near-saturation exists near the base of the inversion. After precipitation has caused the formation of the lower cloud layer, the thickness of the cloud will increase *downward* as more of the colder air becomes saturated. The higher the inversion base, of course, the higher the lower cloud base and top will be.

Fig. 94. This is a cross-section of the weather conditions and air-mass distribution from *A* to *D* in Fig. 93. Notice that as yet there are no lower clouds associated with the warm front, and that there are ample ceilings and visibilities throughout.

Fig. 95. Weather conditions over the vicinity, *A-D,* of Fig. 93, are shown here after a lapse of six hours. Precipitation attending the wide alto-stratus cloud system has spread. The warm front has moved but little, because of the steady pressure gradient within the cold air to the left. The cold front, on the other hand, has moved considerably and is approaching the warm front at the center of the "low" to form an occlusion. (Remember Fig. 82.) The weather at your observation station has undergone a considerable change.

Continuous rain has caused saturation in the lower levels, and the formation of a stratus cloud deck at 1000 feet, with visibility lowered to one and a half miles. The station just NW of yours has also experienced a lowering of the ceiling from 4000 feet to 700 feet, and of visibility from three miles to two miles, for the same reason.

Fig. 96.   In this cross-section of the weather shown in the preceding illustration, notice that the alto-stratus rain has spread over a wide area and that because of this spreading, considerable low cloudiness has formed within the lower, colder air. Under conditions such as these you can fly safely on instruments from the cold air into the alto-stratus cloud system, and out into the open warm sector—provided there are no icing hazards.

If the precipitation takes the form of snow, try to steer clear of the alto-stratus clouds, for the temperature will be below freezing and there will probably be icing in the clouds. You may know, of course, in advance that there is very low temperature with negligible icing of the rime type, *but without that definite knowledge,* do not experiment too long with flight through the cloud. Experimentation with icing hazards leads to trouble!

When there is alto-stratus rain, you will usually find warmer air aloft. In the freezing rain condition, keep out of the lower cold air and seek the level at which the rain is forming at a temperature above freezing. You can figure out for yourself that any clouds which form in the lower, colder air during the precipitation of snow or freezing rain will have icing potentialities. Let me warn you again—keep out of areas where icing is likely. Ice forms so quickly under favorable conditions that it can literally get you down in no time at all.

When there is an inflow of cold air at a cold front in winter, you may find negotiable weather over an area *away from water.* But over water, the weather at the front will be intensified by increased snow, particularly in the lowering of ceilings and visibilities. (If you have forgotten why this is, turn back to the section on lake squalls and study Fig. 52.) After the cold front passes, keep your eye on the weather within the cold air, for even without interaction with a warmer mass, weather within the cold air can become quite hazardous. This, as I pointed out in the discussion of lake squalls, is a result of modification by warmer water surfaces. Obviously, if you can get to your destination before the cold front, you won't have to worry about it. But if you can't, you'd better figure out in advance just how much ceiling

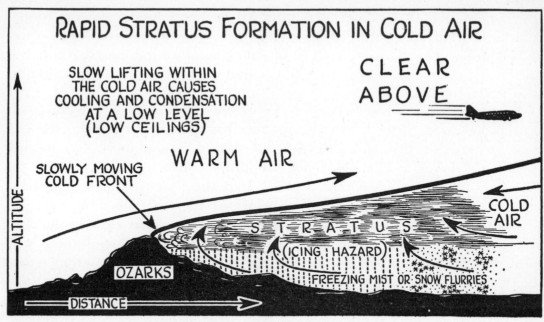

SLOW LIFTING WITHIN
THE COLD AIR CAUSES
COOLING AND CONDENSATION
AT A LOW LEVEL
(LOW CEILINGS)

CLEAR
ABOVE

WARM AIR

SLOWLY MOVING
COLD FRONT

COLD
AIR

S T R A T U S

(ICING HAZARD)

OZARKS

FREEZING MIST OR SNOW FLURRIES

ALTITUDE

DISTANCE

FIG. 97

and visibility you can expect if you arrive simultaneously with the front or just after it has passed.

FIG. 97.   During the colder seasons of the year there are frequent station reports that an extensive area of low cloudiness has formed within cold air after the passage of a cold front. Precipitation in the form of mist, freezing mist, or snow flurries from the stratus cloud layer, may also be reported. This development always takes Cloudy Joe and the uninitiated by surprise, though the seasoned airman and the experienced meteorologist are usually on the alert for just such a formation.

Now, as you know, low clouds do not form within the cold air behind a rapidly-moving front because of the depth of the cold air behind the front and the turbulence within the cold air which is usually moving quite rapidly. But when the cold air outbreak has reached its maximum depth and is beginning to move out, the edge of the cold front either becomes stagnant or moves very slowly. This is your first sign that conditions are favorable for the formation of low clouds.

You saw in Fig. 69 how an air flow favorable to the formation of a front must necessarily bring together the air masses involved. In Fig. 97 just

110

such a circulation is shown, with the cold air, a comparatively shallow mass, being overrun by a warmer mass. To compensate for the piling up of air at the cold front, there must, as you know, be a slow rising of the cold air *behind* the front. After the cold front has been retarded, this cold air is generally considerably modified by the addition of more moisture at the lower levels. This added moisture increases the relative humidity of the mass while rather constant temperature prevails.

The slow rising of the cold air behind the cold front causes adiabatic cooling, and, because of the high relative humidity, the condensation level (or level at which actual condensation of the contained moisture begins) is reached at a very low level. As a result, low stratus clouds form rapidly within the cold air behind the front.

Weather of this type has a redeeming feature, as you will learn from experience, for the top is usually quite low and you can maintain optimum flight level above the low stratus cloud deck without difficulty. But during the winter there is usually a severe icing hazard both in the clouds and in the freezing mist precipitated from the cloud. So don't make the mistake of trying an extended flight in the cloud layer during winter. Besides icing conditions, you will find that cloudiness of this type presents another hazard —low ceilings and visibilities—as you come down through for a landing.

In anticipating this kind of weather, first—watch for indications that the cold front is slowing down. This decrease in forward movement usually occurs well away from the low center, usually to the SW or SSW of the center. Then try to find out the depth of the cold air just behind the cold front. You can get this information by studying available airplane soundings over the areas involved. The soundings will give you the height of the inversion at the warm, overrunning air. Remember, the height of the *base of the inversion* will be the cloud top, and the stratus will build downward, with lifting of the cold air and additional precipitation, through the air, from the stratus formed at the higher points within the air. At times the inversion will be quite large, and the cloud area will be persistent. In fact, it is not unusual for an extensive cloud deck of this type to last from two to three days within a stagnant cold air mass.

Figs. 98 and 99. If there are any indications that you are apt to meet a cold front moving into an area occupied by warm, tropical air, you had better make a careful study of the weather characteristics of the front before

111

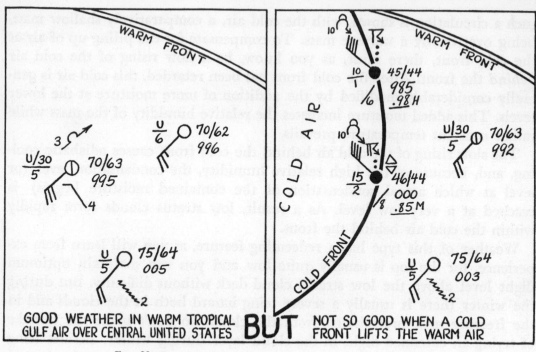

FIG. 98   **FIG. 99**

Within the figures:

WARM FRONT

GOOD WEATHER IN WARM TROPICAL
GULF AIR OVER CENTRAL UNITED STATES **BUT** NOT SO GOOD WHEN A COLD
FRONT LIFTS THE WARM AIR

COLD AIR

COLD FRONT

starting your flight. Thunderstorms, heavy rain and turbulence are apt to develop along the front, as shown in the accompanying illustrations.

An indication of the change in weather which takes place under these conditions is given by the two reports in Figs. 98 and 99, for the station at the left of each drawing. As long as the station was in the southwest flow of air, only a few scattered clouds prevailed at the station. But with the passage of the cold front, the wind shifted to strong NW, rain and a thunderstorm with hail set in, and both ceiling and visibility were greatly reduced.

During the summer, under similar conditions, your best course is to land at a field within the warm air and watch the front go by. You could, however, proceed with extreme caution to the front to see if there were any breaks in the storm chain through which the front could be passed.

The more you know about the location of the storms, the front along which they are occurring, and the rapidity with which they are moving, the better plan of flight will you be able to make. Even Cloudy Joe no longer flies deliberately into a thunderstorm, no matter how mild it looks.

112

FIG. 100

FIG. 100. You have undoubtedly heard a lot about "line squalls" and how tough they can make it for you. These line squalls are frequent along a cold front of the type shown in Fig. 99. In Fig. 100 this squall is shown in cross-section. Line squalls accompany thunderstorms at a cold front. The particular danger of this type of weather as compared to the ordinary thunderstorm lies in the severe turbulence which exists not only within the clouds of the thunderstorm itself but also in the squall cloud and at the surface over which the storm is passing. Retarding of the cold air by surface friction causes the rapidly moving cold air to bulge forward into the warm air above the surface and ahead of the surface cold front. This condition is particularly favorable to the formation of squall-type weather and frequently occurs in summer.

You can identify a line squall by its dark, stormy appearance, and the "roll" or cigar-shaped cloud at the front of the storm. When you find you can't climb over the top of the clouds or find a sizable break between the storms, my advice is—sit down and watch it go by!

113

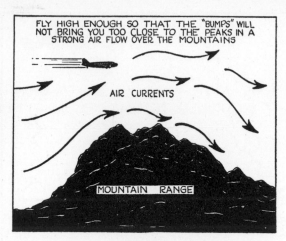

FIG. 101

FIG. 101. In flying over mountainous terrain, remember that the strong air currents develop appreciable turbulence. Be sure to keep enough altitude so that the bumps (which can bounce you up or drop you with equal ease) won't bring you too close to the peaks.

FIG. 102. Another thing to watch out for when you're flying over mountains is cloud formation caused by the lifting of the air over the mountains. Even if the weather is clear in the distance, as shown in Fig. 98, the lift due to the mountains may be sufficient to release the potential instability of the air and cause thunderstorms or heavy showers. Even in air that is not potentially unstable, the lifting may cause it to reach saturation and form clouds which will mask the mountain peaks. One of the dangers here is that the clouds may be unreported along the route, since the area affected may not be near a reporting station.

FIG. 102

Don't be discouraged if your initial attempts at weather forecasting fall short of the mark. You will learn with experience. Observe changes which occur from time to time, and if you do not know just what type of change each one is, ask a meteorologist. Remember that some changes occur within air masses where there is no interaction of air masses, and that other changes take place through interaction —say, with the active overrunning of cold air by warmer air, or the underrunning of warm air by colder air. Determine the various changes that take place within air masses as they pass over a varied terrain, such as the forma-

114

tion of clouds on the windward side of mountains, and the dissipation of clouds on the lee side.

Every time you find the correct explanation for a weather change by your own observation, you automatically increase your ability to forecast similar changes in the future. An accurate observer usually develops with experience into a good, practical forecaster.

A blunder is the result of acting before thinking—
not only in flying.

FLIGHT PLAN NC 17336 A.M. 7/7 12-22-37

From	To	Mileage	Magnetic Course	Compass Course	Drift Correction	Altitude	Wind	Temperature	Horse-Power	Ground Speed	Estimated Flying Time
NK	MI	40	315	297	−18	↗6000	WSW 45	10	600	↗104	:22
MI	EA	135	314	301	−13	6000↘4000	WSW 45	10 to 20	"	155	:52
EA	BJ	111	319-272	305-266	−14 to −6	4000↘	WSW 45	20 to 30 to 35	"	150	:48
											2:02
BJ	PJV	68	271	261	−10	↗2000	SW 40	30	600	↗127	:32
PJV	PSV	88	269	259	−10	2000	SW 40	35	"	132	:40
PSV	DO	75	220-268-330	228-263-325	+8 to −3 to −5	2000↘	WSW 35	32	"	135	:33
											1:45
DO	DT	16	270	265	−5	↗4000	WSW 35	30	600	↗105	:10
DT	AO	53	256	259	+3	4000	W 40	28	"	130	:24
AO	GO	76	265	267	+2	4000	W 40	28	"	130	:35
GO	ML	74	240-271	248-271	+8 to 0	4000-2500	W 35	28	"	135	:34
ML	CG	36	VARIABLE LAKE SHORE		———	2500↘	WSW 35	30	"	132	:17
											2:00

ESTIMATED FUEL CONSUMPTION | ALTERNATES

Total Flying Time : 5:47
Sched.   Time: 5:32

	Gals. Per Hour :	Gallons	*Necessary gallons aboard for this leg of trip.	ALTERNATES
REFUELING POINTS	From: NK To: BJ	212	600	DT
	From: BJ To: DO	183	422	GO
	From: DO To: CG	208	456	GO
	From: To:			
	From: To:			
	From: To:			

PILOT _J. Jones_

FLIGHT SUPT. _J. Doe_

State destination in case of total radio failure BJ-DO-CG

* Inclusive of lawful reserve   (ORIGINAL)

FIG. 103

X

WEATHER AND AIRLINE FLYING

IN THE "good old barnstorming" days, flights were usually conducted according to impulse and individual judgment. The airman set out with the firm determination to get where he was going if he could; to come back if he couldn't; or, barring either of these, to sit down somewhere in between. Cloudy Joe and some of his friends still use barnstorming methods, but so far as the airlines are concerned, those days are gone forever. Today each airline flight is as much a predetermined operation as the limits of human ingenuity will allow. From our later discussions you will become familiar

DEFINITIONS
OF
ABBREVIATIONS
USED IN
FLIGHT
RELEASE

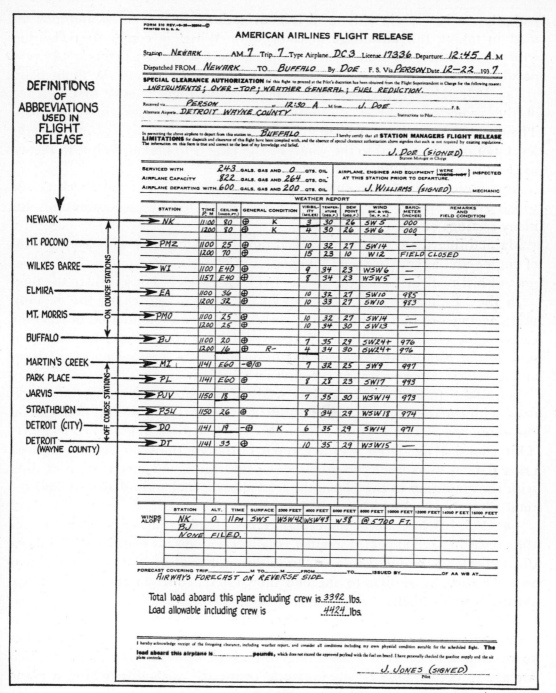

FORM 210 REV.—9—36—200M—©
PRINTED IN U. S. A.

AMERICAN AIRLINES FLIGHT RELEASE

Station __NEWARK__ AM __7__ Trip __7__ Type Airplane __DC 3__ License __17336__ Departure __12:45 A__ M

Dispatched FROM __NEWARK__ TO __BUFFALO__ By __DOE__ F. S. Via __PERSON__ Date __12-22__ 193__7__

SPECIAL CLEARANCE AUTHORIZATION for this flight to proceed at the Pilot's discretion has been obtained from the Flight Superintendent in Charge for the following reason:
__INSTRUMENTS ; OVER-TOP ; WEATHER GENERAL ; FUEL REDUCTION.__

Received via __PERSON__ at __12:30 A__ M from __J. DOE__ F. S.
Alternate Airports __DETROIT WAYNE COUNTY__ .... Instructions to Pilot

In permitting the above airplane to depart from this station to __BUFFALO__ I hereby certify that all **STATION MANAGERS FLIGHT RELEASE LIMITATIONS** for dispatch and clearance of this flight have been complied with, and the absence of special clearance authorization above signifies that such is not required by existing regulations. The information on this form is true and correct to the best of my knowledge and belief.

__J. DOE (SIGNED)__
Station Manager in Charge

SERVICED WITH __243__ GALS. GAS AND __0__ QTS. OIL
AIRPLANE CAPACITY __822__ GALS. GAS AND __264__ QTS. OIL
AIRPLANE DEPARTING WITH __600__ GALS. GAS AND __200__ QTS. OIL

AIRPLANE, ENGINES AND EQUIPMENT [WERE / WERE NOT] INSPECTED AT THIS STATION PRIOR TO DEPARTURE.

__J. WILLIAMS (SIGNED)__ MECHANIC

WEATHER REPORT

STATION	TIME P.M	CEILING (HNDS.FT.)	GENERAL CONDITION	VISIBIL- ITY (MILES)	TEMPER- ATURE (DEG.F.)	DEW POINT (DEG.F.)	WIND DIR. & VEL. (M.P.H.)	BARO- METER (INCHES)	REMARKS AND FIELD CONDITION
NK	11:00	80	⊕ K	3	30	26	SW 5	000	
	1200	80	⊕ K	4	30	26	SW 6	000	
PMZ	1100	25	⊕	10	32	27	SW14	—	
	1200	70	⊕	15	23	10	W12		FIELD CLOSED
WI	1100	E40	⊕	9	34	23	WSW6	—	
	1157	E40	⊕	8	34	23	WSW5	—	
EA	1100	36	⊕	10	32	27	SW10	985	
	1200	32	⊕	10	33	27	SW10	983	
PMO	1100	25	⊕	10	32	27	SW14	—	
	1200	25	⊕	10	34	30	SW13	—	
BJ	1100	20	⊕	7	35	29	SW24+	976	
	1200	16	⊕ R-	4	34	30	SW24+	976	
MI	1141	E60	-⊕/⊘	7	32	25	SW9	997	
PL	1141	E60	⊕	8	28	23	SW17	993	
PJV	1150	18	⊕	7	35	30	WSW14	973	
PSW	1150	26	⊕	8	34	29	WSW18	974	
DO	1141	19	-⊕ K	6	35	29	SW14	971	
DT	1141	33	⊕	10	35	29	WSW15		

Station labels (left margin):
NEWARK → NK
MT. POCONO → PMZ
WILKES BARRE → WI
ELMIRA → EA
MT. MORRIS → PMO
BUFFALO → BJ
(ON COURSE STATIONS)
MARTIN'S CREEK → MI
PARK PLACE → PL
JARVIS → PJV
STRATHBURN → PSW
DETROIT (CITY) → DO
DETROIT (WAYNE COUNTY) → DT
(OFF COURSE STATIONS)

WINDS ALOFT	STATION	ALT.	TIME	SURFACE	2000 FEET	4000 FEET	6000 FEET	8000 FEET	10000 FEET	12000 FEET	14000 FEET	16000 FEET
	NK	0	11 PM	SW5	WSW42	WSW43	W38	@ 5700 FT.				
	BJ											
	NONE FILED.											

FORECAST COVERING TRIP _____ M TO _____ M FROM _____ TO _____ ISSUED BY _____ OF AA WB AT _____
AIRWAYS FORECAST ON REVERSE SIDE

Total load aboard this plane including crew is __3392__ lbs.
Load allowable including crew is __4424__ lbs.

I hereby acknowledge receipt of the foregoing clearance, including weather report, and consider all conditions including my own physical condition suitable for the scheduled flight. **The load aboard this airplane is** _____ **pounds,** which does not exceed the approved payload with the fuel on board. I have personally checked the gasoline supply and the air plane controls.

__J. JONES (SIGNED)__
Pilot

FIG. 104

with the various radio aids to airline avigation and with the instruments used in taking full advantage of these aids. When it comes to reckoning with the weather, no stone is left unturned in finding out *beforehand* every possible weather development which may cause alteration of the flight plan.

FIG. 103. Here is a typical plan for an airline flight. Notice that *each* leg of the projected flight is a carefully planned, carefully executed problem. The captain uses every available facility to determine his optimum flight level, not only in regard to the winds he can expect to find aloft, but in regard to clouds and precipitation as well.

Also notice that the compass courses are computed between check points which are so spaced that the captain can make his own computations for many sections of the projected flight.

Maintaining these carefully worked out flight schedules with a minimum of engine and aircraft wear and a maximum of passenger comfort is the keynote of airline flying, with the rule, "SAFETY FIRST" constantly to the fore.

In the "Estimated Fuel Consumption" section of the chart, the captain, using averages of fuel consumption worked out over a long period of time for each engine type, computes the necessary fuel for completing the flight *not only to the planned destination, but to an alternate landing point,* with an ample reserve after arrival at the alternate destination.

FIG. 104. In addition to a close study of weather maps and general forecasts, with the trend of weather established by reports over several hours along the route, an airline captain is furnished with a flight release or clearance. This contains the latest weather reports from stations on and off course, other data as to weather conditions along the route, and information dealing with the condition of the plane, the load aboard, fuel and oil aboard, and the total allowable load which can be carried.

FIG. 105. Before an airline captain takes his plane upstairs, he talks over the prevailing and expected weather conditions along his route with the flight dispatcher and the meteorologist. In addition, he is furnished with a detailed weather forecast, similar to the one shown here, which he uses for reference throughout his flight.

Think back over the section on meteorology, and you will remember that "summarizing" weather over a route usually leads to trouble when it comes to making a flight plan. The thing to do is to *anticipate the changes* which are apt to occur. This is why everyone connected with dispatching a plane

OPER. FORM 525 A-3-35
90M—10-35 ©

TO: __NEWARK__

AMERICAN AIRLINES, INC.

TRIP FORECAST

Station __NEWARK__

Time Filed __12:05__ AM

Date __12/22/37__

Forecast for trip(s) AM. __7 TRIP 7__ __NK-CG__ sector. To be used until __8:00__ A. M.

Pilots are requested to grade this forecast as follows:

1. Cross out any incorrect portion of the forecast.
2. Write in the actual weather encountered when it differs from that forecast.
3. Grade the various sections according to your own judgment.
4. Sign the forecast and write any remarks you wish to make on the back.

---

1. Terminals:

   NK; INTMDT BRKN CLDS TO OVC AT 7000 OR ABOVE; VSBY 7 OR BETTER.
   BJ; OVC WITH INTMT LGT SNOW OR LGT MIST; CIG 2000 OR BETTER; VSBY
   5 TO 8.
   DO-DT; HI BRKN CLDS TO OVC; CIG OVR 9000. VSBY 5 TO 8 HAZY.
   CG; INTMDT BRKN CLDS TO OVC WITH FEW LWR SCTD CLDS NEAR 2500.
   RISK OCNL SNOW FLRYS. VSBY 5 TO 8.

   (20)

---

2. General:

   INTMDT AND HI BRKN AND OVC GENERAL ALL PORTIONS. LWR CLDS GENERALLY
   BRKN AND OVC. PMO TO PJV AND ANOTHER NARROW AREA LCLY VCNTY PSU.
   INTMT LGT SNOW. RISK OCNL MISTING CONDITIONS LCLY BJ. OCNL LGT
   CLR ICE IN PRECIPITATION LCLY BU AND LGT TO MODERATE ICING CONDITIONS
   IN CLDS.

2-a. Special:
   (icing, hail, temperature, dust, etc.)
   (Grade included in general)

   (20)

---

3. Ceilings:
   6 TO 8000 NK TO EA THEN LWRG TO 2000 TO VCTY PJV AND AGAIN
   VRBL NEAR 3000 THR PSU AREA BREAKING TO 9000 OR OVER THENCE
   TO VCTY GO AND VRBL 5 TO 7000 REMAINDER RTE.

3-a. Top of Lower Clouds:

3-b. Upper Clouds:

   (20)

---

4. Visibilities:
   GOOD EXCEPT IN SNOW OCNLY REDUCED TO NEAR 3.

   (20)

---

5. Upper Winds:

   FLIGHT PLAN.

   (20)

BROWN _____ Meteorologist

JONES _____ Pilot

Total %

PRINTED IN U. S. A.

FIG. 105

from its point of departure discusses in detail every change, however slight, that is likely to take place along the route during flight. Since even the most expert forecasting may not always be entirely right, allowance is always made by the airline for an alternate procedure if below-minimum weather conditions exist at the planned destination. The alternate airport selected is one which is reasonably safe from any radical weather change that might make it inoperative.

Much has been done to make instrument flying safe and to minimize icing hazards, but the greatest enemy to safe flying is still bad weather. It is airline policy not to try to "outwit" the weather but to follow the safest procedure in each case of anticipated weather change, frequently to the point of canceling the flight when flight into unfavorable weather conditions, *existing or anticipated,* might be dangerous.

Confidence based just on self-opinion is a dangerous asset—especially in flying.

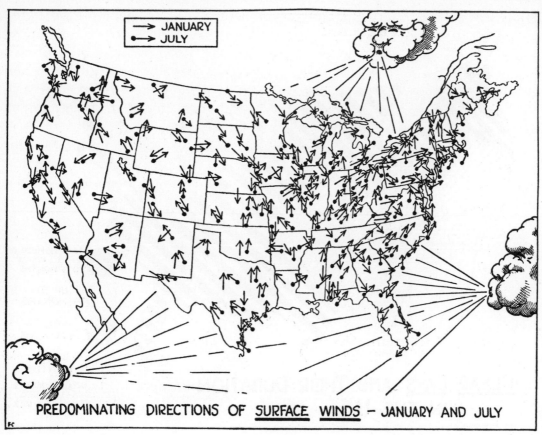

PREDOMINATING DIRECTIONS OF SURFACE WINDS — JANUARY AND JULY

FIG. 106

XI

WEATHER AVERAGES
(Climatology)

TAKE the climate of California and New York, Florida and New England, Texas and the Lake Region, and what do you find? Heaven in California, says the Californian, and the reverse everywhere else. He may be right or he may be wrong, but what you actually find is that each of these localities has a tendency toward a definite type of weather during a given season, and that this tendency is tied up with wind direction, precipitation, fog, and clouds. A knowledge of weather averages is worth having; it gives

121

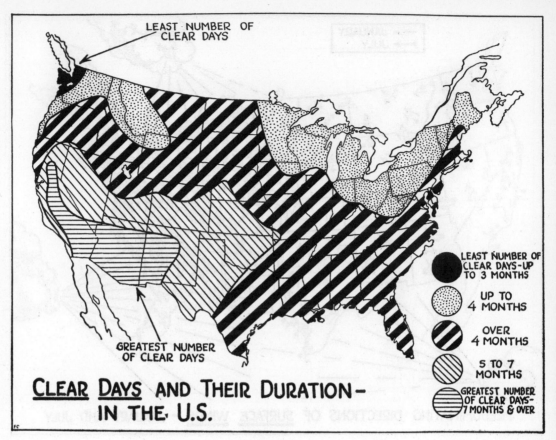

FIG. 107

you an idea, before you start planning your flight, of what to expect, and where, and when.

FIG. 106. This and the following illustrations are largely self-explanatory. Study the January and July arrows and you will see how wind direction varies in different localities during summer (July) and winter (January). In the summer the predominating influence is the inflow of warm tropical maritime air which travels through the country from a southerly direction as far north as the vicinity of the Great Lakes and the Northern Plains States. Here it meets the polar front which moves intermittently southward. During this season winds are more in accordance with the prevailing westerlies of the middle latitudes, in which the United States is situated.

In winter, the flow of warm, tropical maritime air is altered by a more

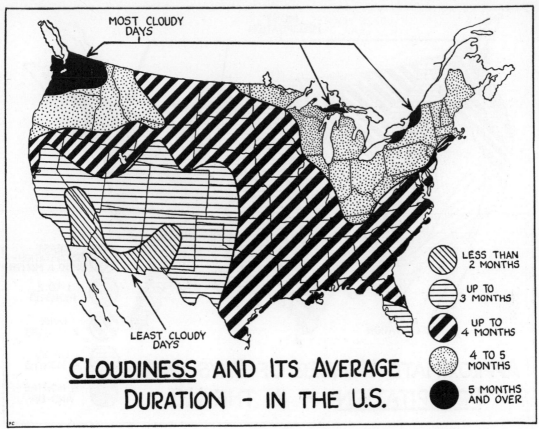

MOST CLOUDY DAYS

LEAST CLOUDY DAYS

CLOUDINESS AND ITS AVERAGE DURATION – IN THE U.S.

LESS THAN 2 MONTHS

UP TO 3 MONTHS

UP TO 4 MONTHS

4 TO 5 MONTHS

5 MONTHS AND OVER

FIG. 108

southerly movement of the polar front. This movement is brought about by intense circulation and the predominantly colder surface which permits a deeper flow, with little modification, of Polar Continental and Polar Pacific air into the lower continental areas.

Notice particularly the reversal of the prevailing wind direction, from July to January, over northern California and the Washington-Oregon area. There is a tenacious low-pressure area in winter over the Aleutian Region, and this causes a pronounced circulation of polar-type air masses from the Rockies to the Coast.

Examine the map closely and you will find that there are many purely *local* variations in wind directions. What causes them? Stop a minute and think. Terrain and other surface conditions, of course.

123

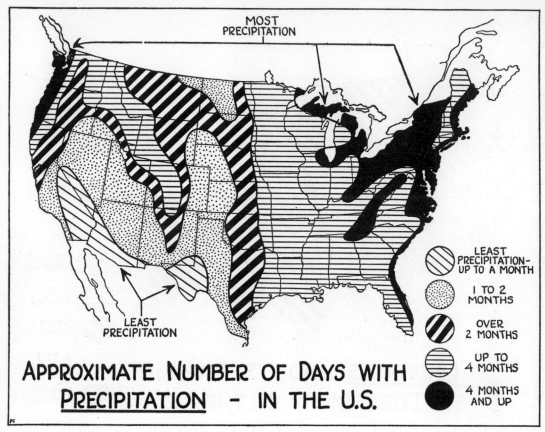

MOST PRECIPITATION

LEAST PRECIPITATION

LEAST PRECIPITATION— UP TO A MONTH

1 TO 2 MONTHS

OVER 2 MONTHS

UP TO 4 MONTHS

4 MONTHS AND UP

APPROXIMATE NUMBER OF DAYS WITH PRECIPITATION — IN THE U.S.

FIG. 109

FIG. 107. Here you have a partial explanation of the Californian's over-weening pride in the climate of his State, which, with another section of the Southwest, has seven months or more of clear days. Why? The prevalence of certain air-mass types and the interaction of air-mass types of different characteristics have a good deal to do with the weather types of various localities. In the southwest part of the United States, hot, dry air masses prevail for the greater part of the year. The intermittent flow of this clear, warm air through the remaining southwestern section of the country accounts for its share of clear days—from five to seven months.

Now look at the sections where there are the smallest number of clear days—the northwestern region, the Great Lakes region, the northern Ohio Valley and the area west of the Alleghanies. Here the explanation lies in the

124

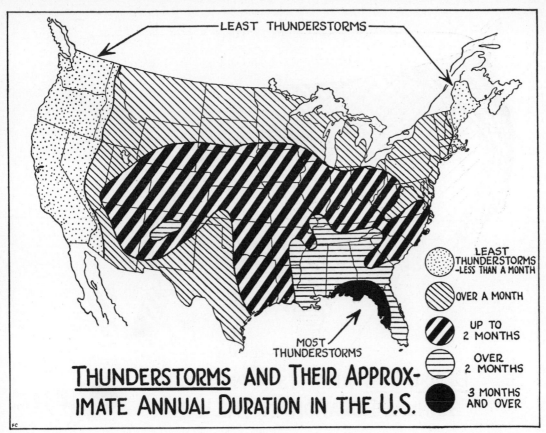

FIG. 110

constant interaction of air masses along cyclonic paths, and in the lifting of moist air by the terrain.

The greatest variation exists in those areas (shown by heavy cross-hatching) where air masses interact along moving fronts.

FIG. 108. The same influences which bring about clear days also account for the reverse condition of cloudiness.

FIG. 109. If you stop to analyze the reasons which underlie the conditions shown on this chart, you will see that the smallest amount of precipitation occurs where hot, dry air masses prevail; that the greatest amount of precipitation is closely allied with cloudiness, particularly where the cloudiness is caused by terrain, cyclonic paths and the passage of fronts. Precipitation along the Rockies and the Alleghanies, as you know, is the result of the lift-

125

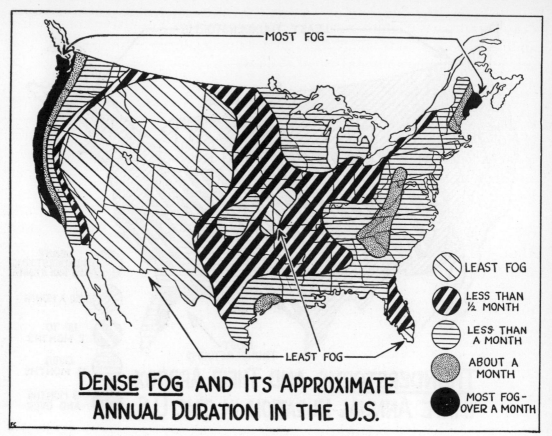

MOST FOG

LEAST FOG

LEAST FOG

LEAST FOG

LESS THAN ½ MONTH

LESS THAN A MONTH

ABOUT A MONTH

MOST FOG— OVER A MONTH

DENSE FOG AND ITS APPROXIMATE ANNUAL DURATION IN THE U.S.

FIG. 111

ing of moist air by the terrain. Along the Atlantic Coast, the explanation lies in the occurrence of cyclones off the coast, while maximum precipitation along the Great Lakes is caused by modification through surface contact. The variable amounts of precipitation which fall over other portions of the country are the result of the interaction of air masses, chiefly along moving fronts.

FIG. 110. Compare this chart with the two preceding ones and you will discover that the prevalence of thunderstorms is not directly associated with either the maximum precipitation or cloudiness areas. Instead, thunderstorms predominate over areas where weather types are controlled by warm, potentially unstable, tropical maritime masses. This is why the maximum thunderstorm area occurs over the Gulf States, where the air mass undergoes its original modification, and to a smaller degree over the central and east central parts of the United States, where there is a displacement of warm air by colder air and mountain ranges. Thunderstorms quite naturally prevail during summer months when tropical maritime masses are carried far north.

FIG. 111. You know from the section on fog that this particular menace is apt to develop wherever air is modified by passage over colder surfaces. A glance at the illustration will show you how true this is. Since the West Coast is subjected to a long, seasonal flow of this modified air, it is subject to extensive fogs, as is the "Down East" section of New England. The areas just inland from these two regions are next when it comes to fogginess.

There is considerable fogginess along the Rockies and Alleghanies, and over the Gulf Coast, caused by land modification of the air. In the central United States there is considerable variation, not only in the amount but in the type of fog, which may be either low stratus or ground. The smallest amount of fog occurs (even Cloudy Joe can guess the answer to this one) over the high western portions of the United States and over the dry southwestern portions.

One of the things that set people apart is—that some of them refuse to call their mistakes lessons.

127

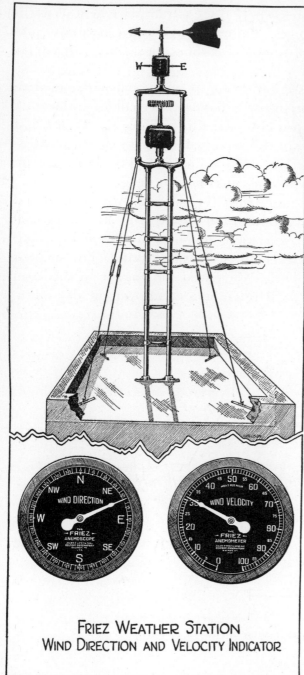

FRIEZ WEATHER STATION
WIND DIRECTION AND VELOCITY INDICATOR

XII

WEATHER INSTRUMENTS

THE job of being a weather detective is considerably simplified by various instruments which are used, figuratively speaking, to fingerprint the weather. Unless you take up weather detection as a career, you probably won't use these instruments yourself, but since they increase your safety in flight by supplying advance information about the conditions upstairs, you ought to know something about how they function.

FIG. 112. A weather-station wind-direction and velocity indicator is motivated by the simplest of all weather instruments. A single-blade, metal wind vane rotates the shaft of a self-synchronous position generator directly beneath the vane. Each movement of the vane, however slight, is transmitted to the pointer on the face of a wind-direction dial located at some distance from the vane structure. In some cases the dial may be several hundred feet below the motivating unit. Accurate transmission to

FIG. 112

FRIEZ
~Direction and Wind Velocity Recorder

FIG. 113

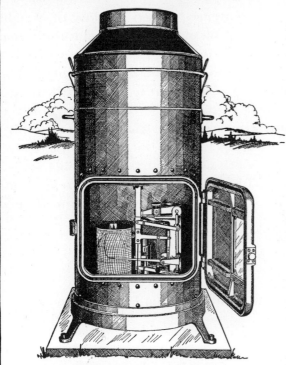

Friez Weighing and Recording Rain and Snow Gage

FIG. 114

this dial is accomplished through the use of two self-synchronous motors, the rotors of which always maintain the same geometrical position in relation to their stators.

Underneath the generator which activates the wind-direction indicator is a second self-synchronous motor topped by a rotor. This rotor is made up of a number of cups—set parallel to the axis of the rotor—which catch the wind but are prevented from spinning with it by a special restraining device. The action of the rotor is transmitted to a velocity-indicator dial with such sensitivity that every gust and lull is repeated by the moving pointer. The final recording on the face of the dial is in linear measurement.

FIG. 113. A recorder which keeps a continuous pen-and-ink record of wind direction and velocity can also be used in conjunction with the main station "weatherman" shown in the preceding illustration. Two self-synchronous motors, one connected with the velocity transmitter of the weatherman, the other with the wind-direction transmitter, op-

129

erate pens which chart velocity and direction on a continuously moving roll of graph paper. The markings at the left of the chart indicate velocity up to 100 miles an hour; on the right, they show direction for all compass points. The chart itself is moved by electricity or by a spring at a rate varying from three-quarters of a minute to twelve minutes an hour, depending upon the unit used. Standard speeds are three inches a minute, or three inches an hour. The principal advantage of this and other instruments employing graphic charts is that they furnish continuous, accurate and permanent records of weather conditions.

FIG. 114. Cloudy Joe thinks that this represents an old-fashioned stove used in remote stations to thaw out the weather detectives. What this instrument does, however, is to collect rain, snow, hail or sleet in a bucket, weigh it by means of a heat-treated spring, and transmit the record through levers and links to a pen which records the weight (that is, the amount of precipitation) on a moving chart.

In order to prevent even slight inaccuracies caused by loss of weight through evaporation, the weight of the rain or snow is recorded at the *actual moment of precipitation*. The upward and downward curves shown on the chart in this illustration each represent a weight of .02 inch of rainfall. The weighing mechanism is so sensitive, however, that it reacts to as little as one-quarter of .02 inch of precipitation, and is capable of weighing as much as nine or twelve inches, depending upon the size of the gauge. For every third of the recording capacity of the gauge, the pen reverses itself, thus increasing the recording scale to three times the width of the chart. The rubber-sealed, weatherproof door has been provided with a strong, efficient lock to keep our friend Cloudy Joe from crawling into the "stove" to see how the darned thing really does work.

Safety in flight begins on the ground.

FRIEZ HYGRO-THERMOGRAPH

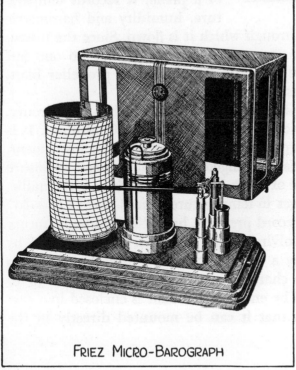

FRIEZ MICRO-BAROGRAPH

FIG. 115

FIG. 115. Hygro-thermograph is a long name for a compact instrument which records temperature by means of an alcohol-filled bourdon tube, and humidity by means of human hair. (You may not know it, but human hair records relative humidity without recourse to computations or tables, and is unsurpassed for its accuracy in both high and low humidities and in its freedom from deterioration. Just in case Cloudy Joe tries to sell some of his girl friend's hair, I ought to warn him that bleached hair, or curly hair, won't do.) The instrument shown here uses fifty strands of processed hair to move the lower, humidity-recording pen, through the wide arc of the 3-inch chart cylinder. The upper pen is used to record temperature changes.

FIG. 115-a. The micro-barograph gets its name from the fact that it records readably pressure fluctuations as small as 0.01 inch of mercury. Enough force to move the arm of the instrument through more than six inches of chart space is provided by two pressure-registering elements, one above

FIG. 115-a

the other. In order to prevent

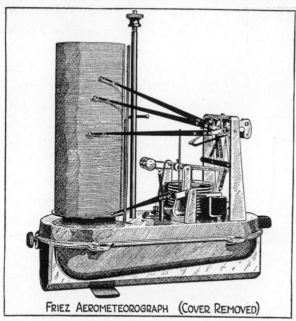

FRIEZ AEROMETEOROGRAPH (COVER REMOVED)

FIG. 115-b

the slightest vibration from entering into and spoiling the accuracy of the barometric recording, a special, liquid-filled dash pot is used to supply ink to the recording pen. The ink recording is arranged in such a way that every two and a half inches on the chart represent one inch of mercury change in barometric pressure.

FIG. 115-b. This instrument has contributed considerably to your safety by supplying accurate knowledge of upper air conditions. Mounted on the outside of a plane, it records temperature, humidity and barometric pressure of the atmospheric level through which it is flown. Since the instrument is used to record barometric pressure, it is obvious that no one but Cloudy Joe would mount it where it would be exposed to propeller blast, exhaust or other aerodynamic pressure changes.

The aerometeorograph records pressure in millibars, inches of mercury, or millimeters of mercury, and covers a range of 1050 to 400 millibars. It is motivated by an evacuated diaphragm located at the base of the instrument. Humidity is recorded by human hair arranged in a banjo-spread to insure greater sensitivity and covers a range of 10 to 100 per cent, while a bimetallic, thermostatic strip registers all changes in temperature from $+45°$ C. to $-35°$ C. Three separate arms are used to record pressure, humidity and temperature on overlapping sections of the revolving chart. A fourth arm, operated by electricity and controlled at will by a push button in the cockpit, records the time—on the lower part of the chart—of passage through a cloud or of some other special weather event. The entire instrument is enclosed in a case which is streamlined in such a way that it can be mounted directly in the wind stream.

132

FRIEZ WIND DIRECTION AND WIND VELOCITY TRANSMITTERS FOR USE WITH AIRPORT WEATHERMAN PANEL

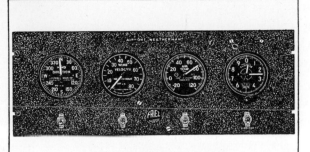

FRIEZ AIRPORT WEATHERMAN PANEL

FIGS. 116 AND 116-a. The airport weatherman shown here detects wind velocity and direction, temperature and barometric pressure changes, transmitting its findings to more or less remote indicator dials. Instead of the multi-cup rotor used on the indicator shown in Fig. 112, this unit uses a three-cup anemometer for registering wind velocity. The anemometer spins a self-synchronizing generator connected with a duplicate self-synchronous receiver in the indicator. A magnetic drag unit between the receiving motor and the indicator changes the speed of the cup rotation into a linear indication of wind velocity in miles per hour.

FIG. 116

The difference between the dry adiabatic and the observed temperature lapse rate is that the first is constant.

FIG. 116-a

133

XIII

AIRPLANE INSTRUMENTS

A SHORT time ago, safe flying depended upon seeing the ground. Today, when you fly on instruments, you don't even want to look at the ground. You rely, instead, upon instruments to tell you the relative attitude, altitude and direction of your plane. Therefore you must know your flying partners—the instruments—well.

Airplane instruments, such as the air speed indicator, altimeter, vertical speed indicator and others, function under pressure exerted by the atmosphere on a diaphragm inside the instrument. This pressure, static or dynamic, causes a linear expansion of the diaphragm which is transmitted as angular motion to the hand or hands on the face of the instrument.

The air which envelops our earth has, as you know, weight and elasticity. Half of the mass of this atmosphere lies between the earth's surface and an 18,000-foot level, and atmospheric pressure and temperature both decrease with altitude. You will recall from our previous discussions that pressure and temperature are affected not only by altitude but by a number of other factors as well, such as air density, nature of the air mass, etc. It is these changes in pressure and in temperature which react upon your pressure instruments and cause them to operate.

TABLE I. While the changes in pressure and temperature are variable rather than constant, the United States Bureau of Standards has established standard atmospheric values of pressure, temperature and mean temperature for the various levels below and above sea level. These values have also been adopted by the International Commission on Air Navigation. Table I gives the values for every 500 feet of change up to 35,000 feet only. Pressure instruments such as the altimeter and the air speed indicator are calibrated in accordance with these standard atmospheric values.

Before you go any further, be sure to memorize the standard atmospheric values for sea level, for these are highly important in relation to pressure instruments. Standard sea-level pressure is 29.921" Hg. (29.92" Hg. is all you need remember); temperature is 15° C., and mean temperature is 15° C. Remember that these values, and the others set up for higher and lower levels, rarely exist; they have simply been set up as a standard, and to serve as a reference line.

It won't take you long to figure out that with pressure instruments calibrated according to values which rarely exist, you must make full allowance for variations from these standards before you can obtain accurate information from your instruments. (This is something Cloudy Joe will never learn; he thinks that if his altimeter says he is 3000 feet above sea level, he *is* 3000 feet above sea level—whether the pressure is standard for that level or has dropped to a lower value. As for temperature, he refuses to believe that it has any effect at all upon a pressure instrument.) Before you can use your instruments intelligently you must learn how to make the necessary corrections from the indicated reading, and how to adjust your instrument to compensate for variations from standard atmospheric conditions.

Before we get into a discussion of the different pressure instruments, there is a point I would like to clear up for Cloudy Joe, if I can; and that is the meaning of the word "static." Cloudy Joe thinks static is a loud crackle that gets into his ears when he is trying to listen to a radio program. Actually, a static condition exists when a body or mass is subjected to only one force—gravitation. This force, as everyone but Cloudy Joe knows, is equal to the weight of the body and is measured with man-made, arbitrary values such as pounds, kilograms, etc. When we speak about the static condition of the air, or static pressure, we are concerned only with weight of the atmospheric column under a motionless condition.

TABLE I
ALTITUDE PRESSURE TABLE OF U. S. STANDARD ATMOSPHERE

Altitude, feet	Pressure in. Hg.	Pressure mm. Hg.	Temperature °C.	Mean Temperature °C.
−1,000 ...	31.02	787.9	+17.0	+16.0
− 500 ...	30.47	773.8	16.0	15.5
0 Sea Level	29.921	760.0	15.0	15.0
+ 500 ...	29.38	746.4	14.0	14.5
+1,000 ...	28.86	732.9	13.0	14.0
1,500 ...	28.33	719.7	12.0	13.5
2,000 ...	27.82	706.6	11.0	13.0
2,500 ...	27.31	693.8	10.0	12.5
3,000 ...	26.81	681.1	9.1	12.0
3,500 ...	26.32	668.6	8.1	11.5
4,000 ...	25.84	656.3	7.1	11.0
4,500 ...	25.36	644.2	6.1	10.5
5,000 ...	24.89	632.3	5.1	10.0
5,500 ...	24.43	620.6	4.1	9.5
6,000 ...	23.98	609.0	3.1	9.0
6,500 ...	23.53	597.6	2.1	8.5
7,000 ...	23.09	586.4	1.1	8.0
7,500 ...	22.65	575.3	+ 0.1	7.5
8,000 ...	22.22	564.4	− 0.8	7.0
8,500 ...	21.80	553.7	− 1.8	6.5
9,000 ...	21.38	543.2	− 2.8	6.0
9,500 ...	20.98	532.8	− 3.8	5.5
10,000 ...	20.58	522.6	− 4.8	5.0
10,500 ...	20.18	512.5	− 5.8	4.5
11,000 ...	19.79	502.6	− 6.8	4.0
11,500 ...	19.40	492.8	− 7.8	3.5
12,000 ...	19.03	483.3	− 8.8	2.9
12,500 ...	18.65	473.8	− 9.8	2.4
13,000 ...	18.29	464.5	−10.8	1.9
13,500 ...	17.93	455.4	−11.7	1.4
14,000 ...	17.57	446.4	−12.7	0.9
14,500 ...	17.22	437.5	−13.7	+ 0.4
15,000 ...	16.88	428.8	−14.7	− 0.1
15,500 ...	16.54	420.2	−15.7	− 0.6
16,000 ...	16.21	411.8	−16.7	− 1.2
16,500 ...	15.89	403.5	−17.7	− 1.7
17,000 ...	15.56	395.3	−18.7	− 2.2
17,500 ...	15.25	387.3	−19.7	− 2.7
18,000 ...	14.94	379.4	−20.7	− 3.2
18,500 ...	14.63	371.7	−21.7	− 3.7
19,000 ...	14.33	364.0	−22.6	− 4.3
19,500 ...	14.04	356.5	−23.6	− 4.8
20,000 ...	13.75	349.1	−24.6	− 5.3
20,500 ...	13.46	341.9	−25.6	− 5.8
21,000 ...	13.18	334.7	−26.6	− 6.3
21,500 ...	12.90	327.7	−27.6	− 6.9
22,000 ...	12.63	320.8	−28.6	− 7.4
22,500 ...	12.36	314.1	−29.6	− 7.9
23,000 ...	12.10	307.4	−30.6	− 8.4
23,500 ...	11.84	300.9	−31.6	− 9.0
24,000 ...	11.59	294.4	−32.5	− 9.5
24,500 ...	11.34	288.1	−33.5	−10.0
25,000 ...	11.10	281.9	−34.5	−10.5
25,500 ...	10.86	275.8	−35.5	−11.1
26,000 ...	10.62	269.8	−36.5	−11.6
26,500 ...	10.39	263.9	−37.5	−12.1
27,000 ...	10.16	258.1	−38.5	−12.7
27,500 ...	9.94	252.5	−39.5	−13.2
28,000 ...	9.72	246.9	−40.5	−13.7
28,500 ...	9.50	241.4	−41.5	−14.3
29,000 ...	9.29	236.0	−42.5	−14.8
29,500 ...	9.08	230.7	−43.4	−15.3
30,000 ...	8.88	225.6	−44.4	−15.9
30,500 ...	8.68	220.5	−45.4	−16.4
31,000 ...	8.48	215.5	−46.4	−16.9
31,500 ...	8.29	210.6	−47.4	−17.5
32,000 ...	8.10	205.8	−48.4	−18.0
32,500 ...	7.91	201.0	−49.4	−18.6
33,000 ...	7.73	196.4	−50.4	−19.1
33,500 ...	7.55	191.8	−51.4	−19.6
34,000 ...	7.38	187.4	−52.4	−20.2
34,500 ...	7.20	183.0	−53.4	−20.7
35,000 ...	7.04	178.7	−54.3	−21.3

An air speed indicator gives you the speed of your plane *in relation to the surrounding air.* The indicated air speed shown on your instrument, however, will equal the true air speed of your plane only when the instrument functions under standard atmospheric conditions at sea level. Theoretically from your indicated air speed you can obtain your actual air speed for a given altitude through the use of the following equation:

$$\text{True air speed} = \text{Indicated air speed} \sqrt{\frac{\text{Actual temperature}}{\text{Standard temperature}} \times \frac{\text{Standard barometric pressure}}{\text{Actual barometric pressure}}}$$

Study this equation for a minute and you will see that with any decrease in barometric pressure there is an increase in true speed, while with any decrease in temperature there will be a decrease in true speed.

Here is an important point to remember in connection with your air speed indicator. You realize, of course, that you must fly faster at higher altitudes to maintain level flight than you do at sea level because of the decreased density of the air. Yet *at whatever altitude* you fly at the minimum speed to maintain level flight, you will get exactly the same reading on your instrument as you would for minimum speed *at sea level.* In other words, if you must fly fifty miles an hour (indicated) to maintain level flight at sea level, and sixty miles (actual) at some higher altitude where the air density is lower, you will get the same reading in either case—fifty miles an hour.

FIG. 117. The mechanism of the air speed indicator is enclosed in a case in the bottom of which are two openings. Through these openings run pipes, or lines, connecting the instrument to the pitot-static tube. One of these pipes —the static connection—goes to the inside of the case, while the other—the pitot connection—goes to the inside of the diaphragm, *D.*

Now look at the sketches of the pitot-static tube shown at the bottom of this illustration and you will see that the tube itself also has two openings. When air goes past the pitot-static tube, its speed is changed into *dynamic* pressure at the pitot opening, while the static opening is subjected only to the *static* pressure of the atmosphere.

The air admitted through these two openings causes pressure in the connecting tubes, *static* atmospheric pressure being transmitted to the inside of the case through the static connection, and *dynamic* pressure being transmit-

137

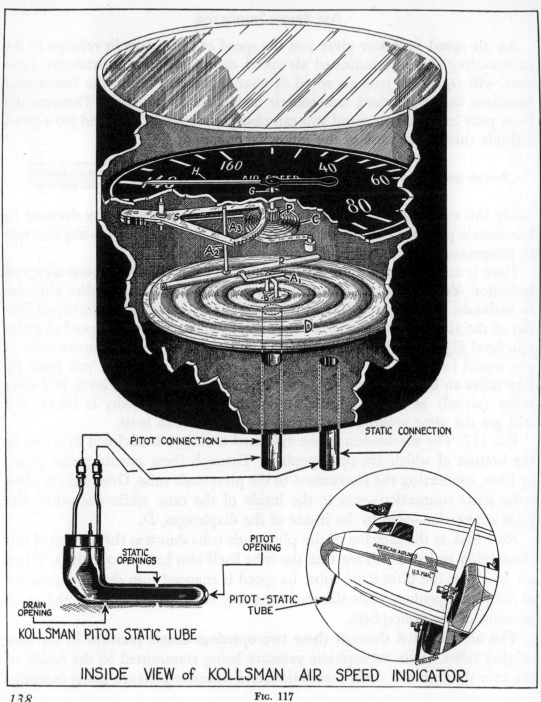

PITOT CONNECTION

STATIC CONNECTION

STATIC OPENINGS

PITOT OPENING

DRAIN OPENING

PITOT - STATIC TUBE

AMERICAN AIRLINES

U.S. MAIL

CARLSON

KOLLSMAN PITOT STATIC TUBE

INSIDE VIEW of KOLLSMAN AIR SPEED INDICATOR

Fig. 117

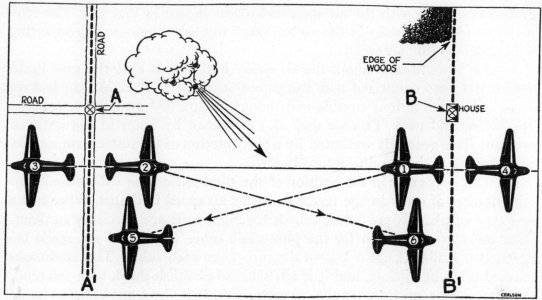

FIG. 118

ted to the inside of the diaphragm through the pitot connection. The net difference between these two pressures acts upon the diaphragm and causes it to expand. The expanding diaphragm pushes the arm, *A-1,* which rotates the rocker, *R,* and the lever, *A-2.* This lever moves a second lever, *A-3,* on sector *S;* the sector turns the gear, and the gear, in turn, rotates the hand of the instrument.

Now that you understand how the mechanism works, you can easily see that the faster you fly at a given level, the greater the dynamic force of the air, and the greater the pressure on the diaphragm of the indicator. Increased pressure causes further expansion of the diaphragm and results in a higher reading on the face of the instrument.

Whenever you wish to know the true air speed of your plane at any altitude, and extreme accuracy is not required, you can disregard the free air temperature and simply add 2 per cent of your indicated air speed for each thousand feet of altitude. If, for example, you are flying at an indicated altitude of 10,000 feet at an indicated air speed of 120 miles per hour, your approximate true air speed will be 144 miles per hour.

If, on the other hand, you must know your true air speed exactly, you can easily calculate it with the air speed calculator shown in Fig. 119. The temperature and the density of the air are taken into consideration in converting indicated into true air speed.

A point to remember about the air speed indicator is that the case itself, once it has been connected with the pitot-static tube, is air-tight. Any leakage of air will cause serious trouble and should be guarded against by frequent inspections and tests. Trouble may also be caused by water in the static or pressure line, generally indicated by a jerky motion of the instrument needle, or by failure of the hand to return to zero.

FIG. 118. Any error in the position of the pitot-static tube will cause a certain amount of error in the reading of your air speed indicator. Whenever a new type of plane is produced, exhaustive flight tests are necessary to determine the correct position for the pitot-static tube. These tests are made between two landmarks at a known distance from each other. The landmarks selected must be distinct, and it is advisable to establish them, with reference to other objects, on lines parallel to each other. It is also a good idea to locate one of the landmarks on a long, straight road.

The distance between the landmarks depends upon the speed of the plane to be tested. The faster the plane, the greater the distance. It has been found by experience that planes with a speed of 100 miles an hour should be tested over a distance of not less than one mile, and that, as a general rule, the distance between the check points should be increased at least a mile for each additional 100 miles an hour plane speed.

Best results are obtained when the tests are made on a windless day or when the wind is blowing in the direction of a line connecting the two landmarks. But even when the wind is not blowing in the desired direction, we can still obtain satisfactory results as long as the test flights are made between the two parallel lines running through the landmarks, and the plane is flown on a heading which is the direction between the two landmarks.

The time in seconds, or fractions of seconds, which it takes the plane to fly between the two landmarks serves as a basis for calculating the ground speed. From the ground speed as determined in these tests, the true air speed may be determined, and air-speed-indicator corrections made accordingly. In the course of such flight tests, not only the reading of the indicated air speed should be noted, but also the air temperature. These will provide the data for establishing the air-speed-indicator corrections, or for changing the posi-

140

tion of the pitot-static tube on the plane. Flights during a test, of course, should be made at the same indicated altitude and at the same indicated air speed.

Here the landmarks chosen are *A*, the intersection of two roads, and *B*, a house which, in reference to the edge of the woods, is on a line parallel to one of the roads. If there is no wind blowing, or if a light wind is blowing from the west or the east, then the plane will fly from No. 1 position to No. 3, returning from No. 2 position to No. 4. But suppose a wind is blowing from the northwest. Then the plane will drift during the course of the first lap from No. 1 position to No. 5, and on the return lap, from No. 2 position to No. 6.

Since, as I have said before, the basis of comparison is the true air speed of the plane, the following example will show you how to determine the ground speed, and from that the true air speed. We know that the relation between speed, time and distance is

$$\text{Actual ground speed} = \frac{3600 \times \text{distance}}{\text{Time in seconds}}$$

and that when the wind is blowing,

$$\text{Actual ground speed} = 1800 \times \left(\frac{\text{Distance}}{\substack{\text{Time flying} \\ \text{down-wind in} \\ \text{seconds}}} + \frac{\text{Distance}}{\substack{\text{Time flying} \\ \text{up-wind in} \\ \text{seconds}}} \right)$$

Now, let's assume that the distance, in our case, between A-A¹ and B-B¹ is 2.5 miles, and that with the wind blowing from the northwest it took 45 seconds to fly down-wind and 54 seconds to fly up-wind. Then

$$\text{Actual ground speed} = 1800 \left(\frac{2.5}{45} + \frac{2.5}{54} \right) = 183.3 \text{ mph}$$

Assuming that the test was made at 2500 feet and at a temperature of +20° C., then this 183.3 miles corresponds to 172 miles per hour indicated air speed. If your air speed indicator reads 175 miles during the test, it requires a correction of −3 miles per hour at this speed. This correction will be accomplished either by compiling a correction chart for the type of plane tested, or else by relocating the pitot-static tube until closer agreement is obtained between the reading of the air speed indicator and the correct indicated air speed.

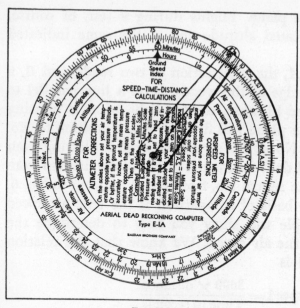

FIG. 119

It is important to distinguish between the *air speed reading*, which is the air speed as given by the reading of the air speed indicator, the *indicated* air speed, which is the air speed reading *after* correction for instrument errors and pitot-static tube position error, and the *true* air speed which is the *actual* speed of the airplane in relation to the air.

FIG. 119. This is a calculator which can be used in flight to find true air speed and actual altitude above sea level from the indicated values of the air speed indicator and the altimeter. The calculations are based on two main factors—indicated speed (or indicated altitude) and temperature at a given level. Each calculator is supplied by the manufacturer with complete instructions for its use.

SENSITIVE ALTIMETER

The altimeter is not an instrument that measures *altitude*. It measures atmospheric pressure, or the weight of the air column. It is, in fact, nothing but a scale, and the indication on the dial varies in the same way that the indicator on the face of an ordinary scale varies when you measure two, and two and a half, pounds of cheese. Only after a thorough realization of the fact that the altimeter is not a device that measures altitude, will you be able to use this instrument intelligently. (This is a point that Cloudy Joe will never understand.)

But since the atmospheric pressure decreases with altitude and continuously changes its value, you would be unable to determine the true weight of the air column unless you had a definite knowledge of change in altitude. The dial of the altimeter, therefore, is graded in feet, with each gradation corresponding to a definite atmospheric pressure (or weight of the air column).

142

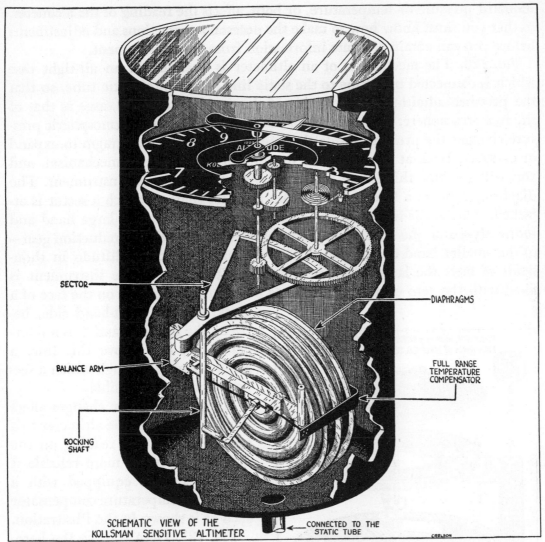

SECTOR

DIAPHRAGMS

BALANCE ARM

FULL RANGE
TEMPERATURE
COMPENSATOR

ROCKING
SHAFT

SCHEMATIC VIEW OF THE
KOLLSMAN SENSITIVE ALTIMETER

CONNECTED TO THE
STATIC TUBE

CARLSON

FIG. 120

The name of the sensitive altimeter is derived from the fact that the pointers on the face of the instrument react to even the slightest variation in pressure. Unlike the air speed indicator, however, the sensitive altimeter responds only to the static pressure of the atmospheric column, which, figuratively speaking, is *weighed* by the multiple diaphragm of the instrument. Any variation from

143

standard pressure or temperature, or both, affects the reading of the altimeter, so that you must know how to make the necessary corrections and adjustments before you can obtain accurate information from your instrument.

FIG. 120. The mechanism of an altimeter is enclosed in an air-tight case which is connected by a tube to the static line of the pitot-static tube, so that the pressure admitted to the inside of the case is always the same as that of the free atmosphere. Any increase or decrease in the outside atmospheric pressure changes the pressure inside the case and causes the diaphragm to expand or contract. Look at the schematic drawing of the altimeter mechanism, and you will see how this action of the diaphragm operates the instrument. The diaphragm moves a lever which rotates a rocker shaft to which a sector is attached. The sector transmits the rotary motion direct to the large hand and indirectly—after the rate of motion has been decreased by a reduction gear—to the smaller hand on the dial. The small hand indicates altitude in thousands of feet; the large hand, in hundreds. The face of the instrument is fixed with the zero occupying the same position as the twelve on the face of a clock. On the right-hand side, between the figures 2 and 3, is a reference line, and above this line, a small opening through which a second—sub-dial—is visible.

Since temperature changes affect the *mechanism* of the altimeter to a certain degree, the reading on the dial will be much more reliable if the altimeter is equipped with a full-range temperature compensator such as is shown in the illustration.

FIG. 121. Here you see the barometric dial which lies underneath the face of the sensitive altimeter. Notice the knob and gear arrangement which rotates the entire mechanism, including the barometric dial and the hands on the instrument dial, and which is used to

SCHEMATIC VIEW of BAROMETRIC DIAL OPERATING MECHANISM of KOLLSMAN SENSITIVE ALTIMETER

FIG. 121

FIG. 122

adjust the altimeter to varying atmospheric conditions. The barometric dial is, of course, calibrated in accordance with the United States standard atmospheric values, and is so constructed that when the figure 29.92 (standard pressure for sea level) is brought to the reference line on the face of the instrument, and the actual pressure is 29.92″ Hg., the hands of the instrument point to zero, or sea-level, altitude.

FIG. 122. This illustration shows the mechanism of the sensitive altimeter mounted on its frame.

So long as standard conditions prevail, the altitude indicated by the sensitive altimeter corresponds with the actual altitude. But, as all of us know—except Cloudy Joe—standard conditions are rarely found, and your indicated altitude, as I have said before, must be corrected before you can obtain your true altitude.

First, let's consider the effect upon your altimeter of a variation from standard barometric pressure. At sea level, an altimeter will show zero altitude only if conditions are standard. Any *increase* in pressure over the standard will give you a *lower* indicated altitude, while any decrease in pressure will give you a higher indicated altitude. Suppose, for example, that you are at sea level and that the pressure has risen to 30.47″ Hg.; your altimeter will indicate an altitude of −500 feet. If the pressure drops to 29.38″ Hg., then your indicated altitude at sea level will be 500 feet.

Air temperature variations must also be taken into consideration in interpreting the reading of your altimeter, as you will see later. An increase in temperature above the standard value will give you a lower indicated altitude; a decrease in temperature will give you a higher indicated altitude. The only exception is that at any *known* altitude, such as a landing field located at 3000 feet, you can eliminate the temperature correction by setting the hands of

145

the instrument to the actual altitude. At all other indications above or below the known altitude, you must correct the indication for temperature.

Variation from the standard air temperature can sometimes produce a difference of as much as 20 per cent between the indicated and actual altitude of your plane.

Kollsman Number

It is because of the discrepancies between real and indicated altitude that the altimeter is provided with a barometric dial. This dial can be adjusted to show the barometric pressure at a given level. This pressure figure, generally known as the kollsman number, is obtained as follows:

The knob of an airport altimeter is turned until the hands on the face of the dial point to the altitude of the airport. The reading on the barometric dial after this adjustment has been made is the "kollsman" number for that particular airport at that particular time. This number is supplied by radio to planes using the airport as a reference point. The barometric dial of the plane altimeter is then rotated by means of the knob until the same kollsman number comes into position. On landing at the airport supplying the number, the indicated altitude of the plane will be the true altitude of the airport.

The kollsman number is known by other names, as well, with which you should be familiar. The Bureau of Air Commerce term is "standard atmosphere sea-level pressure"; other names include "indicated sea-level pressure," "local indicated sea-level pressure," "altimeter sea-level pressure." You will have to watch your step here, or these various names may mix you up. The kollsman number, or "the standard atmosphere sea-level pressure" is *not* the standard atmospheric value for sea level, which, as you know, is 29.92" Hg. Neither is it the actual barometric pressure at sea level, which is known as the "Weather Bureau" sea-level pressure. You will understand more fully what the kollsman number is as we get deeper into the subject; for the time being, all you need to know is that the kollsman number *at any given time* for any given airport is the figure which appears on the barometric dial when the hands of the instrument are brought to the altitude of the airport.

In obtaining the kollsman number, certain corrections must be made at the airport to allow for scale errors. If a mercury barometer is used to obtain the kollsman number at the field, corrections must be made for scale errors, gravity and temperature to obtain station pressure. This is converted into flying-field pressure from which the kollsman number is calculated.

Instead of setting your sensitive altimeter to the kollsman number, you can adjust it to the actual barometric pressure at the field where you intend to land; your altimeter will then give you your altitude above the airport instead of above sea level, and when you land at the field, the hands of the instrument will point to zero.

Before we go any farther, let me explain what is meant by *pressure altitude*. It is the altitude on the table of standard atmospheric values which corresponds to a particular barometric pressure. In other words, if the actual barometric pressure is 28.33, then the pressure altitude will be the altitude given on the table of standard atmospheric values for that particular pressure. Turn to Table I and you will see that the altitude corresponding to 28.33″ Hg. is 1500 feet. Although the *pressure altitude* for 28.33 is 1500 feet, the actual altitude for this pressure at a certain temperature may be some other figure—for example, 1540 feet, as explained later.

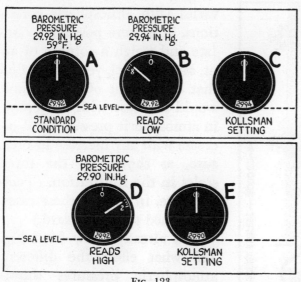

FIG. 123

FIG. 123. Here you see the effect of barometric pressure upon a sensitive altimeter, located at sea level. Under standard atmospheric conditions, if the hands of the instrument are brought to zero (actual altitude) the number 29.92″ (standard barometric pressure at sea level) appears on the barometric dial, as shown at *A*. Now see what happens when the barometric pressure increases to 29.94. The hands swing to the left to indicate a lower altitude. If the hands are again brought back to zero, the reading on the barometric dial changes to 29.94, which, in this case, is the kollsman setting for the instrument, as shown at *C*. If, on the other hand, the pressure *drops* from 29.92″ Hg. to 29.90, the hands of the altimeter will swing to the right, as shown at *D*, to indicate a higher-than-actual altitude. To obtain the kollsman number under these conditions, the hands of the instrument are again brought back to zero, the actual known altitude, and the number 29.90 appears on the barometric dial, as shown at *E*. The same procedure is used to obtain the kollsman number at any other altitude. The knob is turned until the hands show the actual altitude, whereupon the kollsman number appears on the barometric dial.

In each of the examples shown here, the kollsman number corresponds to the actual barometric pressure. This condition exists *only* at sea level. As you will see in Fig. 127, the kollsman number for an altimeter at 3000 feet may, under certain conditions, be 29.54″ Hg., although the actual barometric pressure at that level may be 26.47″ Hg.

FIG. 124. Air, as you know from our previous discussions, has definite

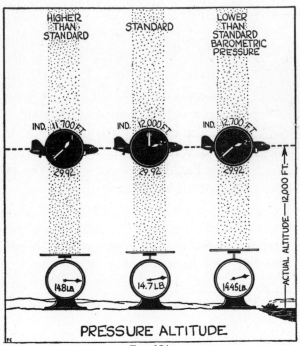

FIG. 124

weight, although this weight varies with atmospheric conditions. If it were possible to isolate and weigh a column of air at, say, sea level, you would find that the weight of the column would decrease with a decrease in atmospheric pressure, and increase with any increase in pressure, as shown by the three scales in the illustration. (Temperature, in each of these cases, is assumed to be standard.)

You already know from Fig. 123 what effect the different atmospheric pressures shown there will have upon the reading of your altimeter at sea level. Now, suppose we lift the altimeter, set for standard conditions at kollsman number 29.92, to 12,000 feet (actual), where the standard barometric pressure is 19.03″ Hg. As long as the barometric pressure remains at 19.03″ and the instrument is set at 29.92, the indicated altitude will correspond with the actual altitude of 12,000 feet. The pressure altitude will also correspond with the actual altitude under these conditions. If the baro-

148

metric pressure at 12,000 feet drops to 18.47″ Hg., and the barometric dial is left at 29.92, then the hands of the altimeter will indicate an altitude of 12,700 feet. Since 18.47″ is the standard barometric pressure for an altitude of 12,700 feet, the indicated altitude in this case will correspond to the pressure altitude. Now, if the barometric pressure increases to 19.21, the hands of the instrument will indicate a lower-than-actual altitude, 11,700 feet. Here, again, the indicated altitude corresponds with the pressure altitude.

PRESSURE, TEMPERATURE, AND ALTITUDE RELATIONSHIPS

When a true reading of the altimeter is necessary, corrections must always be made for pressure and temperature under conditions other than standard. But before you can make these corrections you must know the relationship of these three elements to each other. Both theory and experience have shown that this relationship is accurately expressed by the following equation:

$$H = 221.152 \ T_{ma} \ \log \frac{P_o}{P} + H_o$$

where

      H is the altitude in feet
      T_{ma} is the mean temperature in degrees Centigrade absolute
          of the air column from the ground up to H
      P is the pressure at altitude H
      H_o is the altitude of the ground above sea level
      P_o is the pressure at the ground

While the above equation expresses the relationship between pressure, temperature and altitude, corrections are made in accordance with still another equation, given below, or from a correction scale shown in Fig. 128.

$$H_t = \frac{T_{ma}}{T_{ms}} (H_i - H_o) + H_o$$

In this equation:

      H_t equals the true altitude
      H_i equals the indicated altitude
      H_o equals the ground altitude for which the barometric
          scale is set to give indicated sea level pressure
      T_{ma} is the actual mean temperature, in degrees absolute,
          of the air between altitude H and altitude H_o
      T_{ms} is the standard mean temperature, in degrees absolute,
          of the air between altitude H and altitude H_o

149

Study this equation and you will see that the lower the temperature in relation to the standard, the lower the actual altitude in relation to the indicated altitude. Under extreme conditions this difference may be as great as 20 per cent; that is, if the indicated altitude is 10,000 feet and the temperature at the indicated altitude is extremely low, the actual altitude may be only 8000 feet. I think even our friend Cloudy Joe will realize from this statement how important it is to make the necessary temperature correction while flying over mountainous territory when very low temperatures prevail. At least, I hope he will; otherwise, if he thinks he is clearing an 8002-foot hill when he is flying through the overcast, there may be no more Cloudy Joe!

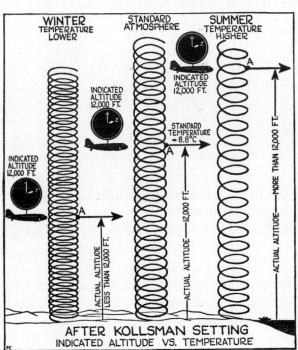

FIG. 125

Fig. 125. This illustration will help to clarify the effect of the atmospheric temperature conditions upon the reading of your altimeter. The atmospheric column is shown in the form of a spring, since the air actually expands and contracts like an ordinary spring. The middle spring represents standard atmospheric conditions; the one to the left, atmospheric conditions when the temperature is below standard; the one to the right, atmospheric conditions when the temperature is above standard.

Remember that an altimeter indicates *pressure* levels, and that these levels go up and down according to the prevailing temperatures.

Let's assume that you are flying a plane with your altimeter set at the correct kollsman number for sea level, and that your actual altitude is 12,000 feet above sea level. If atmospheric conditions are standard, as shown by the middle spring, with the temperature at *A* (the 12,000-foot level) −8.8° C., your *indicated* altitude will correspond with the *actual* 12,000-foot altitude. Now see

150

what happens when the temperature drops below standard. The pressure altitude, *A*, drops below the 12,000-foot level, as shown by the spring at the left, but *your altimeter still shows an indicated altitude of 12,000 feet.* When the temperature rises above standard, the air column expands, carrying the pressure altitude level, *A*, above the 12,000-foot level, as shown by the right hand spring. Yet here again, your altimeter shows an indicated altitude of 12,000 feet. Higher-than-standard temperatures generally prevail in the summer, and lower-than-standard in the winter, as you know; but don't let this mislead you. It is possible to have higher-than-standard temperatures in the winter, and lower-than-standard in the summer.

You can see how important it is to be able to interpret your indicated altitude correctly, particularly when you are flying through the overcast over mountainous terrain, or when you are flying over established airways. The Air Commerce regulations in the United States stipulate that east-bound flights must be made at the odd numbers of thousand feet, indicated altitude, and west-bound flights at the even numbers. You can imagine how necessary it is to have the proper clearance between planes moving in opposite directions. *Indicated* altitudes above sea level are used for air traffic clearance; *actual* altitudes, for avoiding mountain peaks.

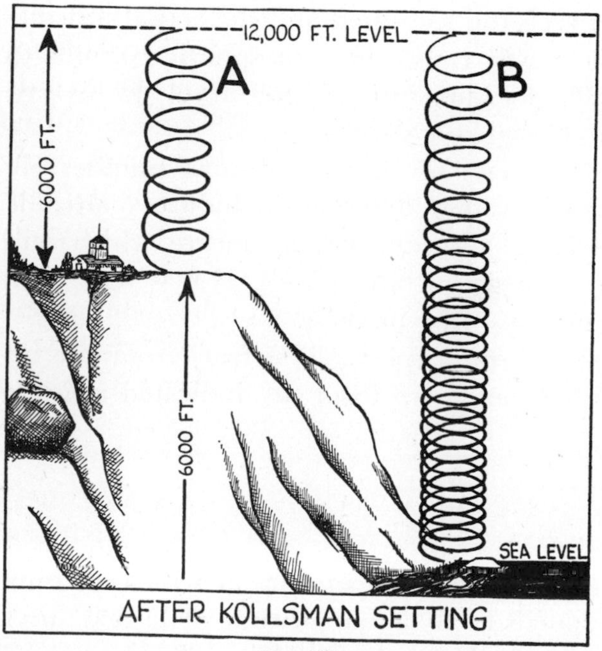

Fig. 126. After your altimeter is set to the correct kollsman number, your actual altitude, you will remember, may be as much as 20 per cent below the indicated altitude if the temperature is far below standard. Now let's see what would happen if you simply set your altimeter at the right kollsman number, during a flight, and did not take temperature variation into consideration. Suppose, for instance, that you are flying at an indicated altitude of 12,000 feet

AFTER KOLLSMAN SETTING

Fig. 126

151

above sea level with your altimeter set to the kollsman number for a sea-level airport, and that the temperature is extremely low. Now, without taking the actual temperature into consideration, but assuming that it is such as to cause a 20 per cent error, what is the maximum error for which you must allow in the reading of your instrument?

Twenty per cent of 12,000 is 2400, so that it is quite possible that you are flying 2400 feet lower than your altimeter indicates. Suppose, however, that you have obtained your kollsman number from an airport 6000 feet above sea level, and that you are still flying at an indicated altitude of 12,000 feet above sea level. The maximum error possible here is 20 per cent of 6000 feet (the difference between your indicated altitude and the 6000-foot air-port), or 1200 feet. In other words, it is possible that with an indicated altitude of 12,000 feet, you are flying 1200 feet nearer the 6000-foot-elevation airport. After these two examples, it is needless for me to emphasize that you must always take into consideration the elevation from which you have obtained your kollsman number, since this fact has an important bearing on the amount of error in your indicated altitude.

Now, let's find the minimum temperature at a given flight level which will cause a difference of 1000 feet between the indicated and the actual altitude —that is, a temperature so low that it will cause the atmospheric column to shrink to such an extent that a 12,000-foot-pressure altitude level, let us say, will be brought down to an actual 11,000-foot altitude.

Suppose that your plane has its altimeter set to the kollsman number obtained from an airport at a 3000-foot elevation, and that the indicated altitude of your plane is 12,000 feet. What is the minimum temperature which will bring the indicated altitude down to an actual altitude of 11,000 feet? You can find this temperature by using the following method:

First, subtract the actual altitude of the airport (3000 feet) from the actual altitude of the plane (11,000 feet) and also from the indicated altitude of the plane (12,000 feet). Then:

$$\frac{8000}{9000} \times 264° \text{ A.} = 234° \text{ A., or } -39° \text{ C.}$$

The conclusion, then, is that the minimum temperature at which an indicated altitude of 12,000 feet corresponds to an actual altitude of 11,000 (after the altimeter has been set to the correct kollsman number) is −39° C.

152

Now, let's look at another extreme case, where a very low temperature causes a difference of 2000 feet between indicated and actual altitudes. This time the plane is flying at an indicated altitude of 13,000 feet with its altimeter again set to the kollsman number for the 3000-foot airport. What is the minimum temperature which will cause a difference of 2000 feet between the indicated altitude (13,000 feet) and the actual altitude of the plane? Follow the same procedure given in the previous example, and you get:

$$\frac{8000}{10000} \times 262° \text{ A.} = 210° \text{ A., or } -63° \text{ C.}$$

The method we have just used for figuring the minimum temperature, which can cause an error of between 1000 and 2000 feet, is based on observed temperature at the indicated altitude and does not take the mean temperature of the air column into consideration. An error of approximately 2° exists when this method is used, but the error is fortunately higher than it would be if the mean air column temperature were used in the calculation.

Flying indicated altitudes over airways where flat terrain predominates does not present any serious problem, but when you fly over mountainous terrain, you must allow for a sufficient clearance between the mountain peaks and your plane, not only over your projected course, but also over a sufficient area to the right and left of your course. Then free air temperature must be respected—unless you wish your plane to get into head-on contact with some of the hills.

*It is in thick, not in clear weather, that
airmanship is proved.*

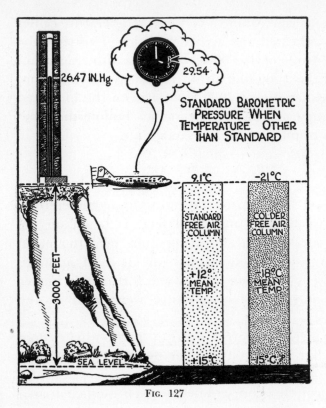

FIG. 127. Temperature correction of an altimeter is highly important when you are flying over mountains in cold weather, but temperature correction must also be taken into consideration even when you fly at low altitudes, as you will see for yourself if you study the adjoining illustration.

The airplane shown is flying at a true altitude of 3000 feet—that is, at the same level as the airport located 3000 feet above sea level. Now, if standard pressure prevails both at sea level and at the 3000-foot level, and temperature conditions are also standard (as shown in the left-hand column), the altimeter of the plane will show the true altitude, 3000 feet, when the barometric scale is set at 29.92.

But suppose that, on a certain day in winter, the temperature conditions change to those shown in the right-hand column, although the atmospheric pressure is still 29.92 at sea level. If the plane continues to fly at a true altitude of 3000 feet with its altimeter set at 29.92, the hands of the instrument will show an altitude of 3353 feet. You can prove this to yourself by taking the equation given on page 149:

$$H_t = \frac{T_{ma}}{T_{ms}} (H_i - H_o) + H_o$$

and, substituting the following values, solving for H_i:

$$T_{ms} = 273 + 12$$
$$T_{ma} = 273 - 18$$
$$H_t = 3000$$
$$H_o = 0$$

154

Then:

$$H_1 = \frac{285}{255} \times 3000 = 3353$$

The standard atmospheric pressure for the 3353-foot level is 26.47. This, then, is the true barometric pressure at the 3000-foot field under the conditions shown in the right-hand air column. Now, think what happens when the hands of the airport altimeter are brought to 3000 feet (the true altitude of the field). As long as the temperature conditions shown in the right-hand column prevail, the kollsman number appearing on the barometric dial will be 29.54. (This is the pressure value given in the standard atmosphere-altitude-pressure tables for the 353-foot level.) The "Weather Bureau" sea-level pressure, remember, is still 29.92, but the standard atmosphere sea-level pressure, or kollsman number, is 29.54. Here again you see the importance of setting the barometric scale of your instrument at the kollsman number, and not at the "Weather Bureau."

In addition to affecting the location of pressure altitudes above sea level, temperature also affects the *mechanism* of your altimeter. If your instrument is equipped with a temperature-compensating unit for sea level, the maximum error at sea level resulting from the effect of temperature upon the mechanism will not be greater than plus or minus 150 feet between two extreme temperatures such as plus or minus 40° C. At all other altitudes, when extremely high or low temperatures prevail, the maximum error will not be more than 500 feet. Following is the maximum error limit for a temperature range of −40° C. to +40° C. on an altimeter equipped with full-range, temperature-compensating unit: 0 feet = 40-foot error; 6000 feet = 70-foot error; 12,000 feet = 90-foot error; 18,000 feet = 125-foot error. For temperatures nearer to standard, errors will be proportionately less.

Fig. 128. This is a nomograph or chart for solving the altitude-temperature problem graphically. The way the chart is used is illustrated by the two sets of lines, both for the indicated altitude of 10,000 feet. (The standard atmosphere temperature, at this altitude is −4.8° C., or approximately −5° C.)

The broken line connects B (−5° C.) on Scale T_h with A (10,000 feet) on Scale H, crossing X-X at C. From C a second broken line is drawn to the indicated altitude 10 (thousand feet) at D on Scale H_i, crossing the scale H_t at the true altitude of 10 (thousand feet) at point E. In other words, for a stand-

155

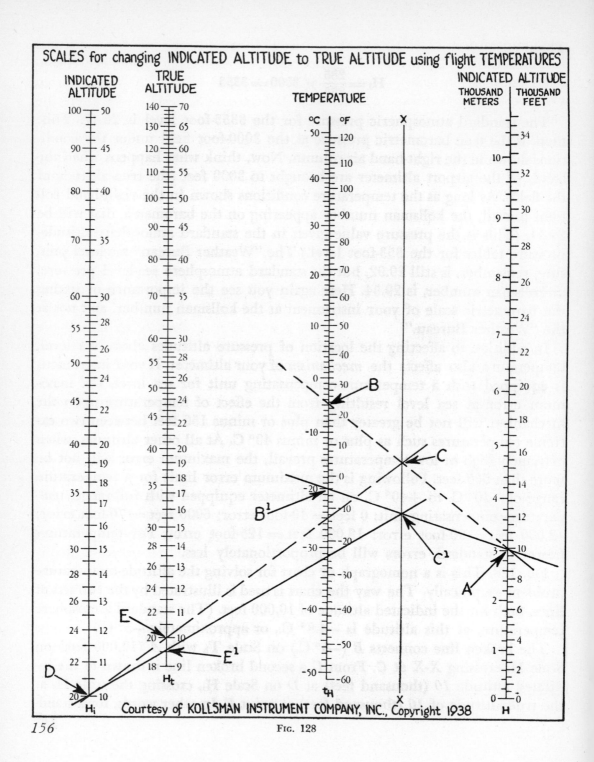

SCALES for changing INDICATED ALTITUDE to TRUE ALTITUDE using flight TEMPERATURES

Courtesy of KOLLSMAN INSTRUMENT COMPANY, INC., Copyright 1938

Fig. 128

ard temperature of −5° C., the true altitude is equal to the indicated altitude.

The solid line is drawn for a temperature of −20° C. at 10,000 feet. It connects point B^1 on Scale T_h with point A on Scale H, crossing X-X at C^1. From C^1 a second line is drawn to D on Scale H_i, crossing Scale H_t at E^1 where the value is 9550. This is the true altitude corresponding to an indicated altitude of 10,000 feet for a temperature of −20° C.

This chart can be used to find the true altitude corresponding to any indicated altitude at any temperature. The numerals on Scales H_i and H_t may be taken as any altitude values; that is, the figure, 35, may be used for 350 meters, 3500 meters, 3500 feet, or 35,000 feet. The numerals on the left-hand side of H_i must be used with the numerals on the left-hand side of H_t, while those on the right-hand side of H_i must be used with those on the right-hand side of H_t.

Fig. 129. You can always utilize two altimeters effectively during a flight.

FIG. 129

With one, you can obtain the pressure altitude by setting the barometric scale at 29.92 and taking the reading. Pressure altitude is important when it comes to adjusting the power for your engines, since in this case you are primarily interested in air density. With this same altimeter you can also adjust the barometric scale to show the indicated altitude above sea level, thus establishing your approximate altitude during the flight. Under adverse weather conditions, when greater precision is needed in landing, you can use the first altimeter by setting it at the kollsman number of the airport, and the second altimeter (the lower one in the illustration) by setting it for the

157

SCHEMATIC
VIEW OF THE
KOLLSMAN
SIMPLE
ALTIMETER

FIG. 130

pressure altitude of the same airport. Thus at the time your plane makes contact with the runway of the airport, the first altimeter will show the airport's elevation above sea level, and the second one will read zero.

FIG. 130. The simple or standard altimeter is the same as the sensitive altimeter except that it has only one hand, which makes one turn for 10,000

SCHEMATIC VIEW
of KOLLSMAN
ENGINE MANIFOLD
PRESSURE GAUGE

CONNECTED TO
INTAKE MANIFOLD

FIG. 131

feet, as does the short hand of the sensitive altimeter. The barometric scale, not shown in this schematic drawing, is set in the same way as the barometric scale on the sensitive altimeter. Naturally, the accuracy of the simple altimeter is not as great as that of the sensitive altimeter.

FIG. 131. The engine manifold pressure gauge, which is connected with the

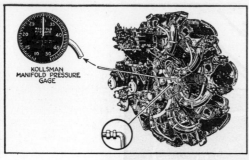

FIG. 132

KOLLSMAN MANIFOLD PRESSURE GAGE

engine, operates on the same principle as the altimeter. In other words, the diaphragm expands and contracts according to the pressure exerted upon it from the intake manifold of the engine.

FIG. 132. This shows the way in which the manifold pressure gauge is connected with the engine.

FIG. 133. The vertical speed indicator functions under the effect of differential pressure when the instrument is carried up or down in the atmosphere. You will notice in the illustration that a pipe connection is provided to the static line of the pitot-static tube, and that this connection is joined to a capillary tube ending inside the instrument case, and to a larger tube leading to the diaphragm itself. Now imagine what happens when the pressure in this common static connection suddenly increases (as it will, of course, with any decrease in the altitude of your plane). Pressure is transmitted to the diaphragm through the larger tube much faster than it is to the inside of the case through the smaller, capillary tube. Consequently the pressure inside the case lags behind the pressure inside the diaphragm. The difference between the pressure inside the diaphragm and pressure inside the case causes the instrument to show descent.

Now, what happens when you climb and pressure *decreases?* The air leaks from the diaphragm through the large pipe much faster than it does from the inside of the case through the smaller pipe, and this difference operates upon the instrument in such a way that it registers *ascent.* The pointer of the instrument will show zero only when the pressure inside the case and the pressure inside the diaphragm have been equalized.

It is well to remember that there is a certain amount of lag in the action of the vertical speed indicator. In other words, after you climb, or descend, and have leveled off the plane, it will take a few seconds for the pointer on the instrument to come back to zero. Taking the maximum possible lag (which is generally measured between 2000 feet per minute down to 200 feet per minute indication), you will find, if you are climbing at a rate of 2000 feet per minute, and you suddenly level off, that if will take about eight seconds for the pointer on the face of your vertical speed indicator to get back to the 200-

160

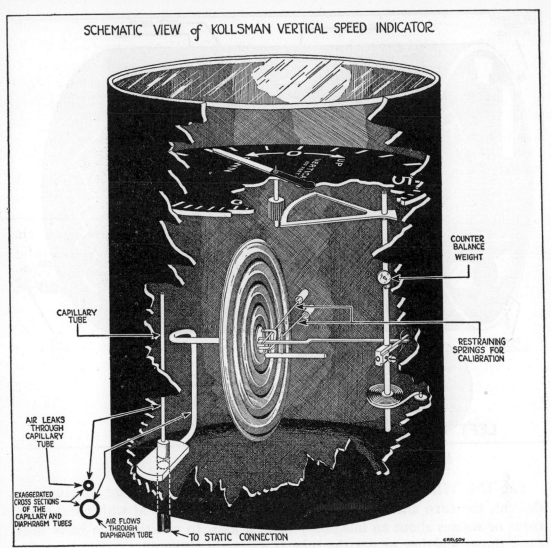

SCHEMATIC VIEW of KOLLSMAN VERTICAL SPEED INDICATOR

COUNTER BALANCE WEIGHT

CAPILLARY TUBE

RESTRAINING SPRINGS FOR CALIBRATION

AIR LEAKS THROUGH CAPILLARY TUBE

EXAGGERATED CROSS SECTIONS OF THE CAPILLARY AND DIAPHRAGM TUBES

AIR FLOWS THROUGH DIAPHRAGM TUBE

TO STATIC CONNECTION

CARLSON

Fig. 133

foot mark. It will, of course, take slightly longer for the hand to come to zero, or the neutral position. This characteristic of the instrument is important to know, so that you won't wonder why, when you have leveled off after a climb and the altimeter no longer shows a change in altitude, the vertical speed indicator is still "taking its time." Another point is that the lag in seconds of the vertical speed indicator increases slightly with altitude.

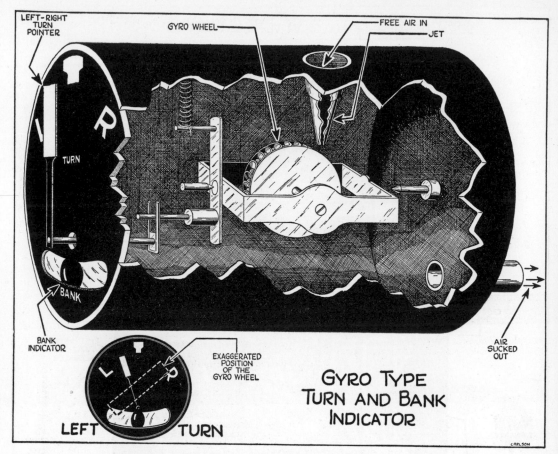

LEFT-RIGHT TURN POINTER

GYRO WHEEL

FREE AIR IN

JET

L R

TURN

BANK

BANK INDICATOR

AIR SUCKED OUT

L R

LEFT TURN

EXAGGERATED POSITION OF THE GYRO WHEEL

GYRO TYPE
TURN AND BANK
INDICATOR

CARLSON

FIG. 134

FIG. 134. While the vertical speed indicator shows the rate of climb or descent, the turn and bank indicator gives you the rate at which the plane turns or rotates about an imaginary vertical axis. In addition, the bank indicator shows whether or not the turn is correctly executed.

The principle upon which the gyro-type turn and bank indicator works is based upon "precession." You probably know that a gyro wheel must have considerable mass for its size. The wheel spins around its axis under air pressure injected through a jet. As long as the plane and instrument do not turn around their vertical axes, the spinning gyro cannot cause a change in the position of the pointer. But as soon as a turn is made along the vertical axis, the gyro leans to the right (or left) as shown in an exaggerated man-

162

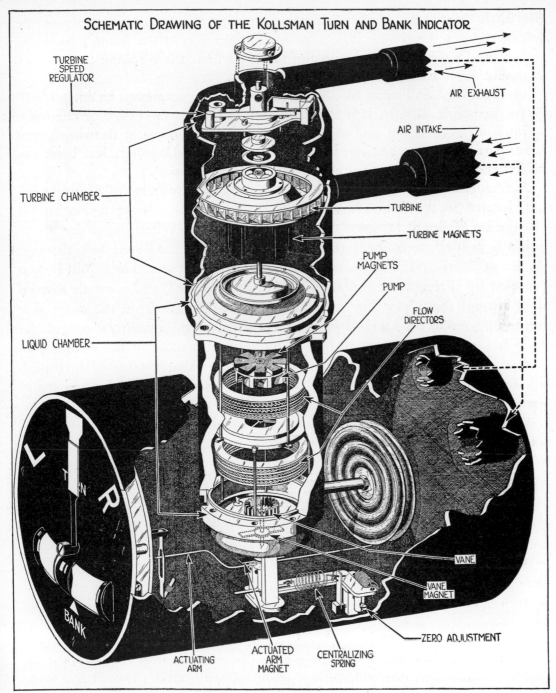

SCHEMATIC DRAWING OF THE KOLLSMAN TURN AND BANK INDICATOR

TURBINE SPEED REGULATOR

AIR EXHAUST

AIR INTAKE

TURBINE CHAMBER

TURBINE

TURBINE MAGNETS

PUMP MAGNETS

PUMP

FLOW DIRECTORS

LIQUID CHAMBER

TURN

L

R

BANK

VANE

VANE MAGNET

ZERO ADJUSTMENT

ACTUATING ARM

ACTUATED ARM MAGNET

CENTRALIZING SPRING

FIG. 135

163

ner in the lower part of the illustration, causing the pointer to move to the left or right of the center. The amount of deflection of the pointer from the center of the dial depends upon the rate at which the airplane and the instrument turn around their vertical axes.

FIG. 135. The Kollsman turn and bank indicator operates on an entirely different principle. Briefly, it is made up of three chambers—a turbine chamber, a liquid-filled chamber, and the case itself. In the schematic drawing given here, part of the mechanism, including the turbine chamber, has been enlarged and pulled out of the case for explanatory purposes.

A magnet attached to the turbine rotates a pump (by means of a pump magnet) located in the lower, liquid-filled chamber, thus causing a continuous circulation of liquid between the blades of the vane. When the entire mechanism is properly assembled and placed in operation, the liquid flows through the lower flow directors, striking the vane toward its center. The liquid is then pumped up through the center portion of the chamber, and is evenly distributed around the upper flow directors. After it emerges from the outer side of the upper flow directors, it again enters the lower flow directors and the cycle is repeated without interruption. The sole purpose of the double diaphragm shown in the illustration is to prevent excessive pressure in the liquid-filled chamber. This is done by allowing the liquid in the chamber to expand under increased pressure.

While the instrument is motionless, the vane remains motionless, since under this condition the liquid spray does not strike the plates of the vane at an angle. But the instant the instrument starts to rotate around the vertical axis, the fluid spray strikes the plates at an angle, causing the vane to turn. A magnet rigidly attached to the vane transmits this rotary motion to the pointer on the instrument dial, by means of an actuating arm to which another magnet is also rigidly attached. Whether the pointer turns to the right or left of the reference line depends, of course, upon the direction in which the instrument is being turned.

TACHOMETERS

There are several types of tachometers (the instruments used to show engine revolutions per minute), some of them operating under centrifugal force,

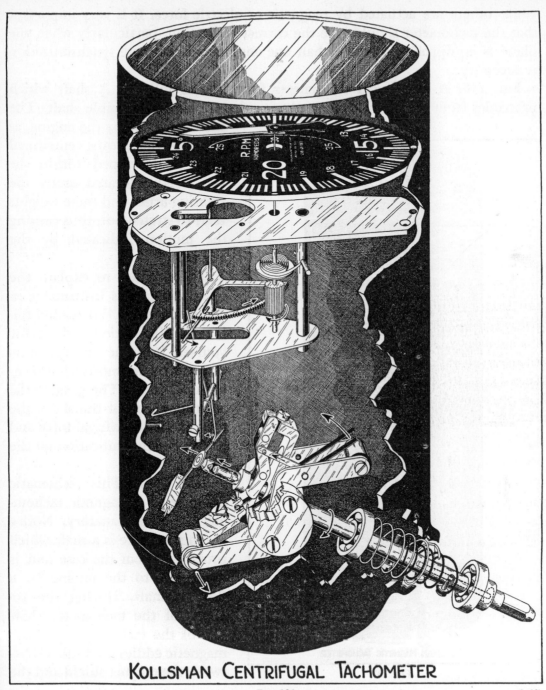

KOLLSMAN CENTRIFUGAL TACHOMETER

Fig. 136

while others are actuated by magnetic or electric force. It is very important that the tachometer should give the correct indication, particularly when the plane is equipped with more than one engine and complete synchronization is necessary.

FIG. 136. A centrifugal tachometer functions as follows: A shaft which protrudes from the case is connected with the engine by a flexible shaft. The shaft is rotated by the engine, as shown by the arrows; centrifugal force is developed within the two weights located under the rotating arms, and these weights tend to stretch out, thus causing the motion indicated by the arrows.

It is needless to explain the operation of this instrument in detail, since you can readily follow the illustration and see for yourself how the various parts respond to the motivating (centrifugal) force. The greater the rotating speed of the shaft, the greater the centrifugal force and the higher the indication on the dial.

FIG. 137. This schematic drawing of a magnetic tachometer is self-explanatory. Notice that again there is a shaft which protrudes from the case and is connected to the engine by a flexible shaft. During the rotation of the tachometer shaft and of the tachometer magnet, magnetic eddies are built up between the magnet shield and the

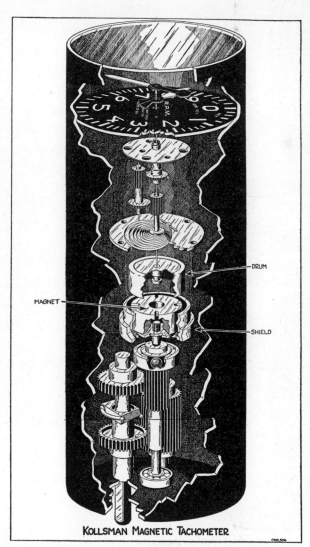

KOLLSMAN MAGNETIC TACHOMETER

FIG. 137

166

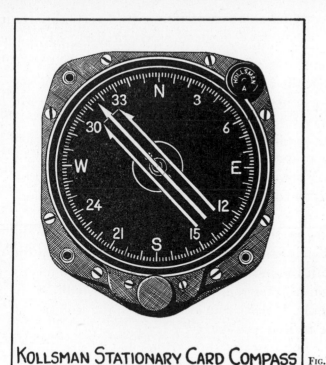

KOLLSMAN STATIONARY CARD COMPASS Fig. 138

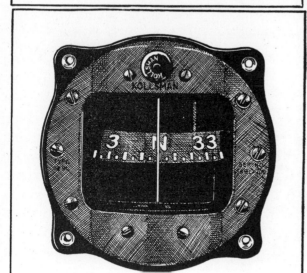

KOLLSMAN MOVING CARD COMPASS Fig. 139

drum. (This drum, incidentally, is actually located between the magnet and the shield.) The greater the speed of the magnet, the greater the force of the eddies which drag the drum along and thus move the pointers on the dial.

The *electric* tachometer (not shown here) functions in about the same way as the magnetic tachometer. An electrical generator at the engine itself transmits its electrical output to a synchronous motor which in turn rotates a magnetic tachometer mechanism.

FIG. 138. There is a wide variety in compass design, particularly in regard to the location of the compass card. Some compasses are less steady than others in rough air, but all compasses have the same general characteristics. In this illustration you see the very latest development in compass design— a *dial* type that continuously indicates the direction of your plane with respect to the earth's magnetic field.

This particular type of compass has a fixed dial, a pointer, and two parallel reference lines which are mounted just in front of the dial and are rotated by means of an adjustment knob at the bottom of the case. During flight you set these lines to the desired heading and guide your plane so that the pointer remains parallel to them. Once the lines are set, you don't have to worry about the individual number to which the needle points. The pointer itself is operated by a magnetic element inside the instrument.

The rose which is engraved on the fixed dial is graduated into the usual degree divisions, with the north point at the top and the east point at the right, and conforms with the customary compass headings printed on topographic maps and charts. The compass is so constructed that it can be read accurately from any angle.

FIG. 139. The card of the compass shown in this illustration rotates around a vertical axis. The actuating principle is the same as that of the dial type, but here the compass case moves, with the movement of the plane, around a card.

You may as well know, right now, that the compass has a bad habit of lying, not occasionally, but habitually. Unless you know when the compass is concealing the truth, it is liable to lead you astray.

The compass is subject to the influence of the various metal parts on the plane, so that corrections for these errors must be made. These corrections are always made after the compass has been installed on the plane, and after it has been "swung." The process of swinging the compass is shown in the illustrations on the next page.

"Ceiling—zero" does not apply to the weather alone.

ERROR

DUE NORTH

ERROR

DUE WEST

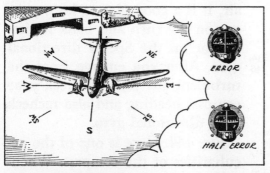

ERROR

HALF ERROR

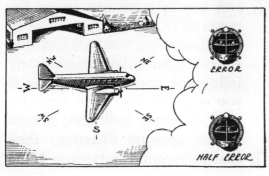

ERROR

HALF ERROR

Fig. 140

Fig. 141

Fig. 142

Fig. 143

FIG. 140. First the plane is turned to a *true north* heading. If the compass fails to show this heading, the *full* error is taken out, as shown in the lower part of the illustration, by means of the compensating magnets located in the compass. (The arrangement and use of such magnets differ with the various compass designs.) In this way the compass card is brought to due north position.

FIG. 141. Then the *next* step is to turn the plane to a true west heading, and again the full error as shown by the compass is removed by means of the compensating magnets so that the compass reads due west.

FIG. 142. Now the plane is heading due south. The same procedure is again followed—except that only *half* of the error is taken out by means of the compensating magnets.

FIG. 143. Finally the plane is swung to a due east heading; the compass is read, and again only *half* the error is taken out. After the "swinging" process has been completed, notation of the reading of the compass is taken on different headings.

During a flight, when your plane travels from one part of the country to another and continually crosses lines of equal magnetic variation,

169

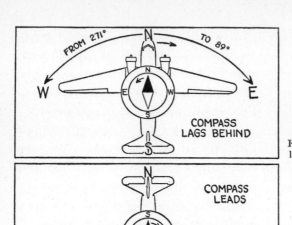

FROM 271°   TO 89°

W   E

COMPASS
LAGS BEHIND

FIG.
144

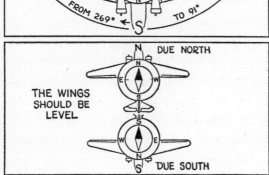

COMPASS
LEADS

W   E

FROM 269°   TO 91°

FIG.
145

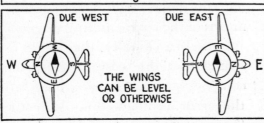

DUE NORTH

THE WINGS
SHOULD BE
LEVEL

DUE SOUTH

FIG.
146

DUE WEST   DUE EAST

W   E

THE WINGS
CAN BE LEVEL
OR OTHERWISE

FIG.
147

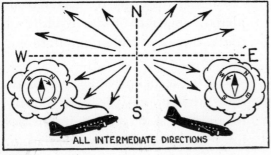

N

W   E

S

ALL INTERMEDIATE DIRECTIONS

FIG.
148

170

you must take these magnetic variations into consideration and allow for them in determining the compass course which will head your plane toward its destination.

Your compass tends to tell you the truth only when your plane has been flying straight and level for a sufficient length of time to allow the compass card to steady itself. But as soon as your plane strikes rough air, the chances are that the compass will become very temperamental and will begin to show you all sorts of directions. Therefore, once your general heading has been established and you are flying through turbulent air, it is a good idea to keep your eye on the turn and bank indicator, or on the Sperry directional gyro. After you emerge from the turbulent air, you can check your compass heading and also recheck your directional gyro.

FIG. 144. Here is one of the peculiarities of the compass. Whenever you fly a compass course between 271° and 89°, as shown in the illustration, you will find that your compass will not immediately follow the nose of your plane if you make a left or right turn. Instead, it starts indicating a turn in the *opposite* direction; then changes its mind and swings in the direction of your turn, eventually steadying itself. The steeper the bank of your plane, the farther back the compass swings. You will find that your compass behaves worst whenever the heading of your plane is near the north. Or imagine that you are flying a 10° compass course, and that you suddenly switch to a 15° compass course. The minute you start turning to the right—that is, to a more easterly direction—your compass card will swing to indicate a *westerly* direction. The swing can be as great as 25° to 30° before the compass card comes back to where it should be.

Fig. 145. If you are flying a compass course of between 90° and 270° in a southerly direction, as shown in the illustration, you will get just the opposite reaction from your compass. The compass is much more sensitive on these headings and always moves in the right direction.

Fig. 146. As long as the wings of your plane are kept level, any change in the position of the nose of the plane in relation to the horizon (above or below) will not disturb the compass, provided you are not making a turn.

Fig. 147. Even though the wings of your plane are not level, you will find that your compass card will behave normally (provided you are not turning) when you fly due east or due west.

Fig. 148. On intermediate headings you will find a combination of the effects which I have just described, depending on your proximity to north, east, south, or west.

As long as you are familiar with the bad habits of the compass, you can outwit it. Remember that when you are flying in a northerly direction, the compass will run ahead whenever you make a turn; and that when you are flying in a southerly direction, it will lag behind the turn. With this temperamental behavior of the compass in mind, try to make your turns at a slower rate and with a more shallow bank—that is, at less than 3° per second. If your plane is equipped with a directional gyro (as I said before) the whole matter will be simplified because you can then make your turns with the help of the gyro rather than with the help of the compass, and once the turn is completed, you can easily check the gyro and the compass against each other.

In this chapter I have outlined the way your compass will behave in the northern hemisphere. If you are flying in the southern hemisphere, you will get just the opposite reactions from your magnetic compass.

XIV

SPERRY GYRO INSTRUMENTS

SPERRY DIRECTIONAL GYRO

CLOUDY JOE is still puzzled over the fact that his airplane must be equipped with a directional gyro when it is already equipped with a compass. But the compass can be relied upon as a directional instrument only when exact and precise flying is not essential, for, as I have said before, while the compass does not lie all the time, it lies often enough to cause trouble. When flight is carried out in "flyable" weather, and over short distances, you can generally rely on the compass; but when it comes to a flight in and out of the overcast, and such aids as radio are used, you will find that you can cope more easily with compass problems if you have a directional gyro as your assistant.

FIG. 149. You probably know that the principle upon which all gyro instruments operate is based on the utilization of certain properties of a spinning flywheel.[1] This illustration shows the mechanism of the Sperry directional gyro without its case, and is largely self-explanatory. The normal position of the gyro in respect to its base is shown at the lower left. The gyro wheel is spun by the dynamic pressure of air which is injected into the case through two jets and acts directly upon the gyro blades. The use of two jets instead of one tends to keep the gyro wheel in position. Whenever the wheel leans to one side, as shown in the lower right of the illustration, more pressure is transmitted to the blades of the gyro from the jet on that side, and the wheel is brought back to normal position.

FIGS. 150 AND 151. These cross-sections of the directional gyro in its case will give you a clearer picture of the general arrangement of the mechanism. You will notice that the spinning gyro is mounted on a gimbal ring, thus permitting the gyro to turn along the vertical as well as the horizontal axis

---

[1] These properties—rigidity in space and precession—as well as the fundamentals of gyro instruments, are explained in *Your Wings*, pages 139-144.

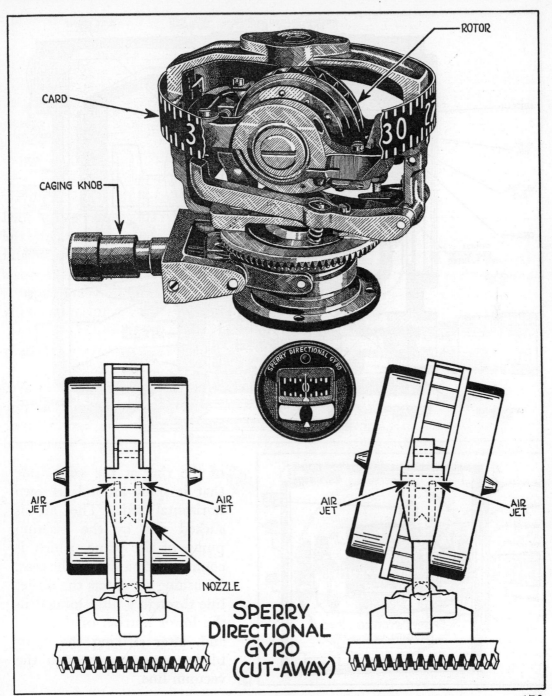

ROTOR

CARD

CAGING KNOB

AIR JET

AIR JET

NOZZLE

AIR JET

AIR JET

SPERRY
DIRECTIONAL
GYRO
(CUT-AWAY)

FIG. 149

173

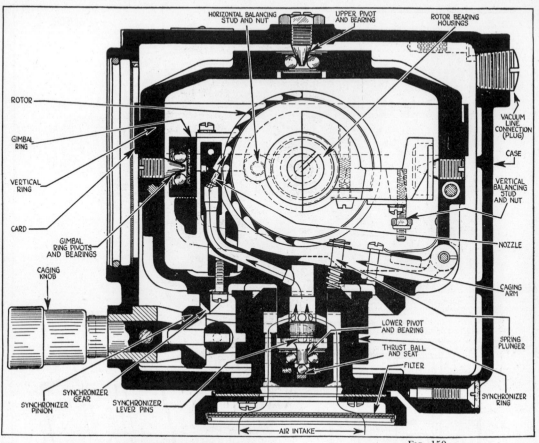

HORIZONTAL BALANCING STUD AND NUT
UPPER PIVOT AND BEARING
ROTOR BEARING HOUSINGS
ROTOR
GIMBAL RING
VERTICAL RING
CARD
GIMBAL RING PIVOTS AND BEARINGS
CAGING KNOB
VACUUM LINE CONNECTION (PLUG)
CASE
VERTICAL BALANCING STUD AND NUT
NOZZLE
CAGING ARM
LOWER PIVOT AND BEARING
THRUST BALL AND SEAT
FILTER
SPRING PLUNGER
SYNCHRONIZER GEAR
SYNCHRONIZER PINION
SYNCHRONIZER LEVER PINS
SYNCHRONIZER RING
AIR INTAKE

FIG. 150

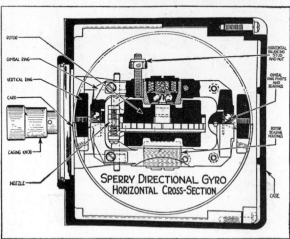

ROTOR
GIMBAL RING
VERTICAL RING
CARD
CAGING KNOB
NOZZLE
HORIZONTAL BALANCING STUD AND NUT
GIMBAL RING PIVOTS AND BEARINGS
ROTOR BEARING HOUSINGS
CASE

SPERRY DIRECTIONAL GYRO
HORIZONTAL CROSS-SECTION

FIG. 151

of the ring at the same time that it spins around its own horizontal axis. The air is sucked out by the vacuum pump of the plane, which is connected by a line to the case. Inrushing air enters the air-jet line through a filter located in the lower portion of the case, and, after striking the rotor blade, passes on through the vacuum line.

174

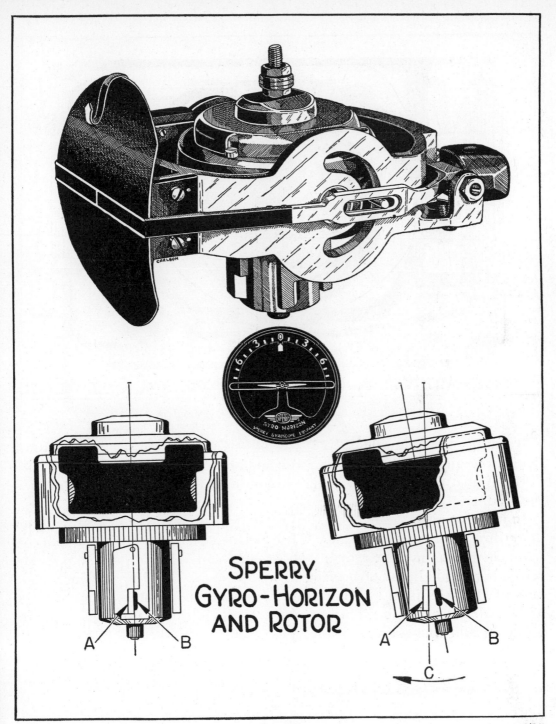

SPERRY
GYRO-HORIZON
AND ROTOR

A   B

A   B

C

FIG. 152

175

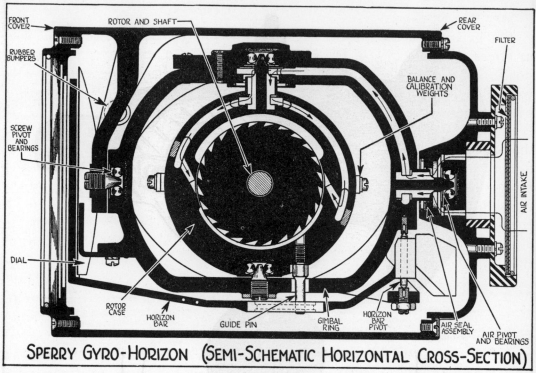

FRONT COVER — ROTOR AND SHAFT — REAR COVER — FILTER — RUBBER BUMPERS — BALANCE AND CALIBRATION WEIGHTS — SCREW PIVOT AND BEARINGS — AIR INTAKE — DIAL — ROTOR CASE — HORIZON BAR — GUIDE PIN — GIMBAL RING — HORIZON BAR PIVOT — AIR SEAL ASSEMBLY — AIR PIVOT AND BEARINGS

SPERRY GYRO-HORIZON (SEMI-SCHEMATIC HORIZONTAL CROSS-SECTION)

FIG. 153

By means of a caging knob, it is possible to turn the whole mechanism—that is, the gimbal ring with the rotor and the card—along the vertical axis of the gimbal ring. In this way the card of the directional gyro is set to match the reading of your compass.

In using your directional gyro, be prepared to allow for a slight drift of not more than 3° in fifteen minutes. When this happens, simply reset your instrument by means of the caging knob. But here is an important point to remember. Your limits of movement are 55° on any heading in climb, glide or bank. If these limits are exceeded, the gimbal ring tumbles about and the gyro card starts to spin. This condition is also corrected by caging and re-setting the instrument with the caging knob.

*The final measure of flying skill is to
know when not to fly.*

176

The gyro (artificial) horizon gives you the relative position of your plane in reference to the true horizon. This relationship is shown by means of a small indicator, in the form of an airplane, which follows the movement of your plane, and a bar which, whatever the position of your plane, remains parallel to the true horizon.

FIG. 152. While the rotor of the directional gyro rotates in a vertical plane, the rotor of the artificial horizon rotates in a horizontal plane. The rotor is housed in a comparatively small case with four pendulum valves at *A* and four ports at *B* in the lower end of the unit. Air ejected from the valves through the ports tends to keep the rotor in a horizontal plane. Any tendency of the rotor to deviate from this position causes an uneven discharge of air from the valves, and the reaction caused by this uneven discharge in turn brings the rotor back to its normal position.

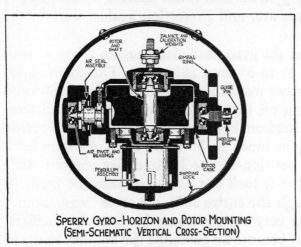

SPERRY GYRO-HORIZON AND ROTOR MOUNTING
(SEMI-SCHEMATIC VERTICAL CROSS-SECTION)

FIG. 154

FIGS. 153 AND 154. These semi-schematic illustrations show the Sperry gyro-horizon, in cross-section, mounted in its case. The rotor is mounted in a gimbal ring, and the passage of the free air is somewhat similar to the arrangement in the directional gyro. Air is sucked out of the case and inrushing air passes through the filter on the intake side of the case and through the channel built along the gimbal ring, until it reaches the two jets. The air ejected from these jets strikes the blades of the rotor, causing it to spin.

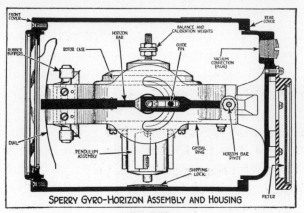

FIG. 155

SPERRY GYRO-HORIZON ASSEMBLY AND HOUSING

FIG. 155. The artificial horizon is housed in a case which is rigidly attached to the plane. The indicator-plane on the face of the instrument (not shown in this illustration) is rigidly attached to the case. You can see for yourself, therefore, that the indicator, the case and your plane all move together, while the bar on the face of the instrument remains parallel to the true horizon, thus giving you the actual attitude of your plane.

At the extreme right of the illustration is a dust filter, a standard part of every gyro instrument. While the gyro-horizon is not affected by dust to any great extent, other gyro instruments are, and protection against dust in the bearings is most important.

You will find by experience that the gyro (artificial) horizon shows a small error on turns, of not more than 3° to 5° on a 180° turn. This error shows up when you return to level. In other words, if you make a turn of 180° at a 30° bank, you will find, on leveling off, that while the wings of the indicator-plane are parallel to the artificial horizon bar, the bar itself, and therefore the wings of your plane, may vary as much as 3° to 5° from the true horizontal position. This error in the position of the horizon bar corrects itself in about the same length of time that it took the plane to make the turn. If, however, you turn the plane through the entire 360°, the error "washes out."

Cloudy Joe claims that during a very severe storm he lost the artificial horizon altogether. If he did, it was because he exceeded the angular limits of the instrument—and went considerably past the vertical bank. After these limits are exceeded, the gyro upsets, and by the time the plane levels off, the artificial horizon may be 45° to 50° off on each axis. When the plane has been leveled, the gyro comes back to the vertical at the rate of about 4° a minute. It is a good idea during normal flight not to exceed banks of more than 45° when the gyro-horizon is being used.

178

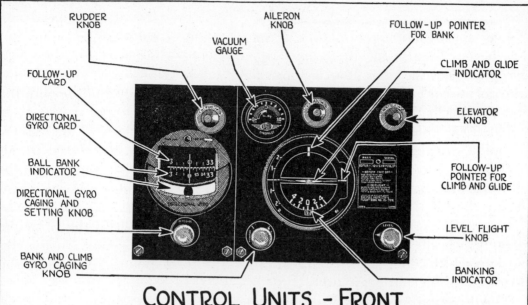

RUDDER KNOB

VACUUM GAUGE

AILERON KNOB

FOLLOW-UP POINTER FOR BANK

CLIMB AND GLIDE INDICATOR

FOLLOW-UP CARD

DIRECTIONAL GYRO CARD

BALL BANK INDICATOR

DIRECTIONAL GYRO CAGING AND SETTING KNOB

BANK AND CLIMB GYRO CAGING KNOB

ELEVATOR KNOB

FOLLOW-UP POINTER FOR CLIMB AND GLIDE

LEVEL FLIGHT KNOB

BANKING INDICATOR

CONTROL UNITS - FRONT

THE CONTROL UNITS PROVIDE VISUAL INDICATIONS OF THE ATTITUDE AND DIRECTION OF THE AIRPLANE WHETHER FLYING BY AUTOMATIC OR BY MANUAL CONTROL

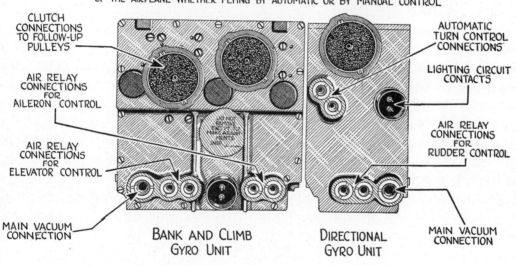

CLUTCH CONNECTIONS TO FOLLOW-UP PULLEYS

AIR RELAY CONNECTIONS FOR AILERON CONTROL

AIR RELAY CONNECTIONS FOR ELEVATOR CONTROL

MAIN VACUUM CONNECTION

AUTOMATIC TURN CONTROL CONNECTIONS

LIGHTING CIRCUIT CONTACTS

AIR RELAY CONNECTIONS FOR RUDDER CONTROL

MAIN VACUUM CONNECTION

BANK AND CLIMB GYRO UNIT

DIRECTIONAL GYRO UNIT

CONTROL UNITS - REAR

THE CONTROL UNITS SLIDE INTO THE MOUNTING UNIT ON TRACKS AND THE CONNECTIONS ENGAGE AUTOMATICALLY AS THE ATTACHING BOLTS ARE TIGHTENED

FIG. 156

Ever since Cloudy Joe found that such a thing as an automatic pilot exists, he has been saving up to buy one so that he can take a nap while the gyropilot does the work. But if I have anything to say about it, I won't allow him to use an automatic pilot until he becomes thoroughly familiar with the way the mechanism functions.

FIG. 156. This illustration shows the front and rear views of the Sperry gyropilot control units—namely, the directional gyro, and a gyro (artificial) horizon used to indicate bank and climb. You can use these combined units either manually, by disengaging the automatic pilot, or automatically, by engaging the pilot.

I am taking it for granted that you are already familiar with the principle upon which the directional gyro and the gyro-horizon operate. In the discussions which follow, I will simply outline the main points involved in the operation of the automatic pilot.

The directional gyro is a directional reference, for either automatic or manual control, by which the gyropilot can be adjusted to steer your plane to any heading desired. In addition, the air pick-offs interconnect the unit with an air diaphragm which operates the oil-pressure distributing valve and regulates the motion of the servo pistons and the rudder.

Whenever you wish to fly in a certain direction under automatic control, you must be sure to set the air pick-offs at neutral at the time your plane points in the direction which gives the desired reading on the directional gyro. The *follow-up card* is directly connected with the pick-offs, which are in a neutral position whenever the readings of the directional gyro and the follow-up card coincide. The follow-up card is controlled by means of the RUDDER knob.

The bank and climb gyro control unit has the same type of air pick-off interconnection as the directional gyro unit and controls the longitudinal and lateral attitude of the plane.

Notice the location of the various knobs as shown in the illustration. With the AILERON knob you can adjust the air pick-offs for any lateral attitude of your plane; with the ELEVATOR knob, you can adjust the air pick-offs to control the longitudinal attitude of the plane.

180

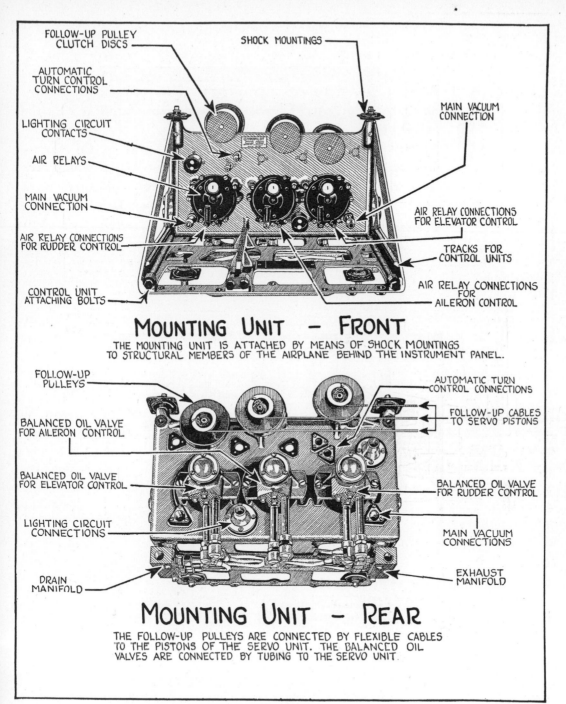

FOLLOW-UP PULLEY
CLUTCH DISCS

SHOCK MOUNTINGS

AUTOMATIC
TURN CONTROL
CONNECTIONS

MAIN VACUUM
CONNECTION

LIGHTING CIRCUIT
CONTACTS

AIR RELAYS

MAIN VACUUM
CONNECTION

AIR RELAY CONNECTIONS
FOR ELEVATOR CONTROL

AIR RELAY CONNECTIONS
FOR RUDDER CONTROL

TRACKS FOR
CONTROL UNITS

CONTROL UNIT
ATTACHING BOLTS

AIR RELAY CONNECTIONS
FOR
AILERON CONTROL

MOUNTING UNIT – FRONT

THE MOUNTING UNIT IS ATTACHED BY MEANS OF SHOCK MOUNTINGS
TO STRUCTURAL MEMBERS OF THE AIRPLANE BEHIND THE INSTRUMENT PANEL.

FOLLOW-UP
PULLEYS

AUTOMATIC TURN
CONTROL CONNECTIONS

FOLLOW-UP CABLES
TO SERVO PISTONS

BALANCED OIL VALVE
FOR AILERON CONTROL

BALANCED OIL VALVE
FOR ELEVATOR CONTROL

BALANCED OIL VALVE
FOR RUDDER CONTROL

LIGHTING CIRCUIT
CONNECTIONS

MAIN VACUUM
CONNECTIONS

DRAIN
MANIFOLD

EXHAUST
MANIFOLD

MOUNTING UNIT – REAR

THE FOLLOW-UP PULLEYS ARE CONNECTED BY FLEXIBLE CABLES
TO THE PISTONS OF THE SERVO UNIT. THE BALANCED OIL
VALVES ARE CONNECTED BY TUBING TO THE SERVO UNIT.

FIG. 157

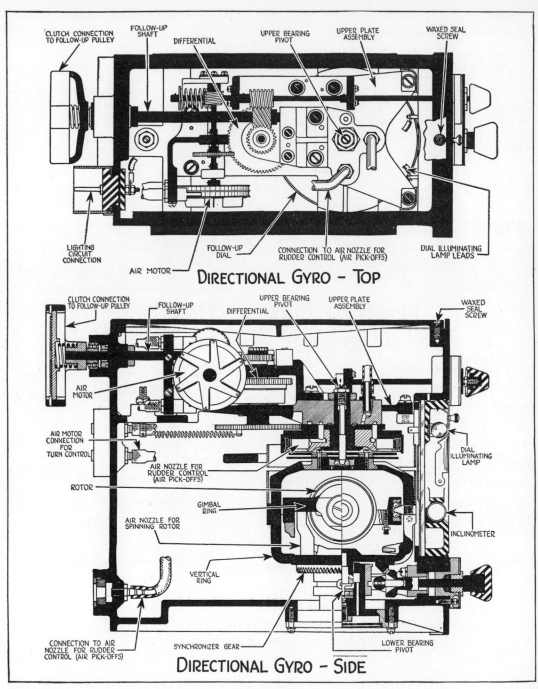

CLUTCH CONNECTION TO FOLLOW-UP PULLEY

FOLLOW-UP SHAFT

DIFFERENTIAL

UPPER BEARING PIVOT

UPPER PLATE ASSEMBLY

WAXED SEAL SCREW

LIGHTING CIRCUIT CONNECTION

AIR MOTOR

FOLLOW-UP DIAL

CONNECTION TO AIR NOZZLE FOR RUDDER CONTROL (AIR PICK-OFFS)

DIAL ILLUMINATING LAMP LEADS

DIRECTIONAL GYRO - TOP

CLUTCH CONNECTION TO FOLLOW-UP PULLEY

FOLLOW-UP SHAFT

DIFFERENTIAL

UPPER BEARING PIVOT

UPPER PLATE ASSEMBLY

WAXED SEAL SCREW

AIR MOTOR

AIR MOTOR CONNECTION FOR TURN CONTROL

AIR NOZZLE FOR RUDDER CONTROL (AIR PICK-OFFS)

ROTOR

AIR NOZZLE FOR SPINNING ROTOR

DIAL ILLUMINATING LAMP

GIMBAL RING

INCLINOMETER

VERTICAL RING

CONNECTION TO AIR NOZZLE FOR RUDDER CONTROL (AIR PICK-OFFS)

SYNCHRONIZER GEAR

LOWER BEARING PIVOT

DIRECTIONAL GYRO - SIDE

182

FIG. 158

Fig. 157. The control units just described are located in a *mounting* unit which not only supports the control units but also contains the air diaphragms, the oil pressure distributing valves, etc.

Figs. 158 and 159. These illustrations show the top and side sectional views of the directional gyro unit and the bank and climb indicator unit of the gyropilot.

It is almost impossible to explain every detail involved in the construction and general arrangement of the automatic pilot within so short a space. But if you remember the highlights (particularly the operating rules) and make a study of the instrument itself, you will be able to man the automatic pilot intelligently.

The rotors as well as the air diaphragms of the two gyro units operate because of a vacuum created by a vacuum pump in the respective vacuum lines. Under normal conditions the vacuum shown by the vacuum gauge should read between 3″ Hg. and 5″ Hg. A point for you to remember is that the vacuum pump usually provides enough vacuum at about a thousand engine r.p.m. at lower altitudes and at cruising r.p.m. at higher altitudes. At lower altitudes, and at cruising or high r.p.m., excessive vacuum is created by the vacuum pump. This excess is reduced by a vacuum relief valve.

With the aid of three speed valves, the gyropilot can be adjusted to produce a faster or slower movement (as you wish or the roughness of the air dictates) of the airplane control surfaces. The sole function of the speed valves is to regulate the passage of the oil, in greater or smaller amounts, to the servo units. On the rate at which the oil flows into the pistons of the servo unit depends the alertness or sluggishness of the gyropilot.

The pressure necessary to operate the servo units varies with different types of plane.

The oil supply tank in the hydraulic system of the gyropilot has an oil pressure regulator as well as a filter. A constant oil supply pressure is maintained by the pressure regulator.

Operating Points

Before you take off on a flight where you are going to use the automatic pilot, be sure to:

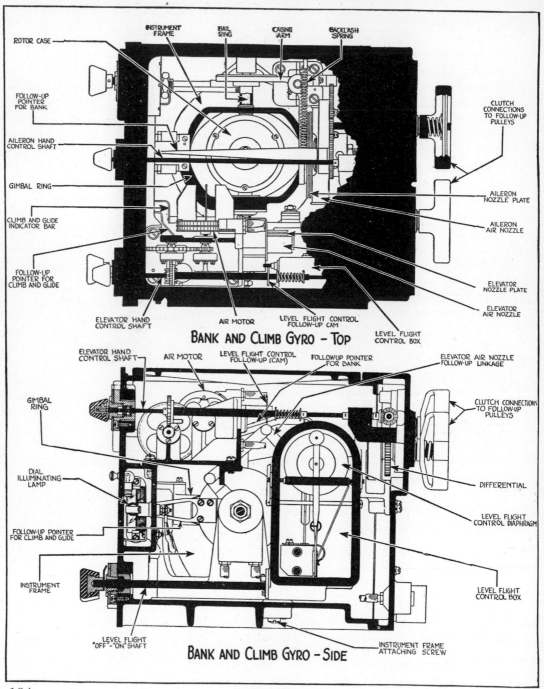

ROTOR CASE

INSTRUMENT FRAME

BAIL RING

CAGING ARM

BACKLASH SPRING

FOLLOW-UP POINTER FOR BANK

CLUTCH CONNECTIONS TO FOLLOW-UP PULLEYS

AILERON HAND CONTROL SHAFT

AILERON NOZZLE PLATE

GIMBAL RING

AILERON AIR NOZZLE

CLIMB AND GLIDE INDICATOR BAR

FOLLOW-UP POINTER FOR CLIMB AND GLIDE

ELEVATOR NOZZLE PLATE

ELEVATOR AIR NOZZLE

ELEVATOR HAND CONTROL SHAFT

AIR MOTOR

LEVEL FLIGHT CONTROL FOLLOW-UP CAM

LEVEL FLIGHT CONTROL BOX

BANK AND CLIMB GYRO - TOP

ELEVATOR HAND CONTROL SHAFT

AIR MOTOR

LEVEL FLIGHT CONTROL FOLLOW-UP (CAM)

FOLLOW-UP POINTER FOR BANK

ELEVATOR AIR NOZZLE FOLLOW-UP LINKAGE

GIMBAL RING

CLUTCH CONNECTIONS TO FOLLOW-UP PULLEYS

DIAL ILLUMINATING LAMP

DIFFERENTIAL

LEVEL FLIGHT CONTROL DIAPHRAGM

FOLLOW-UP POINTER FOR CLIMB AND GLIDE

INSTRUMENT FRAME

LEVEL FLIGHT CONTROL BOX

LEVEL FLIGHT "OFF"-"ON" SHAFT

BANK AND CLIMB GYRO - SIDE

INSTRUMENT FRAME ATTACHING SCREW

184

FIG. 159

(a) Turn the valve which engages the gyropilot to "ON" prior to starting your engine, and after setting your airplane controls to about a neutral position.

(b) Open the speed valves and start to move the controls. If they feel locked, there is no air in the respective servo cylinder, and you can disengage the gyropilot. If they seem somewhat resilient, the cylinder contains air. This is removed by turning the engaging valve to the "OFF" position, starting the engine and moving each control separately to the extreme positions. Within approximately 30 seconds, the air will have been carried into the oil supply tank by the oil.

(c) Check the oil pressure by closing the speed control valves. Indicated pressure should be within about ten pounds of the pressure stipulated for your particular plane.

(d) Check the vacuum. At 1000 r.p.m. the vacuum should read at least 3″ Hg., and at the maximum ground r.p.m. the vacuum should not exceed 5″ Hg.

(e) Uncage bank and climb gyro; if functioning properly, it will indicate the position of your plane in relation to the horizon within a few minutes.

(f) Set and uncage the directional gyro.

(g) Open speed control valves.

(h) Set level control to "OFF."

(i) Set follow-up indices to correspond with gyro indications, using the rudder, aileron and elevator knobs with manual controls in about neutral position.

(j) Now engage the gyropilot again. See that it functions properly by turning the rudder, aileron and elevator knobs to find out if the controls move with the same speed in each direction. An uneven rate of motion of the controls indicates that something is not functioning properly and that an adjustment must be made before take-off.

(k) Prior to taking off, disengage the gyropilot.

Once in the air, see that the speed valves are open and the follow-up indices aligned before you engage the gyropilot. After engaging the gyropilot, tune it to the plane. If the plane has a tendency to oscillate or "hunt," you can damp this condition with the aid of the speed valves. Actual practice with the gyropilot is the best way to familiarize yourself with the rest of the flight operations.

After a climb during which the automatic pilot has controlled the plane and upon reaching the desired altitude, turn the gyropilot off before leveling off. Be sure that the level knob is also turned off by the time the plane has leveled itself. Then, while you keep the plane in level position manually, adjust the level knob to level position while the gyropilot is STILL DIS-

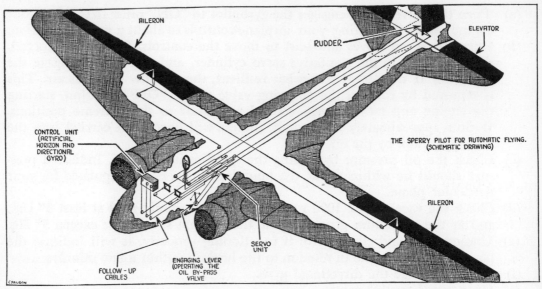

FIG. 160

ENGAGED. As soon as the displacement of the elevator follow-up index pointer stops, re-synchronize the pointer with the miniature airplane bar by means of the elevator knob and re-engage the gyropilot. Remember that the level control must always be turned to "OFF" position before disengaging the gyropilot or attempting to change altitude.

Fig. 160. The schematic drawing given here shows the connections between the gyropilot and the various controlling surfaces of the plane.

*No man-made mechanism is better than
the man who runs it.*

186

XV

A CHAT ON THE AIRCRAFT POWER PLANT

THE aircraft power plant—the engine that pulls your plane through the air—can be divided into various classes. There are liquid and air-cooled types; Diesel and gasoline; supercharged and non-supercharged, with each type designed to fit a specific purpose just as each type of plane is built to perform certain duties.

One of the requirements which the present-day engine must meet is a wide flexibility in power output. High power is necessary on the take-off of a heavily loaded plane, while only half that power is needed at cruising speed. It is also essential that the engine deliver its power on as little fuel as possible per horsepower hour.

During recent years great strides have been taken in the development of the engine. Through an improvement in cylinder-head design, for instance, it has been possible to improve the cooling of the combustion chamber. Through the use of better alloys, it has been possible to produce more resistant bearings which, in turn, have permitted increased crank-shaft speed and therefore increased horsepower. A stepping up of the compression ratio has permitted a decrease in specific fuel consumption. Improvement in supercharger design has lifted the horsepower output of our modern engine still further.

Reduction in the weight of the engine per horsepower has been brought about by the increased power output of the engine. During the past ten years, the mean effective pressure in the cylinders of the Wright Cyclone, for example, has been increased from about 115 lbs. per square inch to about 220 lbs., while the weight of the engine has been decreased from over 2 lbs. per horsepower to a little over a pound. The compression ratio, which used to be a little over 5 to 1, is now rapidly approaching 7 to 1 because of the use of high octane-number rating fuel. The rotational speed of the engine crankshaft has been raised from below 1700 r.p.m. to above 2300; and last, but by no means least, the specific fuel consumption has been decreased, as a result of all these improvements, until today it rates as low as .40 lb. per brake horsepower hour output. These improvements do not cover the whole story of engine development by any means, but they will give you some idea of the background of the power plant in your plane and thereby help you to a better understanding of the engine.

Liquid vs. Air-Cooled Engines

For many years most airplane engines were liquid-cooled. When the first air-cooled engine was developed, it had the definite advantage of lighter weight, but it also had the serious disadvantage of increased drag. With the increase in the size of planes, however, and the development of radial engine cowling, this disadvantage was overcome, and before long the radial, air-cooled, high-power engine took the lead in this country over the liquid-cooled. Any wide use of the air-cooled engine, however, would have been impossible if ways had not been found to bring its fuel consumption down to where it compared favorably with that of the liquid-cooled engine. The fuel consumption of the liquid-cooled engine is still below that of the air-cooled as the result of a higher compression ratio permissible with this type of engine. The critical parts of the engine—those which become heated—are more easily cooled in the liquid than in the air-cooled engine. But the possibilities of overheating in the air-cooled engine have been reduced to within safety limits through the use of high octane-rating fuels, and the difference in fuel consumption between the two types of engine has been reduced to a minimum.

Other points which favor the air-cooled over the liquid-cooled engine are the development of cylinders which provide 300 per cent more fin area, and lower maintenance and operating cost. Since the air-cooled engine has less plumbing than the liquid-cooled, it is less apt to develop trouble and requires less repair work.

Inline Air-Cooled vs. Radial Air-Cooled

Cloudy Joe cannot understand why all air-cooled engines are not inline, with a relatively small frontal area, instead of radial, with a large frontal area,

188

since the radial type would seem to offer greater resistance to the air. The choice between inline and radial depends upon the type of plane in which the engine is to be used. If you use a small engine with a very small frontal area (inline engine) in front of a large body, the total resistance to the air is increased. But the resistance to the air is also increased when a large engine of the radial type is installed in front of a small body. In other words, your engine must be matched to the plane in order to produce the best results.

The structure behind the engine itself is also important. A propeller functions more efficiently when it is placed in front of a *round* body, such as the engine nacelle. This arrangement, in which the engine is an integral part of the streamlined body, results in a total drag equal to, or probably less than, that of an inline engine of the same power.

Cloudy Joe wishes to know why the engines of a plane are not submerged in the wings. With the present type of plane and power plant, such an arrangement would be impractical, but I must admit that for once Cloudy Joe has had a good idea. Eventually, I believe, with an increase in the size of plane and power plant, engines will come to be submerged in the wings.

SUPERCHARGED VS. NON-SUPERCHARGED

A non-supercharged engine develops its maximum power at sea level and gradually loses power whenever it functions in an atmosphere of lower-than-sea-level density—that is, at higher-than-sea-level altitudes. The supercharged engine, because of a blower which supplies greater atmospheric pressure in the intake manifold, can maintain its maximum power until it reaches its critical altitude. As soon as any engine is lifted to its critical altitude, it begins to lose power. The critical altitude for a non-supercharged engine is sea level; for a supercharged engine, it may be 5,000, 10,000, 15,000 feet or more above sea level, according to the purpose for which the engine was designed. But *above their critical altitudes, all engines are non-supercharged and begin to lose power.* As you will see later, only 47 per cent of an engine's sea-level power is left at 20,000 feet.

Another point to remember is that whether you are flying a supercharged or non-supercharged engine, the more power you draw out of it, the more heat is generated. Part of this heat is diverted to mechanical work, and the rest (about 65 per cent of the total) must be released into the free atmosphere. The

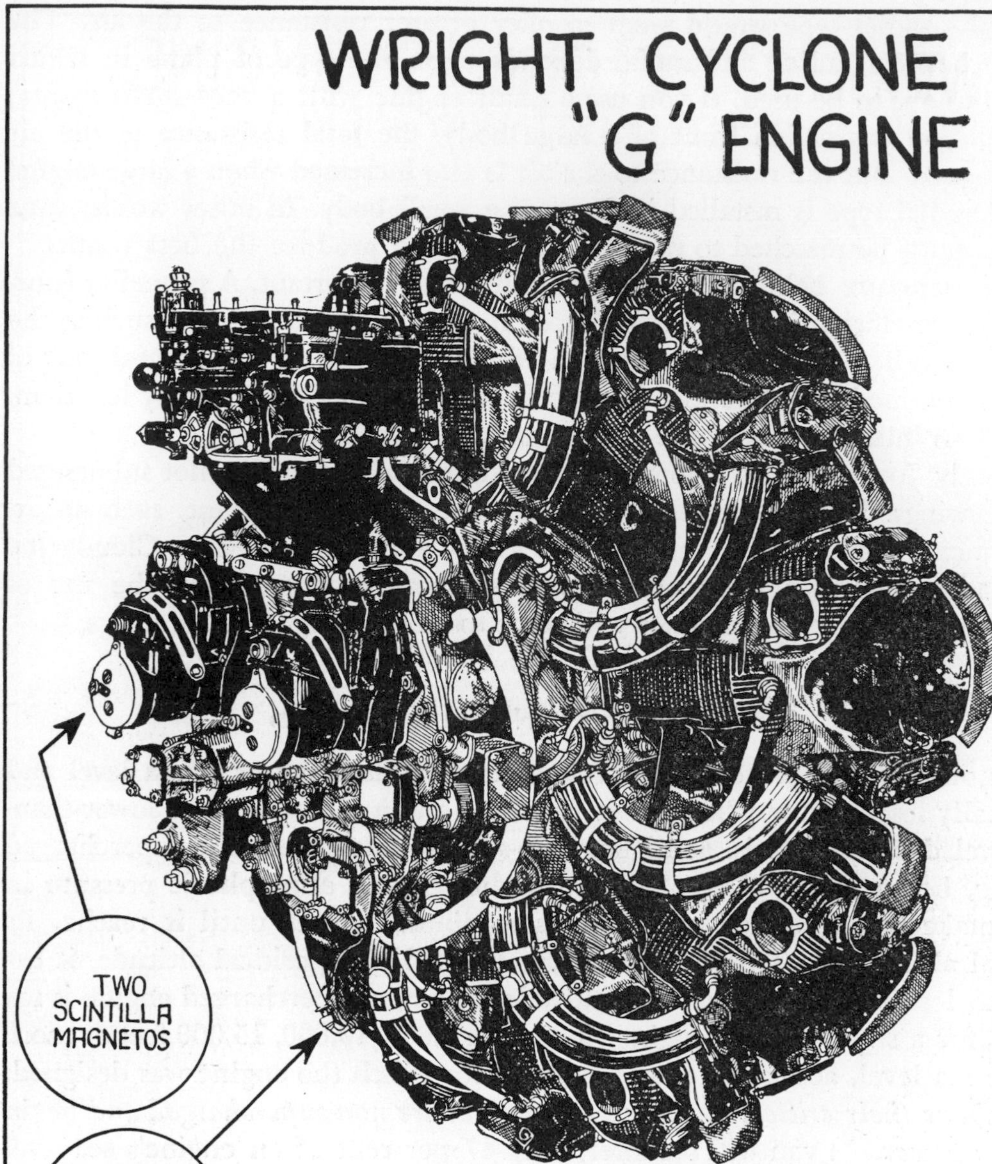

WRIGHT CYCLONE
"G" ENGINE

TWO
SCINTILLA
MAGNETOS

BG
SPARK PLUG
(FINNED)

1000 H.P.

REAR VIEW

Fig. 161

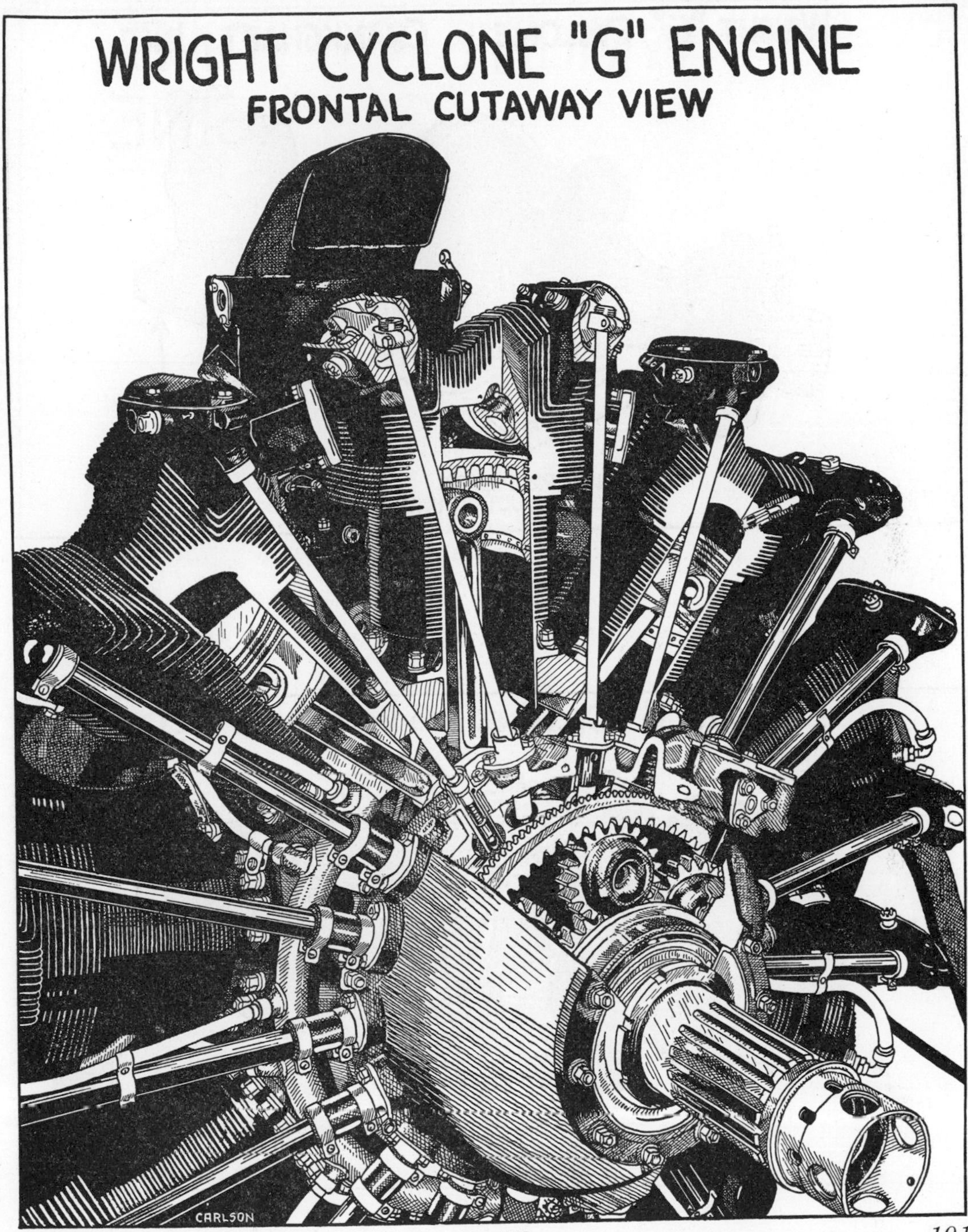

WRIGHT CYCLONE "G" ENGINE
FRONTAL CUTAWAY VIEW

CARLSON

Fig. 162

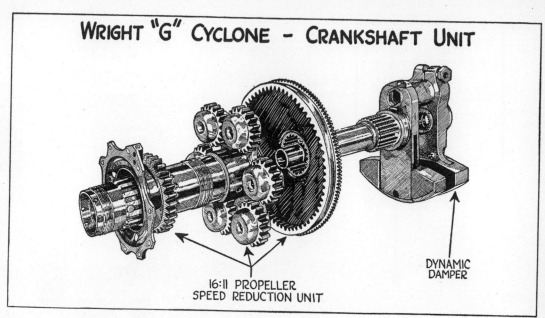

WRIGHT "G" CYCLONE – CRANKSHAFT UNIT

16:11 PROPELLER
SPEED REDUCTION UNIT

DYNAMIC
DAMPER

Fig. 163

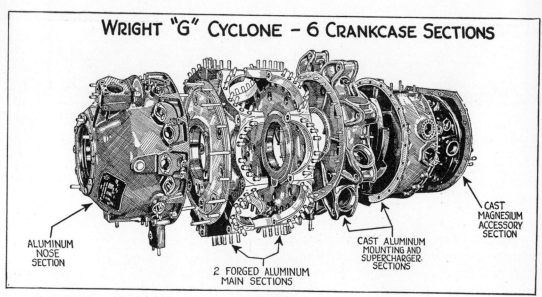

WRIGHT "G" CYCLONE – 6 CRANKCASE SECTIONS

ALUMINUM
NOSE
SECTION

2 FORGED ALUMINUM
MAIN SECTIONS

CAST ALUMINUM
MOUNTING AND
SUPERCHARGER
SECTIONS

CAST
MAGNESIUM
ACCESSORY
SECTION

Fig. 164

192

FIG. 165

cooling of the engine is poorest during take-off when maximum power is drawn out of the engine while the plane's forward speed is comparatively low.

Cloudy Joe is full of questions about the engine, but I cannot take time to answer more than one of these now. He wants to know why some countries favor one type of engine, and others, another. The deciding factor in most cases is fuel. Here in the United States, where we have an almost unlimited supply of high octane gasoline at comparatively low prices, air-cooled engines can be used to great advantage. In England, where gasoline is of poorer quality, the liquid-cooled engine is favored for certain purposes, while in Germany, where any kind of gasoline is difficult to obtain, the oil-burning Diesel engine is popular.

The attitude of the government toward aviation also has an important influence upon engine design. Where aviation is the focal point of a national military program, the industry is largely supported by government subsidies, and engines, as well as planes, are designed chiefly for offensive or defensive purposes. In the United States, however, the aviation industry has had to stand on its own feet *as a commercial venture*. The tendency in this country, therefore, has been to develop heavy-duty aircraft engines which must *earn their own living*.

FIGS. 161 TO 164. These illustrations show the rear view, front cut-away, and major component parts of a typical, American, air-cooled, radial engine.

FIG. 165. The fundamental factors affecting engine horsepower are shown here in a pictorial formula. Notice that there are two variables under your control which can cause an increase or decrease in the power output of an engine. You will find this formula helpful in connection with our further discussions of the power output of supercharged and non-supercharged engines.

POWER CURVES

FIG. 166. While the formula in Fig. 165 gives you a general idea of the factors affecting power, power curves will give you a still better understanding of the behavior of your engine. The curve on the adjoining graph represents full throttle

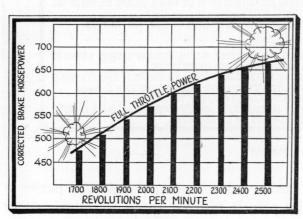

FIG. 166

power at sea level—that is, full brake horsepower delivered to the propeller shaft at different revolutions per minute for a particular engine. In plotting the curve, full corrections are made for variations from standard sea-level pressure and temperature. The same standard atmospheric sea-level values are used as a reference line in obtaining the brake horsepower as are used in calibrating your pressure instruments.

When the propeller load is light enough to allow the engine to run full throttle at 2400 r.p.m., the engine develops 655 horsepower. But when an increased propeller load reduces the r.p.m.'s to approximately 1800, the engine only develops 513 horsepower.

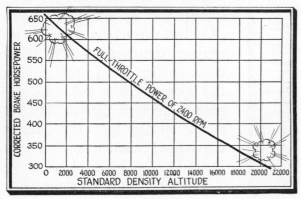

FIG. 167

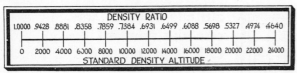

FIG. 168

FIG. 167. How does altitude affect an engine running full throttle? The answer is given in the adjoining graph, where the experimentally determined altitude curve has been plotted after corrections have been made for pressure and temperature for an engine operating at 2400 r.p.m. Horsepower decreases with altitude because the density of the air has decreased, and not, as Cloudy Joe thinks, because the engine has become dizzy with altitude and therefore less efficient. The density of the air, you will remember, is dependent upon two factors—temperature and pressure. Now, if you take the horsepower developed at a given altitude when atmospheric conditions are not standard, and convert it into the horsepower that would have been developed under standard conditions, you get what is known as *horsepower in standard density altitude.*

FIG. 168. The density ratio for any given altitude is the ratio between the weight of one cubic foot of air at that altitude and the weight of one cubic foot of air at sea level, under standard conditions. Under standard atmospheric conditions, the weight of a cubic foot of air is .076 lb. at sea level, and .056 lb. at 10,000 feet, with a ratio between these two values of .738. Fig. 168 gives a conversion scale for obtaining density ratio corresponding to standard density altitudes in even thousands of feet.

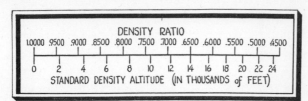

DENSITY RATIO

FIG. 169

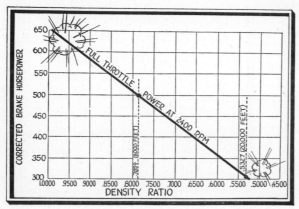

FIG. 170

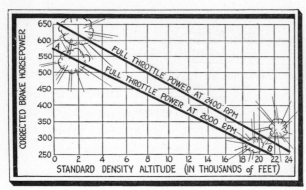

FIG. 171

FIG. 169. Here you have a conversion scale in which equal changes of density ratio (changes of .0500) are shown against even thousands of feet density altitude.

FIG. 170. We plotted the horsepower of an engine running full throttle at 2400 r.p.m. against standard density altitude, in Fig. 167. In this graph, the horsepower of the same engine is plotted against density ratio. Notice that the power curve has become a straight line instead of a curve as in Fig. 167.

FIG. 171. Now let's plot the horsepower of our 2400-r.p.m. engine against standard density altitude another way. In this case the standard density altitude is plotted as a function of the density ratio, and we again get a straight line as shown in the illustration. Notice that while 665 horsepower is available at sea level, only 311 horsepower—or 47 per cent—is available at 20,000 feet. (Cloudy Joe wants to know what the second, 2000-r.p.m. line is for, but we shall have to come back to that later.)

What a firm foundation is to a house,
a good theoretical background is to
any art.

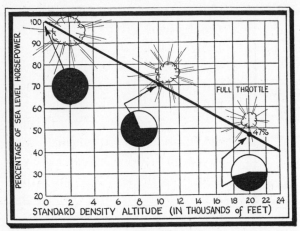

FIG. 172

FIG. 172. The work we have just done establishes a very helpful fact in the construction of power curves, and that is, that the variation of brake horsepower with altitude is a straight-line relationship when plotted against atmospheric density ratio. You can prove how helpful this is by making a graph which shows the percentage of sea-level horsepower (instead of corrected brake horsepower) against standard density altitude. You already know from Fig. 171 that an engine running at 2400 r.p.m. develops 100 per cent horsepower at sea level and only 47 per cent at 20,000 feet, and that a power curve of the engine can be shown as a straight line. Well, then, go ahead and draw a straight line on your new graph connecting the 100-per-cent point (at sea level) with the 47-per-cent point at 20,000 feet. From this line you can get the percentage of horsepower output at any altitude level along the curve. Experience has shown that a curve starting at 100 per cent at sea level and crossing the 20,000-foot ordinate at 47 per cent gives the correct percentage drop in power with increase in altitude for any normal non-supercharged engine now in use, provided it operates at full throttle and at constant r.p.m. (You may be interested in knowing that if you multiply the percentage power at any altitude along the curve by the sea-level power shown in Fig. 170, you will get the same horsepower value as shown in Fig. 170 for the corresponding altitude.)

Now let's apply this knowledge to an engine operating in full throttle at 2000 r.p.m. Turn back to Fig. 166 and you will find that the corrected brake horsepower for an engine operating at 2000 r.p.m. at full throttle is 570. Forty-seven per cent (the horsepower output at 20,000 feet) is 268. Now plot this curve on the graph given in Fig. 171, and you get the second line, *A-B*, that Cloudy Joe was worried about. From this you can obtain the corrected brake horsepower for an engine operating at 2000 r.p.m. at full throttle for any altitude between sea level and over 20,000 feet, if you wish. Power curves,

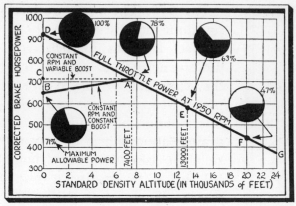

FIG. 173

you see, are far from being the theoretical things Cloudy Joe believes they are.

FIG. 173. You can make good use of the percentage power curve shown in Fig. 172 when it comes to plotting the altitude curve of any given engine at any given altitude, provided you know the horsepower and r.p.m. Let's assume that at 13,000 feet a given engine operates at 1950 r.p.m. full throttle and develops 580 horsepower. How can you find out what percentage of the total horsepower this 580 represents? Simply by turning to the graph given in Fig. 172. The answer is 63 per cent. Cloudy Joe, who never went higher than the fifth grade, has never heard of "proportion" and has no idea of how to go about finding the horsepower at sea level, but you will have no difficulty in figuring out that:

Hp at 13,000 ft. (or 580) : per cent of sea level power delivered at 13,000 ft. (or 63%) = Hp at sea level : 100%

$$63 \times (\text{Hp at sea level}) = 58,000$$
$$\text{Hp at sea level} = \frac{58,000}{63} = 923 \text{ (approximately)}$$

While an engine operating at 1950 r.p.m. on full throttle theoretically develops 923 horsepower at sea level, in actual practice you would find it impossible to operate your engine at that power output without burning it up.

Now suppose we plot the power curve of a *supercharged* engine—that is, of an engine provided with an impeller, or blower, that forces air into the intake manifold, thus maintaining sea-level or even greater-than-sea-level pressure in the intake manifold. The power of the supercharger is primarily limited by the capacity of the engine to develop certain maximum power, and this power, in turn, is limited by cooling problems and the weight and strength of the materials which enter into the structure of the engine.

To get an idea of how a supercharged engine functions, imagine that you are flying a plane equipped with such an engine, and that you wish to maintain 1950 r.p.m. at 34½″ Hg. manifold pressure. You will find that in order

198

to maintain this r.p.m. as your plane climbs into the air, you must open the throttle wider and wider until you finally reach an altitude where you can maintain the given r.p.m. only by operating at *full* throttle. The altitude at which this happens is called the *critical* altitude of your engine, and is the altitude below which you cannot operate your engine at full throttle without exceeding its normal operating ratings.

Tests made on the particular type of engine we are now considering—that is, a supercharged engine operating at a constant r.p.m. of 1950 and at constant boost (intake manifold pressure)—show that it develops 71 per cent of its full theoretical horsepower at sea level, and that it reaches its critical altitude at 7400 feet with a power output of 78 per cent. The power curve for this particular type of engine from sea level to 7400 feet is shown by the curve *B-A*. After the engine reaches the critical altitude, it follows the power curve, *A-G,* so that the complete power curve is *B-A-G.* Tests also show that if this type of engine is operated at variable boost and a constant r.p.m. of 1950, it develops 78 per cent of its full theoretical power at sea level and maintains this power output until it reaches its critical altitude (as shown by the dotted curve, *C-A),* and that it then follows the curve, *A-G.* In other words, the power curve of an engine operating at 1950 r.p.m. and at a variable boost is represented on our graph by *C-A-G.* In both cases, notice that after reaching the critical altitude, the engine loses its supercharger characteristics and follows the same curve that a non-supercharged engine would. This is true of all superchargers after they reach their critical altitude.

As long as you can maintain constant manifold pressure, the power of your engine will increase with altitude. This increase is caused by a decrease in air pressure on the exhaust side of the engine, and also by the fact that the engine labors under lower than sea-level temperatures. Power along the curve *C-A* is constant from sea level to the critical altitude of the engine. Correctly interpreted, this means that the boost at which the engine started to operate at sea level was much higher than the sea-level atmospheric pressure, and that the loss of boost with altitude has been offset by the power added to the engine by decreased pressure in the exhaust manifold. Curve *B-A,* on the other hand, which shows a constant r.p.m. and constant boost, indicates that the engine is working at sea level with the least amount of boost and is therefore developing less power. The gradual increase in power with altitude is caused by the fact that while the pressure in the intake manifold has remained con-

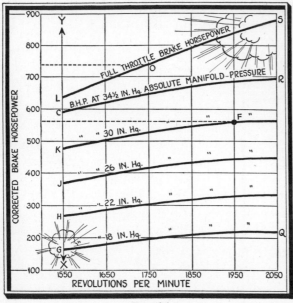

FIG. 174

stant, power has been added to the engine by decreased atmospheric pressure.

FIG. 174. Back in Fig. 166 we plotted the corrected brake horsepower against r.p.m. for an engine operating at full throttle. In the adjoining graph, corrected horsepower is plotted against r.p.m. for different values of absolute manifold pressure. Curve *L-S* represents the power of an engine operating at full throttle. Now, if you vary the load on the propeller shaft so as to cause the propeller to turn at only 1550 r.p.m. with a manifold pressure of 34½″ Hg., the available horsepower will be 593 as shown at *C*. If you continue to adjust the throttle so as to maintain a manifold pressure of 34½″ Hg. at the same time that the propeller load is theoretically or actually decreased, you obtain the curve *C-R,* representing the power output of the engine at a constant manifold pressure of 34½″ Hg., at different r.p.m. The r.p.m. can increase only when the load on the propeller is decreased. Curves for engines operating at 30″, 26″, 22″, 18″ Hg., etc., can be drawn in a similar way, as shown on the graph.

Notice that the full throttle curve is not parallel to the manifold pressure curves, and that it does not show any manifold pressure values whatever, as do the curves below it. The reason for this is that, at full throttle, the manifold pressure of the engine changes as the r.p.m. of the engine vary according to the load of the propeller shaft.

From this chart, which shows the manifold pressure curves at sea level, you can readily obtain the horsepower available at a given r.p.m. and a given manifold pressure. For instance, assume that the engine is operating at 1950 r.p.m. and 30″ Hg. absolute manifold pressure. The manifold pressure curve in this case intersects the 1950 r.p.m. line at point *F*. Now look over on the ordinate scale (I have put in a dotted line to help Cloudy Joe) and you will find that

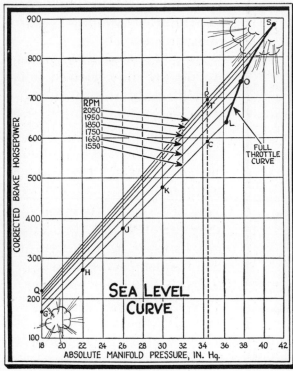

FIG. 175

point *F* corresponds to 560—the available brake horsepower. If the engine operates at full throttle, you do not need to read the manifold pressure in order to find out the power output. All you have to do is to read a given r.p.m.—say, 1750—which immediately gives you point *O* on the full-power brake horsepower curve, and you find that the engine's available power under this condition is 740.

From this graph you can also find the horsepower available along the constant r.p.m. lines under variable manifold pressure. Take the constant r.p.m. line, 1550, for example, where it is joined by the manifold pressure curves at *G, H, J, K, C* and *L*, and find the corresponding brake horsepower. Our engine operating at a constant r.p.m. of 1550 and 18″ Hg. absolute manifold pressure develops only 168 horsepower at sea level. With increase in manifold pressure, notice that the horsepower goes up.

FIG. 175. Now that you have found out how to obtain the horsepower corresponding to a given r.p.m. at a given manifold pressure, you can obtain the data necessary for constructing a new sea-level curve in which horsepower is plotted against absolute manifold pressure. First, transpose values *G, H, J, K, C* and *L* from Fig. 174 to Fig. 175. (Cloudy Joe has already forgotten that these values represent horsepower available at the constant r.p.m. of 1550 at 18″, 22″, 26″, 30″ and 34½″ Hg., manifold pressure, at full throttle.) Still using the values shown on the previous chart, plot the curves for manifold pressure against horsepower for the other r.p.m. (Notice that each one of these curves is a straight line.) By connecting points *L, O* and *S,* transposed from Fig.

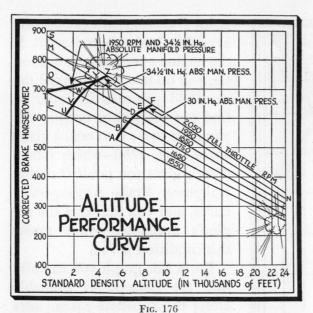

FIG. 176

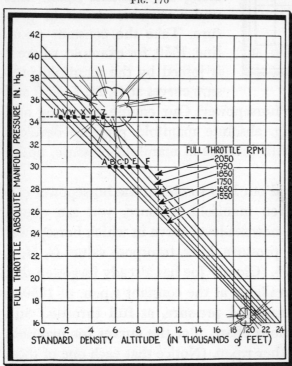

FIG. 177

174, you can now obtain the full-throttle manifold-pressure curve at sea level.

From this new chart you can also obtain the power output with increase in r.p.m. for any given manifold pressure. The dotted line crossing the manifold pressure curves represents the value of $34\frac{1}{2}''$ Hg. absolute manifold pressure. Notice again that at this, and any other constant manifold pressure value, any increase in r.p.m. brings about an increase in horsepower available.

FIG. 176. Now let's see what happens when we plot the corrected brake horsepower of an engine operating at full throttle at various given r.p.m. against standard density altitude. Transpose the full-throttle curve horsepower values from Fig. 175 to the sea-level ordinate of Fig. 176 at points *S, M, O, T* and *L*. You already know from Fig. 172 that an engine operating at constant r.p.m. at full throttle develops 47 per cent of its sea-level power at 20,000 feet. From these two values (100 per cent brake horsepower at sea level and 47 per cent brake horsepower at 20,000 feet) you can plot an altitude performance curve for each of the r.p.m. under consideration, as shown in the adjoining graph. (We will come back to the three heavy black curves a little later.)

Fig. 177. Since it has been experimentally determined that only 47 per cent of the total sea-level manifold pressure is left at 20,000 feet, we can draw another set of curves for our particular engine operating at full throttle and various given r.p.m., by plotting manifold pressure against standard density altitude. Notice that the greater the full throttle r.p.m., the higher the engine can be lifted with a given manifold pressure, as shown by points A, B, C, D, E and F for 30″ Hg., and points U, V, W, X, Y and Z for 34½″ Hg. manifold pressure.

If we now transpose these points to our altitude performance curve, given on the previous graph, we get the curves A . . . F, and U . . . Z. Similar curves can, of course, be drawn for any other manifold pressure. From the graph, as it now stands, you can determine the manifold pressure reading, and the horsepower available, at any given altitude for our particular engine when it operates at full throttle and constant r.p.m.

Turn back to Fig. 175 and locate point T, the maximum theoretical horsepower available at sea level for an engine operating full throttle at 1950 when the manifold pressure reading is 34½″ Hg. Transfer this to the sea-level ordinate of Fig. 176, and connect it by a line with Y, the point where the 1950 r.p.m. line intersects the 34½″ Hg. manifold pressure line. This new curve, T-Y, is a *part throttle* curve and represents the horsepower available at 1950 r.p.m. and 34½″ Hg. manifold pressure for all altitudes at which you can operate under these two conditions. In actual flight you would accomplish this by a gradual opening of the throttle until the throttle is at "full."

You already know, from Fig. 173, that the critical altitude of your engine is the altitude below which you cannot operate your engine at full throttle without exceeding its normal operating ratings. There are various critical altitudes for any particular engine. For instance, if the engine operates at 1950 r.p.m. and at a manifold pressure reading of 34½″ Hg., the critical altitude, as indicated by the curve T-Y, is 4100 feet. If you change the r.p.m. to 1650 and keep the same manifold pressure reading, the critical altitude will be a little under 2000 feet, while the critical altitude of the engine operating at 1950 r.p.m. and 30″ Hg. is a little over 8000 feet.

Figs 178 and 179. Sea-level curves such as we plotted in Fig. 175, and alti-

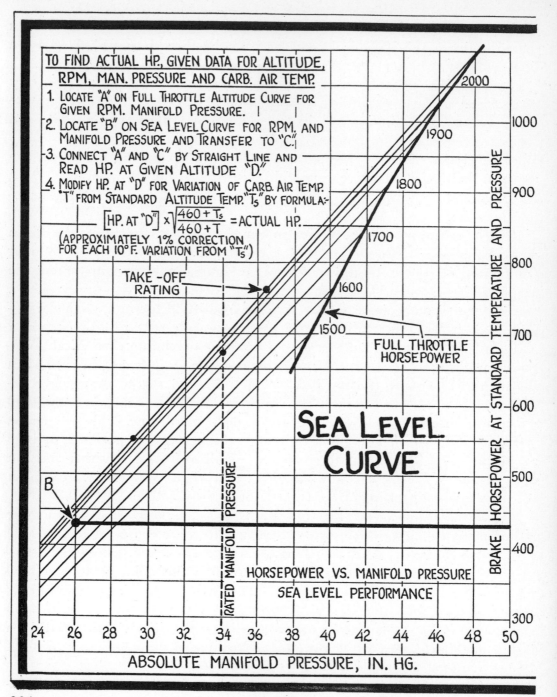

TO FIND ACTUAL HP, GIVEN DATA FOR ALTITUDE, RPM, MAN. PRESSURE AND CARB. AIR TEMP.

1. LOCATE "A" ON FULL THROTTLE ALTITUDE CURVE FOR GIVEN RPM. MANIFOLD PRESSURE.
2. LOCATE "B" ON SEA LEVEL CURVE FOR RPM. AND MANIFOLD PRESSURE AND TRANSFER TO "C."
3. CONNECT "A" AND "C" BY STRAIGHT LINE AND READ HP. AT GIVEN ALTITUDE "D."
4. MODIFY HP. AT "D" FOR VARIATION OF CARB. AIR TEMP. "T" FROM STANDARD ALTITUDE TEMP. "T_s" BY FORMULA:-

$$\left[\text{HP. AT "D"} \right] \times \sqrt{\frac{460 + T_s}{460 + T}} = \text{ACTUAL HP.}$$

(APPROXIMATELY 1% CORRECTION FOR EACH 10° F. VARIATION FROM "T_s")

TAKE-OFF RATING

2000
1900
1800
1700
1600
1500

FULL THROTTLE HORSEPOWER

SEA LEVEL CURVE

B

RATED MANIFOLD PRESSURE

HORSEPOWER VS. MANIFOLD PRESSURE
SEA LEVEL PERFORMANCE

BRAKE HORSEPOWER AT STANDARD TEMPERATURE AND PRESSURE

2000
1000
900
800
700
600
500
400
300

24 26 28 30 32 34 36 38 40 42 44 46 48 50

ABSOLUTE MANIFOLD PRESSURE, IN. HG.

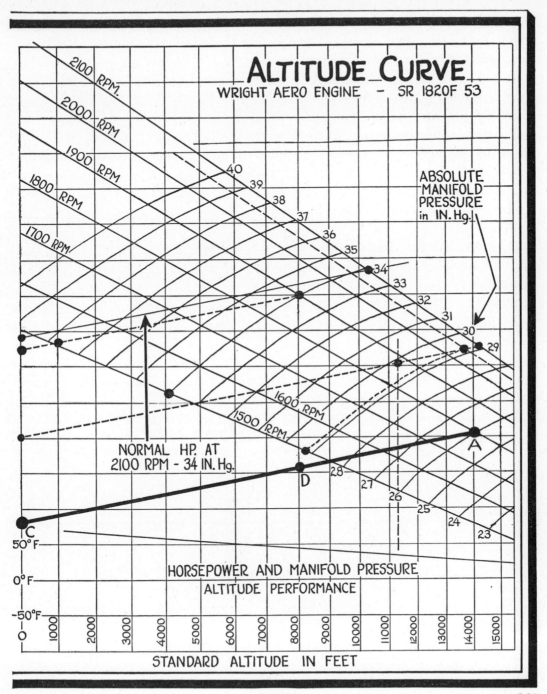

ALTITUDE CURVE
WRIGHT AERO ENGINE – SR 1820F 53

ABSOLUTE MANIFOLD PRESSURE in IN. Hg.

2100 R.P.M.
2000 RPM
1900 RPM
1800 RPM
1700 RPM
1600 RPM
1500 RPM

40 39 38 37 36 35 34 33 32 31 30 29 28 27 26 25 24 23

NORMAL H.P. AT
2100 RPM - 34 IN. Hg.

A
C
D

HORSEPOWER AND MANIFOLD PRESSURE
ALTITUDE PERFORMANCE

50°F
0°F
-50°F
O

1000 2000 3000 4000 5000 6000 7000 8000 9000 10000 11000 12000 13000 14000 15000

STANDARD ALTITUDE IN FEET

FIG. 179

205

tude-performance curves can be used in conjunction to give us the actual horsepower of a given engine, when we know altitude, r.p.m., manifold pressure, and carburetor air temperature.

In Fig. 178 we have manifold pressure plotted against horsepower for a given engine operating at various r.p.m. In Fig. 179 we have r.p.m. and manifold pressure curves plotted horsepower against standard altitude. Suppose that you are interested in finding out the horsepower developed at 1800 r.p.m. by an engine at 26″ Hg. absolute manifold pressure under standard atmospheric conditions. Find the intersection, in Fig. 179, of the 1800 r.p.m. line and the 26″ Hg. manifold pressure curve—point *A*. Find, in Fig. 178, the intersection of the 26″ Hg. line and the 1800 r.p.m. curve—point *B*. This point, as you will see by following the black line, is at 430 Hp. Transfer *B* to *C* in Fig. 179, and connect *C* and *A* by a line. Read along this line and you will find the horsepower developed at any altitude up to 14,000 feet by a particular engine operating at 1800 r.p.m. and 26″ Hg. manifold pressure. At 8000 feet *(D)*, for example, the horsepower developed by the engine is 510.

When the carburetor air temperature, however, does not correspond to the standard atmospheric temperature for that level, a correction must be made according to the formula given in Fig. 178 for this variation. Or instead of using the formula, you can allow 1 per cent correction for each 10° F. variation from the standard temperature. If the carburetor air temperature is higher than the standard, subtract 1 per cent for each 10° F. variation; if it is lower than standard, add the 1 per cent for each 10°.

The human element may play an important part—after poor airmanship.

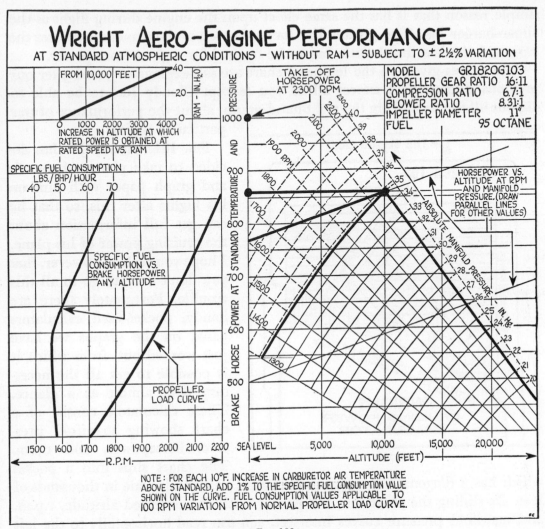

FIG. 180.

FIG. 180. The graphs given here show the performance of the particular engine, the general characteristics of which are listed in the upper right-hand corner. Notice that these analyses are made under standard atmospheric conditions, and without taking *ram* into consideration. *Ram,* as you probably know, is the dynamic pressure exerted by the air which rushes into the engine through the scoop (remember the pitot tube?) and is similar in effect to the action of the supercharger. *Ram* is not taken into consideration for the

207

simple reason that it has the same effect upon the engine during flight as the supercharger has. The greater the forward speed of the plane, the greater the *ram* and the less the throttle has to be opened for a given horsepower.

The curves given on the left-hand chart are self-explanatory, and after our previous discussions I expect all of you (except Cloudy Joe) to be able to dig out all the facts, from the right-hand graph, about the performance of our particular engine.

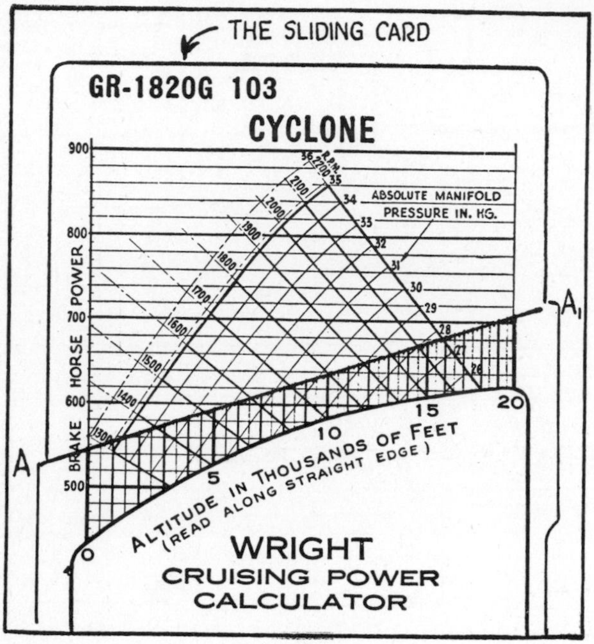

FIG. 181

FIG. 181. Cloudy Joe has decided to take plenty of pencils and graph paper with him on his flights after this, so that he can get full information about the cruising power of his plane. I hope you realize, however, that you don't have to go to all this trouble. Fortunately there are handy, pocket-sized calculators based on the graphs we have just worked out, from which it is possible to get all the necessary data almost at a glance. These calculators consist of a chart showing manifold pressure, horsepower, and r.p.m. The chart slips into a pocket which has a diagonal edge along which runs an altitude scale in thousands of feet. By sliding the chart into the pocket until the observed altitude, r.p.m. and manifold pressure curves intersect, you can read horizontally to the left of the chart and obtain the horsepower for your observed altitude. But remember, whether you use pencil and graph paper or a ready-made calculator, you must always make full allowance for any variation from standard atmospheric conditions before you can obtain the true horsepower of your engine.

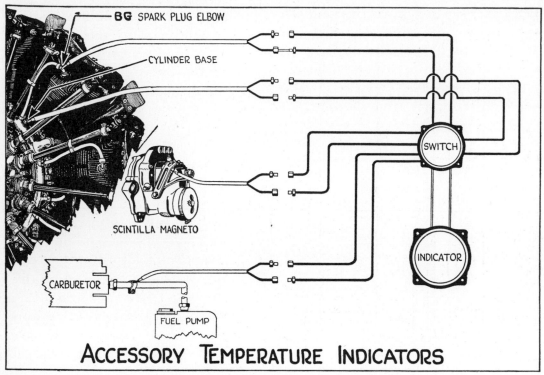

BG SPARK PLUG ELBOW

CYLINDER BASE

SCINTILLA MAGNETO

CARBURETOR

FUEL PUMP

SWITCH

INDICATOR

ACCESSORY TEMPERATURE INDICATORS

Fig. 182

Fig. 182. This illustration shows the general arrangement by which the temperature of the various parts of the engine is measured by means of a single temperature gauge, or indicator. This indicator, which is electrically operated, is connected with a selector switch. Electrical conductors run from the switch to the parts to be measured. To read the temperature of any one of these parts on your temperature gauge, you merely "tune in" that particular part by means of the selector switch. In actual flight you will be chiefly concerned with the temperature of the cylinder heads, the take-off temperature operating limits of which are from 250° to 450° F. At cruising speed, cylinder-head temperatures should be below 400° F.

*Knowing the principle will help you
master the details.*

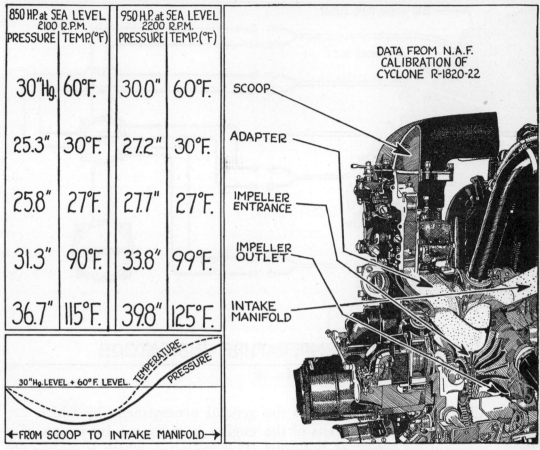

850 H.P. at SEA LEVEL 2100 R.P.M.		950 H.P. at SEA LEVEL 2200 R.P.M.	
PRESSURE	TEMP.(°F)	PRESSURE	TEMP.(°F)
30"Hg.	60°F.	30.0"	60°F.
25.3"	30°F.	27.2"	30°F.
25.8"	27°F.	27.7"	27°F.
31.3"	90°F.	33.8"	99°F.
36.7"	115°F.	39.8"	125°F.

DATA FROM N.A.F. CALIBRATION OF CYCLONE R-1820-22

SCOOP

ADAPTER

IMPELLER ENTRANCE

IMPELLER OUTLET

INTAKE MANIFOLD

TEMPERATURE
PRESSURE
30"Hg. LEVEL + 60°F. LEVEL.
←FROM SCOOP TO INTAKE MANIFOLD→

FIG. 183

FIG. 183. The air which rushes into your engine through the scoop travels through the adapter and the impeller, and into the intake manifold, following the path shown on the right half of the illustration. At the left is a table giving the pressure and temperature of the fuel-air mixture as it follows this path, for two different horsepower outputs at sea level and at different r.p.m. These tables are expressed graphically by the two curves at the lower left corner of the illustration.

Density, pressure and temperature are
partners for life.

XVI

FUEL AND LUBRICATION

YEARS ago, when (like Cloudy Joe) I did not know how much I did not know about fuel and lubricants for the engine which pulled my plane through the air, I used to open the throttle when I wanted to take off, and close it when I wanted to come down. If the engine was properly lubricated, it ran for any length of time. If it wasn't, it fell apart, and down I came for a forced landing. I had no idea how important it is to have a thorough understanding of fuel and lubricants—not for *any* kind of aero engine, but for the *particular* engine I was using.

In the early days, they used to lubricate an engine with whatever commercial lubricant seemed to suit it best, and to feed it whatever fuel seemed to agree with it. Today the lubricants and fuel used in your engine are produced for your particular type of engine by chemists employed by the large petroleum producing companies.

Because of the number of rules connected with its operation, you may have concluded that the present-day, high-powered aero engine is a capricious and delicate affair. The truth is that these rules have been set not only to prolong the life of the engine but to insure its functioning properly during flight. The reliability of an aero engine such as the Wright Cyclone is shown by the fact that overhaul intervals have been stretched from the less-than-200 hours of ten years ago to over 600 hours today. A plane equipped with this type of engine can fly almost a hundred thousand miles before it has to take an engine-overhaul vacation.

But in order to get these results, you must feed your engine food that it can digest easily by the process of complete combustion. You must also lubricate it with an oil capable of providing a film between the moving parts, not only under normal temperatures and high-bearing loads, but also in an emergency where the temperature is far in excess of normal. As long as such a film exists, no matter how thin it is, it will keep the surfaces from coming together.

It is a generally accepted theory that an oil's lubricating qualities, as well as its actual performance in service, can be determined in advance by specification. While this is true to a certain extent, the actual performance of a lubricant in a particular engine remains problematical until after it has actually been tested in that type of engine. The proper lubrication for a given engine, after specifications for the oil have been met, depends largely upon specific characteristics of the original crude oil, and its adaptability to the modern process of refining. You should bear this in mind, particularly if you are responsible for the correct operation of more than one airplane. Your chief problem will be to mate the engine to the lubricant, or vice versa.

Not very long ago I decided that I knew as much about this oil and engine mating process as my friend Cloudy Joe, and that I had better do a little first-hand investigating. One of the oil companies very kindly let me go through its research laboratory, and furnished me with a most attentive guide. Like Cloudy Joe, I did not want to let the guide know how little I knew, so I put on my wisest manner and succeeded in seeming fairly intelligent until he introduced me to "Mr. X—the man whose job is measuring things one millionth to one four-millionth of an inch long."

Mr. X shot a question at me. "You are familiar, of course," he asked, "with Professor Blank's theory of the XYNKRPSLXMKFN around the molecules?" (At least that is the way it sounded to me.) Before I could answer, he had fired another question at me—"And what do you think of the MLFKMSZMKSQY method by which the thickness of the oil film is determined by the various colors of the film when such a film is produced in the laboratory under certain conditions?"

My jaw—and pride—dropped. Here I was, about to be forced into confessing abysmal ignorance before my guide, to whom I had been representing myself as an authority. I could get by on some things, but not on the "XYNKRPSLXMKFN," and the "MLFKMSZMKSQY" method! Just as I had given up all hope, Mr. X beamed at me and rushed on—"Now, in *my* opinion . . ." By the time he had finished, he had told me all about the theory and the method, and a good deal else besides, and had spared me the ignominy of showing my ignorance.

We finally left Mr. X to his measuring work, and continued around the

212

laboratory. I found that tests are constantly being made to determine the best oil for a given engine. Under simulated service conditions, the oil is subjected to even severer stresses than those which would be encountered in actual operation. This precaution provides a safety factor which is invaluable in an emergency where the oil must continue to withstand high temperatures and at the same time must retain its lubricating qualities. In one part of the laboratory they were trying to find the proper oil mate for an engine with a compression ratio of 6.7 to 1, at 2200 r.p.m., and a boost of 43" Hg. A model test engine had been built and installed in the laboratory to operate at a 6.7 to 1 compression ratio, but at *3600 r.p.m. and 68" Hg. boost.*

The right kind of lubricant cannot, of course, be determined from just one test. Countless tests on many types of lubricant must be carried out before the best oil in regard to wear and sludge deposits is evolved. Even the laboratory test may not always provide the final answer, so that it is absolutely essential to subject the oil to prolonged operation in the full-scale aircraft engine for which it is intended. After such a test, made under conditions far beyond normal service operation, the oil giving the outstanding performance is finally selected for actual service use. I am passing this knowledge on to you so that you will have some idea of the thoroughness of the procedure by which the right oil for a given engine must be selected. But remember this—every advance in engine design brings its own lubrication problem. Lubricants which were satisfactory for the "latest" engines two years ago are not suited to the engines of today.

Even when you use an oil that has been properly mated to your engine, you cannot expect perfect lubrication if you run your engine without proper oil cooling, with an extremely low oil supply, or under continuous excessive heat.

The remarkable increase in engine horsepower output which has taken place during recent years without any dimensional changes being made in the engine itself is the result of several factors. One of these is that more fuel is burned per power stroke and that therefore more heat energy is released per unit of time, producing greater mean effective pressure in the cylinders. Since the oil must cool as well as lubricate the engine, the oil is heated to a greater extent than ever before. Not only is combustion pressure exerted directly on the cylinder walls, but it also causes the piston rings to be forced against the cylinder walls, and the oil film has to bear a considerable side-

213

thrust load. This expansion of the piston rings against the cylinder walls subjects the oil film to greater pressure and results in greater heat within the film.

Both the piston and the piston rings of the aero engine transmit a considerable portion of the heat developed during the combustion stroke to the cylinder walls. From there, the heat is dissipated by the cooling fins. During the past ten years the increased heat to which the piston rings, the oil between the rings and the ring grooves are exposed has made it necessary to greatly increase the area of the cylinder cooling fins. If the oil in your engine cannot stand up under such conditions, the inevitable result will be sticking piston rings, low power, and probably serious damage to the engine itself.

The only way you can determine the condition of your oil during a flight is by watching the oil temperature and pressure gauges. Changes in the reading of these instruments indicate trouble, but a slight drop in the pressure gauge is not in itself cause for alarm. Remember that oil must provide considerable cooling as well as lubrication, so that the oil pressure must necessarily be far in excess of that required for lubrication alone. Don't be alarmed, therefore, if your oil pressure gauge begins to drop during a flight. If the normal operating pressure of your engine is 80 lbs., your engine will still continue to operate satisfactorily at, say, 50 lbs. of pressure, provided you draw less power out of it. So you see you won't need to "sit down" just because the oil pressure drops a few pounds.

The *immediate* cause of the pressure drop may be excessive heat, as indicated by your oil-temperature gauge; the *original* cause will have to be found later. If the temperature of the cylinder heads is still within the service limits recommended for your particular engine, the chances are that the cause of the pressure drop in the oil line is outside the danger boundary, and you won't have to make an emergency landing. But if the cylinder-head temperatures begin to rise dangerously, richen your mixture, make an emergency landing, and find out the cause of the low pressure in the engine. You will find with experience that the very last thing that can cause trouble is the oil itself, since it is almost impossible for the oil to change its characteristics enough to upset the oil pressure.

Engines of high output, such as the Wright Cyclone, are possible only because of high octane-number fuels. The high compression ratio of the engine, as well as the high intake manifold pressure, means that a greater amount of fuel, in weight, is being burned per unit of time. This requires fuels which

214

will not detonate under high pressure until the proper time for the combustion stroke. It is the detonation that causes knocks in the engine, resulting in vibration and eventual destruction of the engine. Since detonation is an explosion rather than a slow burning, it results in excessively high pressures and temperatures inside the cylinders. Therefore you might just as well know the various factors affecting detonation. These are:

(1) *Fuel octane number rating:* The higher the octane number, the greater the factor of safety from detonation.

(2) *Cylinder design:* The correct design eliminates the possibility of detonation by removing local hot spots in the combustion chamber. (This factor is beyond your control, since the safety features, good or bad, are incorporated in the cylinder design by the manufacturer.)

(3) *Mixture (fuel-air ratio):* With low octane fuel rating, the wrong mixture for a given boost, particularly on the lean side, will substantially reduce the safety factor of detonation.

(4) *Cooling air temperature:* The higher the atmospheric air temperature, the hotter the cylinder temperature and the greater the tendency to detonate. (In summer be *sure* you run your engine on a higher octane-rating fuel.)

(5) *Horsepower:* The higher the horsepower, the higher the cylinder-head temperature, and therefore the greater the tendency toward detonation.

(6) *R.P.M.:* The lower the r.p.m., the higher the mean effective pressure for a given horsepower, the hotter the cylinders and the greater the tendency toward detonation.

(7) *Carburetor temperature:* The higher the carburetor temperature, the hotter the charge entering the combustion chambers, and the greater the tendency toward detonation.

(8) *Cylinder-head temperatures:* The higher the cylinder-head temperatures, the greater the likelihood of local hot spots inside the combustion chamber, and the greater the tendency toward detonation.

If your engine has been designed for high octane-rating fuels, be sure to use that type of fuel—and only that type. A lower octane-rating fuel will produce detonation and will eventually lead to trouble.

A little while ago Cloudy Joe piloted me on a series of trips around the country. Fortunately I landed whole, though my hair was considerably grayer than it had been at the start, for, besides all the other scrapes Cloudy Joe had gotten us into, he had:

(1) Tried to run his plane on too lean a mixture. ("This is where I show you how to save money," was his explanation.)

(2) Neglected to set his carburetor on full rich for take-off.
(3) Tried to make up for lost time by pushing his engine too hard against headwinds.
(4) Tried to get greater power without increased revolutions, thus heating his engine as he increased the mean effective pressure.
(5) Forgotten to use enough carburetor air heat, with the result that his carburetor froze.
(6) Wound up in a vapor lock caused by overheated gasoline. (The real trouble here lay in the poor plumbing which Cloudy Joe's brother had installed at "special reduced rates.")

But the thing that annoyed me the most about the whole trip was that Cloudy Joe could have reduced the danger from any one of these mistakes if he had used his head in the first place and burned a higher octane-rating fuel.

Even though all the nuts on the plane have been tightened, nothing is safe as long as one is loose.

XVII

CAMBRIDGE FUEL-AIR RATIO INDICATOR

You are already familiar with the fact that the air density is greatest at sea level, or below, and that a cubic foot of air weighs more at sea level than it does at higher altitudes. In order to secure the best combustion in your engine, you must, therefore, maintain the correct ratio between your fuel and the air taken in by your engine. You probably know that the best mixture is 1:13 (.07)—that is, *one unit of fuel (in weight) to 13 weight units of air*, the normal carburetor setting. Any other fuel-air ratio makes either a rich or a lean mixture. If there is too much fuel and not enough air, combustion will not be complete, and a great deal of fuel will be thrown out, unburned, through the exhaust. On the other hand, too much air and too little fuel result in a lean mixture and high engine temperatures.

If you are flying your plane at a given atmospheric pressure level, you are flying, of course, at an approximately constant air density. Once the fuel-air mixture control is adjusted, therefore, you do not need to make any change until you take your plane to a different pressure level. Formerly mixture was adjusted by climbing to about 4000 feet, leaving the throttle at cruising r.p.m., gradually leaning the mixture until the engine lost about 20 r.p.m., and then richening the mixture until the lost r.p.m. were regained. This method of adjusting the mixture is still used on planes equipped with fixed pitch propellers. Throughout the procedure, the only reference line is the tachometer.

With a constant-speed propeller, a different method must be used, since, regardless of how you try to adjust the throttle or the mixture, your tachometer will still give you the same r.p.m. A fuel-air ratio indicator has, therefore, been devised as an exact means of establishing the fuel-air ratio from which to adjust the mixture in your engine.

217

Before we go into the principle upon which this instrument operates, I would like to mention a few of its advantages in controlling the fuel-air mixture ratio in your engine. The analyzer helps you maintain maximum power under any conditions, and helps you run your engine—or engines—for the greatest amount of time on the least amount of fuel, since no fuel can be wasted. This latter is particularly important in case of emergency, where your only guide to what is happening to your fuel is the fuel-air indicator. As a rule, the high-power aero engine consumes, for every four hours' operation at cruising speed, the equivalent of its own weight in fuel. Any waste of fuel, therefore, becomes an important factor, not only from the point of view of economy, but also from the point of view of load and distance performance of the plane for a given amount of fuel. Another advantage of the fuel-air ratio indicator is that it warns you against running your engine on too lean a mixture, which would cause excessive engine temperatures and, eventually, considerable damage.

Figs. 184 and 185. These illustrations show the Cambridge fuel-air ratio indicator for twin and four engines.

So far as Cloudy Joe is concerned, the fewer the gadgets in his plane, the better; he would rather depend on what he calls his uncanny guess work.

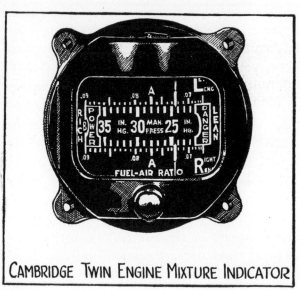

CAMBRIDGE TWIN ENGINE MIXTURE INDICATOR

FIG. 184

The real explanation of his prejudice lies in his failure to understand how these gadgets work. Fortunately your attitude is just the opposite from Cloudy Joe's, for you do understand (or will, by the time we finish) how the gadgets function. As I have said before, everything about the operation of your airplane is simple, once you know what it is all about. Ignorance may be bliss—but it is dangerous in an airplane.

And here is the simple principle around which the Cambridge fuel-air ratio analyzer operates:

218

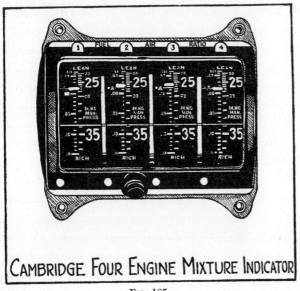

CAMBRIDGE FOUR ENGINE MIXTURE INDICATOR

FIG. 185

FIG. 186. The component gases in the exhaust, as you will see from the illustration, are carbon dioxide, hydrogen, oxygen, carbon monoxide, methane, and water. Upon the proportion in which these gases exist depends the fuel-air ratio value of the mixture. We can take advantage of these gases by measuring their thermal conductivity (which is greater or less, depending upon the predominance of some of the elements in the exhaust gas). Of all the gases in the exhaust, hydrogen has the greatest thermal conductivity.

The exhaust gas analyzer consists of two chambers, S and E. Chamber S is sealed, and contains saturated air; chamber E has an opening through which

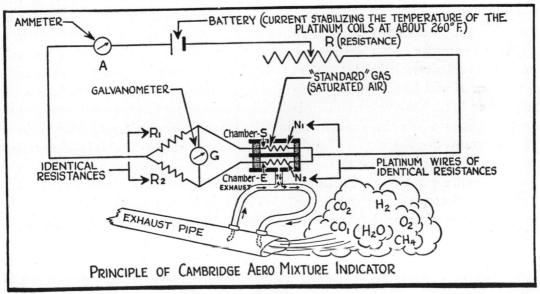

PRINCIPLE OF CAMBRIDGE AERO MIXTURE INDICATOR

FIG. 186

exhaust gas diffuses continuously, as shown by the arrows in the illustration.

There is an electric battery which constantly supplies a current to the closed circuit. Two spiral platinum wires—N_1 and N_2, of identical resistance—are mounted in the two chambers. In the circuit there is a simple Wheatstone bridge which also has two wires, R_1 and R_2 of identical resistance.

Now let's see what happens when the current from the batteries is turned on. First, the current flows through the bridge and heats the two platinum wires. The heat is immediately dissipated through the medium of the gases surrounding the two wires and is quickly conducted to the walls of the two chambers. The thermal conductivity of the standard gas surrounding N_1 is constant, while the thermal conductivity of the exhaust gas surrounding N_2 varies with the result that the wire, N_2, changes its temperature in comparison to N_1. The higher the temperature of the platinum wire (electrical conductor) the greater is its electrical resistance. This difference in electrical resistance unbalances the Wheatstone bridge, causing a voltage drop across the bridge, which in turn causes a deflection of the galvanometer (fuel-air ratio indicator) G, from, say, its neutral position. The bridge is generally out of electrical balance, with the amount of conductivity of the exhaust gases being indicated by the amount of deflection of the pointer. Thermal conductivity of the exhaust gases is proportional to the fuel-air ratio, and you can therefore obtain a direct reading from your indicator (galvanometer) of the fuel-air ratio of the mixture burned.

Whenever the fuel mixture supplied by the carburetor is about normal, or in a fuel-air ratio of 1:13, the thermal conductivity of the exhaust gas in chamber E will be about the same as the thermal conductivity of the air in chamber S, and the value shown by the indicator is .07. If the mixture is too rich—as it is when the fuel-air ratio is 1:11 (.09), for example—the exhaust gas surrounding the air in chamber E has a higher thermal conductivity than the air in chamber S. A reverse condition exists when the mixture is too lean, or when the proportion between fuel and air is about 1:15 (.06). In this case, the thermal conductivity of the analyzed gas in chamber E is lower than standard in comparison with the thermal conductivity of the saturated air in S. You can readily see, therefore, that any change in the proportions of the gases present in the exhaust (such as hydrogen or carbon dioxide) will cause a difference in the thermal conductivity of the gases in the two chambers, and will result in a variation of the temperature and hence of the electrical resistance

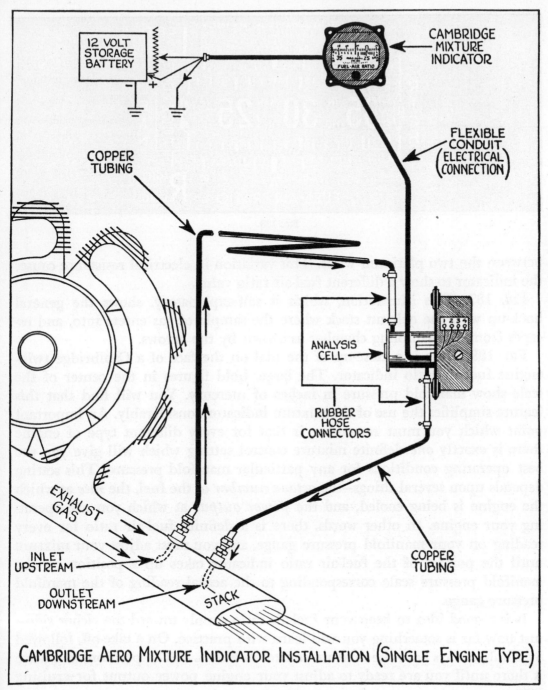

12 VOLT
STORAGE
BATTERY

− +

CAMBRIDGE
MIXTURE
INDICATOR

35 NP 25
FUEL-AIR RATIO

FLEXIBLE
CONDUIT
(ELECTRICAL)
CONNECTION

COPPER
TUBING

ANALYSIS
CELL

RUBBER
HOSE
CONNECTORS

COPPER
TUBING

EXHAUST
GAS

INLET
UPSTREAM

OUTLET
DOWNSTREAM

STACK

CAMBRIDGE AERO MIXTURE INDICATOR INSTALLATION (SINGLE ENGINE TYPE)

Fig. 187

Fig. 188

between the two platinum wires. This variation in electrical resistance causes the indicator to show a different fuel-air ratio value.

FIG. 187. This illustration, which is self-explanatory, shows the general hook-up with the exhaust stack where the sample of gas enters into, and escapes from, the sampling chamber as shown by the arrows.

FIG. 188. Here is a close-up of the dial on the face of a Cambridge twin-engine fuel-air ratio indicator. The large, bold figures in the center of the scale show manifold pressure in inches of mercury. You will find that this feature simplifies the use of the mixture indicator considerably. An important point which you must remember is that for every different type of engine there is exactly *one* definite mixture control setting which will give you the best operating conditions for any particular manifold pressure. This setting depends upon several things—the *octane number* of the fuel, the *rate* at which the engine is being cooled, and the *power output* at which you are operating your engine. In other words, there is a definite fuel-air ratio for every reading on your manifold pressure gauge, and you must adjust your mixture until the pointer of the fuel-air ratio indicator takes up a position on the manifold pressure scale corresponding to the actual reading of the manifold pressure gauge.

It is a good idea to keep your fuel-air ratio supply toward the richer side—just how far is something you will learn with practice. On a take-off, followed by climb, always have the mixture control in FULL RICH position, and leave it there until you are ready to adjust your engine power output for cruising

222

speed. At that time, adjust the mixture until the pointer (or pointers in case of a plane with two or more engines) on the mixture indicator corresponds to the reading of the manifold pressure gauge. You will occasionally find that the mixture control must be readjusted, particularly if you are flying from one atmospheric pressure altitude to another, or if the temperature of the air changes.

The fuel-air mixture indicator, besides showing you the correct fuel-air ratio, also serves to warn you when things are not going as they should. If the throttle, for instance, is moved from the SET position, the fuel-air ratio indicator pointers warn you of the fact by moving automatically from the position to which you have adjusted them. The pointers also move if the carburetor air temperature changes, or if there is an increase or decrease in the carburetor air-scoop pressure, thus increasing or decreasing the supercharging. This deflection in the position of the fuel-air ratio pointers is similar to the deflection caused by changing your flight-level pressure altitude. If the pressure in the fuel supply line drops, the indicator pointers move toward the lean side.

You can also detect any detonation that may be taking place in your engine by means of your fuel-air ratio indicator. Detonation, you will recall, is destructive to the engine, and it occurs most of the time when Cloudy Joe flies the plane. As detonation begins, the pointers of the fuel-air ratio indicator start to fluctuate rapidly. They move gradually toward the rich side of the scale. In other words, if you understand the language of the fuel-air ratio analyzer, it shouts that your mixture control must be adjusted.

If you swallowed a bone, you would
feel just about as good as an engine fed
with food it can't digest.

XVIII

THE SPARK PLUG

CLOUDY JOE thinks only the big things are important. He spends most of his time shining up his airplane, but he never pays any attention to little things like spark plugs. But since the proper functioning of your engine, as well as your own safety, depends upon these small units, I am going to take time right now to tell you how these little "big" things are kept in first-class condition. As a rule, spark plugs should be taken out, cleaned and inspected once in every sixty—or at the very most, seventy-five—flying hours, but they must be handled with the greatest care to prevent damage to any part of the plug.

If you do some of the mechanical work on your plane yourself, here are the various steps to be followed in the proper inspection and maintenance of spark plugs:

(1) After removing the core assembly from the shell and taking out the gasket, place the cores in a bench work tray.

(2) Clean both the core and core electrode, and wash and dry the core.

(3) Measure electrode shoulder diameter; inspect tip diameter and core; lubricate threads and install core assembly gasket.

(4) Clean and inspect shells; form shell electrodes; assemble plugs and adjust electrodes.

(5) Test plugs and replace in engine (or prepare for storing).

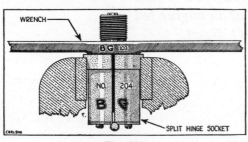

FIG. 189

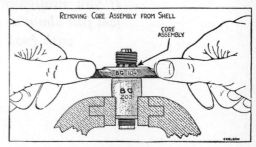

FIG. 190

224

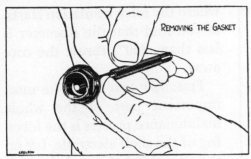

FIG. 191

FIG. 192

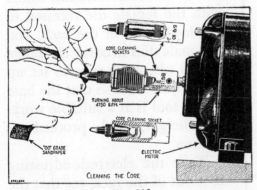

CLEANING THE CORE

FIG. 193

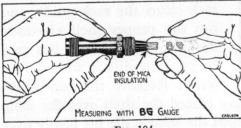

END OF MICA INSULATION

MEASURING WITH **BG** GAUGE

FIG. 194

FIGS. 189 AND 190. To remove the core assembly of a two-piece spark plug, such as the BG, from its shell, place the plug in a vise socket (Fig. 189), or a split hinge socket in a vise (Fig. 190), and use a wrench as illustrated. *Never use an open-end wrench, and never place the shell or core in the jaws of a vise.*

FIG. 191. Here you see how a special punch is used to remove the copper core assembly gasket from a shell of the internal gasket type. On some of the newer shells, you will find the gasket between the top of the shell and the bottom of the coupling nut.

FIG. 192. Spark plugs are easily damaged. Don't let the cores lie around in a box or in piles. Put them into a bench work tray, such as shown here, except when you are actually working on them.

FIG. 193. A core-cleaning collet and 00-grade sandpaper or #150 Aloxite cloth are used to remove all traces of carbon, oil, lead, etc., from the core. You will get the best results if the motor shaft to which the collet is attached turns about 1750 r.p.m. Never use emery, carborundum cloth, paper, steel wool, file or metal buffing wheels for cleaning cores.

FIG. 194. Measure the shoulder or head diameter of the electrode with a micrometer or BG gauge, as shown in the illustration, taking the measurement at the point of the metal electrode

225

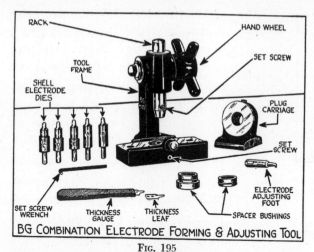

BG COMBINATION ELECTRODE FORMING & ADJUSTING TOOL

RACK
HAND WHEEL
TOOL FRAME
SET SCREW
SHELL ELECTRODE DIES
PLUG CARRIAGE
SET SCREW
SET SCREW WRENCH
THICKNESS GAUGE
THICKNESS LEAF
SPACER BUSHINGS
ELECTRODE ADJUSTING FOOT

FIG. 195

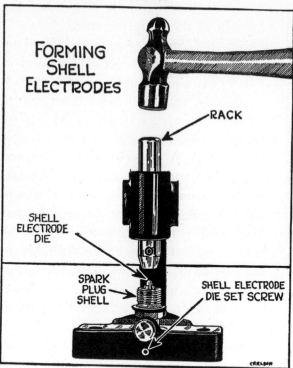

FORMING SHELL ELECTRODES

RACK
SHELL ELECTRODE DIE
SPARK PLUG SHELL
SHELL ELECTRODE DIE SET SCREW

CARLSON

FIG. 196

where the mica insulation starts. If you find that the diameter is less than .260″, throw the core away.

FIGS. 195 AND 196. The most important part of the whole maintenance process is the forming of the shell electrode, for on the way this is formed depends the efficiency with which the plugs will operate in the engine, and the rate of burning of the electrodes. For this work you will need an electrode-forming and adjusting tool mounted on a solid base, and a set of specially shaped dies. The tool shown in the illustration comes with the female die recessed in the lower end of the rack, and five male dies to cover the range of BG plugs. Be sure to set up your equipment so that the base of the tool is at a suitable working height, and proceed as follows:

Take the electrode-adjusting foot out of the rack, see that the screw at the lower end of the rack clears the rack guide, and put the proper shell electrode die into the bed of the tool frame, fastening it with the set screw. Remove the handwheel and pinion from the frame. When you have placed the shell over the male die as shown in Fig. 196, lower the rack until the female die fits firmly over

226

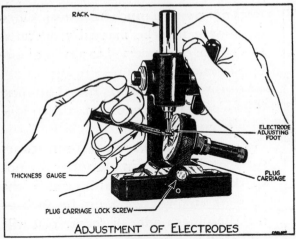

ADJUSTMENT OF ELECTRODES

FIG. 197

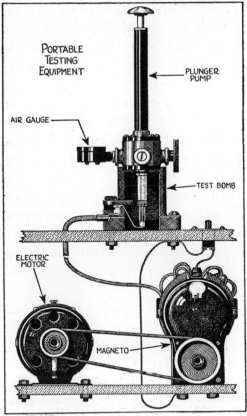

FIG. 198

the shell electrode and strike a sharp blow with a one-pound hammer at the center of the upper end of the rack—but don't try to prove how strong you are. Remember that spark plugs and everything about them must be carefully and gently handled. When the electrode conforms to the shape of the shell, raise the rack and take out the shell.

FIG. 197. The same tool shown in the preceding illustrations is here set up for adjusting electrodes. Bushings are provided to bring spark plugs of varying shell-thread length into position for adjusting. In making the adjustment, be careful not to bend the electrodes too far.

Specifying an electrode setting of .012″ instead of .015″ will lengthen periods between plug overhauls, particularly in high-power-output engines. In lower-power-output engines, longer periods between overhauls are not always worthwhile, since small gaps are apt to result in poor idling characteristics.

FIGS. 198 AND 199. The possibility of insulation failures can be largely eliminated by testing plugs in a test bomb and with the portable equipment shown in these illustrations. (Cloudy Joe thinks that this part of the proceedings may be worth learning, since it

227

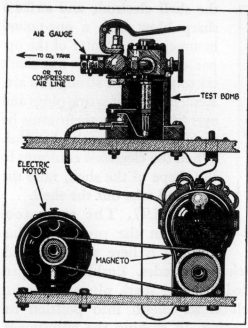

AIR GAUGE

TO CO₂ TANK
OR TO
COMPRESSED
AIR LINE

TEST BOMB

ELECTRIC
MOTOR

MAGNETO

FIG. 199

does not require much headwork.) The test bomb may be manually operated (Fig. 198), or connected to a tank of carbon dioxide under pressure (Fig. 199), or connected to a compressed air line if provision is made to extract the moisture from the air.

Because plugs which sometimes spark at atmospheric pressure may not spark at all under operating conditions in your engine, you must be sure to test the plugs under pressure. You will find that a plug which sparks regularly under 125 lbs. of pressure per square inch with the gap adjusted to .015" generally performs satisfactorily in any engine. For best results, keep the spark gaps properly adjusted. Check and reset them each time the plugs are removed for cleaning. If the gaps are not checked at regular intervals, you may have difficulty in starting your engine; and the actual running of the engine may be ragged and irregular if the gap growth is allowed to proceed too far.

For testing at pressures up to 150 lbs., use either a booster or service magneto in good condition. Current from spark coils or transformers gives misleading results and may damage the insulation.

FIG. 200. A container of the type shown here is convenient for storing or shipping spark plugs, and is widely used by the airlines.

Before you do any work on spark plugs, study a service manual carefully. Be sure to use the right kind of tools, and don't use too much force. Spark plugs may be a small part of your aircraft, but they are important both to the smooth running of your engine and to your own safety.

CONVENIENT METHOD OF STORING AND SHIPPING SPARK PLUGS

FIG. 200

228

XIX

WHIRLING PROPS

CLOUDY JOE doesn't give a hoot about propellers, for the simple reason that they all look alike to him, whether they are wood or metal, have wide or narrow blades, small or large diameters, or fixed or variable pitch. The only difference he has ever been known to observe is in the number of blades. The idea that one propeller might be more efficient than another, or that a propeller should be mated to the engine and plane, has never occurred to him. Such "well-rounded" knowledge, however, is not sufficient for you, and I shall go into the matter of propellers in some detail—not because I expect you to sit down and build your own, but because it is a good idea to know how propellers behave.

In the early days, propellers were made of wood, were of the fixed-pitch type, and gave satisfactory results for average performance. But with the increase in the size of planes, and in the power output of the engine, it was necessary not only to step up the efficiency of the propeller but to make it an integral part of the engine. With the steady increase in power output of the engine, there has been a corresponding increase in the size of the propeller, although the latter is limited by the size of the plane on which it is to be used, by the maximum r.p.m. delivered by the engine at full throttle, and by the speed of the propeller tips. It has been found that 1000 feet per second is the maximum propeller-tip speed permissible without impairing the efficiency of the propeller. Perhaps I ought to explain to Cloudy Joe that the efficiency of a propeller is rated on the amount of horsepower which the propeller has converted into thrust horsepower. If 20 per cent of the total horsepower delivered by the engine to the propeller shaft is lost through slip, friction, or some other cause, the propeller is rated 80 per cent efficient.

Let's assume that an airplane is traveling at 180 miles an hour, or 15,840 feet per minute, with a total air resistance or drag of 1000 lbs. Then:

$$\text{Total thrust hp.} = \frac{\left(\dfrac{\text{feet per minute}}{15{,}840}\right) \times \left(\dfrac{\text{lbs. drag}}{1{,}000}\right)}{33{,}000} = 480$$

Now, if the propeller is operating at 80 per cent efficiency, the brake horse-power which the engine must deliver to the propeller is:

$$\text{Brake hp.} = \frac{\overset{\text{(total thrust hp.)}}{480} \times 100}{80} = 600$$

You are not concerned in actual flight with thrust horsepower, but you are concerned with brake horsepower—that is, with the power delivered by your engine.

Cloudy Joe still thinks that propeller "efficiency" is something theoretical and that he needn't bother his head about it. But getting the right propeller for a particular engine—a propeller that provides the maximum efficiency for your plane—is a matter of vital importance, and may result in a considerable fuel saving. Suppose, for instance, that you are using a propeller that is 70 instead of 80 per cent efficient at 180 miles per hour cruising speed. If your engine develops 500 horsepower at cruising speed, your propeller is wasting 10 per cent, or 50 horsepower. In terms of fuel, this means that you are throwing away approximately four gallons of fuel for every hour that you are in the air. Measure it by miles, and you will find that at the end of a four-hour flight you are 50 miles short of your destination—and all because of a less efficient propeller.

A fixed-pitch propeller may be highly efficient at take-off, *or* during climb, *or* at cruising altitudes, but it can never be equally efficient during all stages of a flight. With a two-pitch propeller—that is, one with a high and low setting—you can get somewhat better results at take-off, while at cruising altitudes the r.p.m. of the engine can be reduced by setting the propeller at high pitch and allowing the engine to operate at its most favorable cruising speeds. You will not be able to get full engine power with your two-pitch propeller at take-off, because the low-pitch setting is usually selected to prevent over-speeding during climb, and will hold the engine down during most of the take-off below rated r.p.m.

A continuously varying pitch (constant-speed) propeller, on the other hand, is capable of absorbing all the power developed by the engine, giving you

230

maximum take-off power, and operates with approximately equal efficiency at take-off, during climb, at cruising or high speed, and during dives and violent maneuvers.

Such a propeller is an engine-speed regulator and gets its more usual name, "constant speed propeller," from the fact that it can be used to maintain a constant r.p.m. in the engine. It accomplishes this by constantly changing its pitch to meet varying propeller air loads. When the load is light, the pitch increases; when the load increases, the pitch decreases. In this way the torque, as well as the r.p.m., is kept constant. The pitch of the propeller is regulated by a governor attached to the engine. You simply set the governor manually to any desired r.p.m., and from then on, everything is automatic. If the engine has a tendency to speed up, the governor increases the pitch of the propeller blades and thus holds the speed of the engine in check.

I have already mentioned that the size of the propeller is definitely limited by the size of the plane, the r.p.m. delivered by the engine, and the speed limitation of the propeller tips. This problem of size limitation can be solved in several ways. For instance, where an increase in the size of a two-bladed propeller would bring the diameter beyond practical limits, a three-bladed propeller has been found to be satisfactory. While the three-bladed propeller is actually about 2 per cent less efficient, it has a better static thrust, and operates with less vibration, especially during side slipping or violent military maneuvers. On large, high-powered planes, larger diameters can sometimes be used if reduction gears are placed between the engine crankshaft and the propeller. Despite the fact that there is a certain mechanical loss throughout the system, the gearing of the engine increases the available power and results in an appreciable increase in the rate of climb. The choice between a propeller with wider blades and one with greater diameter is determined by the purpose for which the plane is intended. A plane intended for high-altitude work, where high climbing and take-off efficiencies are important, needs the largest possible diameter compatible with tip speed and ground clearance. If high speed is of first importance, then a wide-blade propeller is selected in preference to one with a large diameter.

The actual mating of a propeller to an engine and a plane is, of course, an engineering job, but you ought to be familiar with the basis on which the choice is made. From the foregoing discussion you can readily see that constant-speed propellers are more suited to heavy duty, high-performance planes, and that the fixed-pitch propeller is more practical, from the point of view of initial cost and weight, for lighter planes that are called on for average performance only.

You may be interested in knowing that the present-day propeller has a specific weight of between .35 lb. and .50 lb. per horsepower. It has been found that, *wherever practical,* an increase in the weight of the propeller results in an increase in the life of the propeller. But those two words, "wherever practical," are important. Weight added in the wrong place can cause a serious increase in vibration—and vibration is the propeller's worst enemy.

Propellers represent a serious problem on the newer type of plane where at sub-stratosphere levels, the cruising speed is steadily being raised. Theoretically the propeller diameter must be increased in direct proportion to the decrease in air density to provide for the proper absorption of the same amount of horsepower absorbed at sea level. The diameter of a propeller functioning at an elevation where the density is half that of sea level is (theoretically) twice that of a propeller operating at sea level. Actually, such a variation in the size of propellers is impractical for present-day planes, and the problem must be solved by using variable-pitch propellers with more blades. This, as I have said before, means that there will be some loss in efficiency, but it prevents increasing the diameter to excessive proportions; in other words, it is the next best choice.

You may also be interested in knowing, purely from an academic point of view, that, although the propeller tip speed at sea level must be below 1000 feet per second, this speed (again theoretically) must be decreased at higher altitudes where the temperature is lower. This would seem to favor larger diameters for propellers, to provide for better maximum efficiency at sub-stratosphere levels, provided that the structure of the plane permits, and the propeller r.p.m. is decreased through further reduction in the gear ratio between the engine and the propeller shaft.

Before I forget, I must remind you that you should always keep your propeller in perfect condition—that is, you must see to it that your propeller is statically balanced—with all the blades of equal weight. The propeller should also be properly lined up within a plane perpendicular to its rotational axis. Otherwise, because of the high rotational speed of the propeller, the centrifugal force developed by the blades is so great that any difference in the weight of the blades, or any deviation from their correct alignment, no matter

232

how small, will set up a severe vibration throughout the plane that will cause metal fatigue, particularly near the propeller hub, and eventually crystallize and weaken the metal. This is an extremely undesirable thing to have happen in the plane you are flying, as even Cloudy Joe realizes.

You will understand even better what this centrifugal force can amount to when I tell you that it causes an increase in weight from a little over 100 lbs. to over 40,000 lbs. *for each blade* of a propeller absorbing, say, 500 hp. at cruising r.p.m. These figures should be fair warning to you not to let your propeller get out of balance through lack of regular inspection, for the vibration fatigue that results from an unbalanced propeller is simply an invitation to blade failure. The above figures will also give you an idea of the potential forces present in a propeller operating on a plane at normal cruising speed.

The estimated life of the present-day propeller is about 5000 hours or more, but you can shorten—or prolong—these hours by the kind of attention you give to this part of your plane.

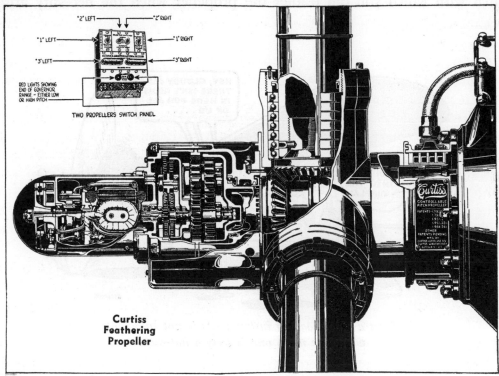

Curtiss
Feathering
Propeller

FIG. 201

FIG. 201. This illustration shows a cut-away of a Curtiss feathering, electrically controlled, constant speed propeller. You can control the pitch of this propeller automatically, by means of an engine-driven governor which maintains constant speed at whatever engine r.p.m. you wish within the normal operating range of your engine. This automatic pitch change is precisely regulated by the electrical circuit of the governor switching device.

The propeller pitch can also be controlled selectively by means of a manually operated toggle switch, with which you can hold the pitch at any point throughout its range while you check the functioning of your power plant by observing the effect of mixture adjustments and throttle changes on the r.p.m. of the engine. With the automatic control, of course, you can rid yourself of all responsibility for change in pitch during take-off, cruising and landing. I don't need to tell you that this leaves you more time for other operations.

On the instrument panel, next to the selective switch, is another toggle switch with which you can feather the propeller when the necessity arises.

Even a plane-load of instruments is not sufficient
when the main one is only a hat-rack.

FIG. 202. Obviously the constant change in propeller pitch requires some motivating force or power. This power is supplied to the propeller shown in the previous illustration, by an electric motor mounted in the nose of the power unit installed on the front of the propeller hub. This small motor has two oppositely wound fields, either of which can be electrically energized to cause the motor to rotate in one direction or the other, thus increasing or decreasing the pitch of the propeller.

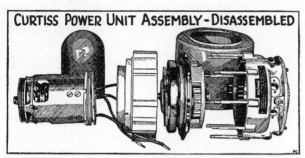

CURTISS POWER UNIT ASSEMBLY - DISASSEMBLED

FIG. 202

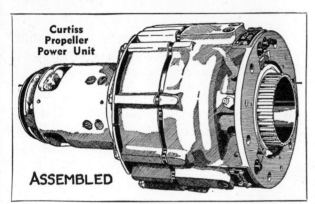

Curtiss Propeller Power Unit

ASSEMBLED

FIG. 203

To prevent overrunning of the electric motor during constant speed operation, an electromatically released, spring-loaded, no-voltage brake is installed on the front of the motor armature shaft. (Overrunning of your motor would, of course, result in "hunting" of the control.) The brake automatically locks the blade-turning mechanism when the controlling current is switched off. This brake allows you to get the full benefit of the precision control made possible by electric equipment.

FIG. 203. The electric motor is connected with a master bevel gear which engages the blade gears by means of a planetary gear-speed reducing unit. This arrangement allows the propeller constant-speed control to keep pace with the changes in aerodynamic conditions, and thus produces the most satisfactory rate of pitch change in degrees per second. During the feathering period, when a faster pitch change is required, the motor operates on boosted voltage.

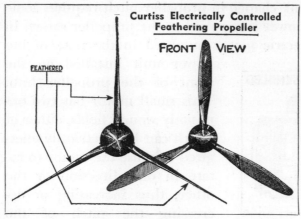

FIG. 204

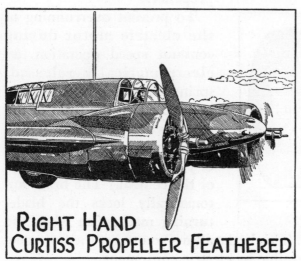

FIG. 205

FIGS. 204 AND 205. You can see what is meant by the term "feathering" if you study the adjoining illustrations. The blades of the feathered propeller are turned, by means of a manual feathering control switch, until they are 85° to 90° to the plane of rotation, the exact number of degrees depending upon the type of blade.

A propeller is feathered when its engine goes dead during flight. Feathering cuts down resistance to the air, prevents the dead engine from rotating, and increases the flight range of the remaining engine or engines by conserving their power. An unfeathered, "windmilling" propeller, on the other hand, by offering greater resistance to the air, causes an extra drag which must be overcome by the working engines. Windmilling propellers may also set up a severe vibration which can be extremely dangerous, especially if there is any structural failure around the dead engine. When the propeller is feathered, this danger is completely eliminated. A feathered propeller, you see, contributes to your safety in more ways than one.

Occasionally, you may wish to feather a propeller engine even though no emergency exists. In that case, be sure to shut off the gasoline supply and run the gasoline out of the engine before you start feathering. This will eliminate the possibility of backfire from an overaccumulation of gases.

There are two or three miscellaneous points about propellers that I want

236

to call to your attention before we go on to a general discussion of airplane behavior. In landing, for instance, set the r.p.m., by means of the governor control lever, to the normal rated r.p.m. of the engine so that as you approach with engines throttled, your propeller blades will be at low pitch. This last precaution will enable you to obtain full power from your engine at once if you find you must continue your flight. Be sure to have the propeller, governor and control system on your plane inspected at regular intervals. It is a good idea to have the governor and propeller disassembled and completely overhauled and greased every time you have a major engine overhaul.

Not all constant-speed propellers are electrically controlled. The motivating force for some types is supplied by hydraulic pressure—that is, by forcing oil under pressure into the mechanism of the propeller.

Cloudy Joe wants me to take out time right now to give him a step-by-step lesson on how to operate a constant-speed propeller. In fact, he would really like to have the knowledge poured into him without any effort on his part. But now that I have explained the principle on which the propeller functions and shown him how it contributes to the performance of his plane, Cloudy Joe will have to get busy and do some thinking of his own.

The words GUESS and KNOW when used in flying
may produce entirely opposite results.

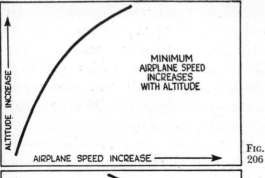

FIG.
206

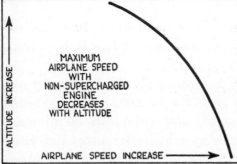

FIG.
207

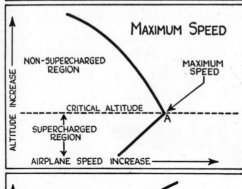

FIG.
208

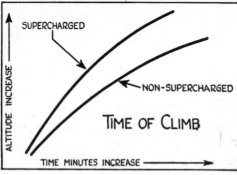

FIG.
209

XX

AIRPLANE BEHAVIOR

I ASSUME that you will do your flying with your head and not mechanically, like Cloudy Joe, who remembers isolated facts and forgets all about the underlying principles. It may be a good idea, therefore, if I give you a general picture of how your airplane behaves under the effect of power and variable air density.

FIG. 206. Since the lift of the wing on your plane for a given speed increases or decreases in direct proportion to the density of the air, you can readily see from the curve in Fig. 206 that the minimum speed which will provide sufficient lift to sustain the plane in the air increases with altitude. If you are taking off from a high altitude, you must have a greater minimum air speed to lift the plane from the ground than you would need at a field nearer sea level.

FIG. 207. On the other hand, if your plane is equipped with a non-supercharged engine, the power of which, as you know, decreases with altitude, the maximum speed of your plane will gradually decrease with altitude—despite the fact that the air density also decreases.

FIG. 208. This curve shows you that if you are flying a plane with a super-

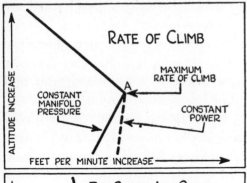

RATE OF CLIMB

ALTITUDE INCREASE →

CONSTANT MANIFOLD PRESSURE

MAXIMUM RATE OF CLIMB

A

CONSTANT POWER

FEET PER MINUTE INCREASE →

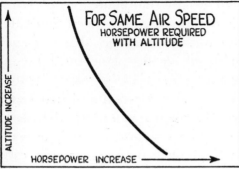

FOR SAME AIR SPEED
HORSEPOWER REQUIRED WITH ALTITUDE

ALTITUDE INCREASE →

HORSEPOWER INCREASE →

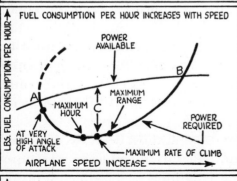

LBS. FUEL CONSUMPTION PER HOUR →

FUEL CONSUMPTION PER HOUR INCREASES WITH SPEED

POWER AVAILABLE

B

A

MAXIMUM HOUR

C

MAXIMUM RANGE

AT VERY HIGH ANGLE OF ATTACK

POWER REQUIRED

MAXIMUM RATE OF CLIMB

AIRPLANE SPEED INCREASE →

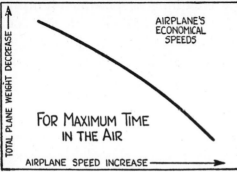

TOTAL PLANE WEIGHT DECREASE →

AIRPLANE'S ECONOMICAL SPEEDS

FOR MAXIMUM TIME IN THE AIR

AIRPLANE SPEED INCREASE →

charged engine—that is, with an engine that maintains constant power up to its critical altitude—the speed of your plane will increase until a maximum is reached at *A*, the critical altitude level. After this point, you will notice, the curve slopes to the left, and the maximum speed decreases as explained in Fig. 207.

Fig. 210

FIG. 209. The time it takes in minutes for your plane to climb to a given altitude depends upon the excess power supplied by your engine. Since the power of a non-supercharged engine drops with altitude, the time for each thousand feet of climb increases with altitude; and since the power of a supercharged engine can be kept constant up to the critical altitude, the time required for each thousand feet of climb also increases, although this increase is slower than for the non-supercharged engine.

Fig. 211

FIG. 210. The number of feet per minute at which your plane can climb to a given altitude again depends upon the excess power supplied by your engine. You will notice in this illustration that, when you are flying at a constant manifold pressure, the rate of climb increases with altitude as the power of the engine increases with altitude. If you climb at constant power, the curve will either be similar to the one shown by the dotted line, or more upright. Once you reach your

Fig. 212

Fig. 213

239

critical altitude, the rate of climb begins to drop, since the supercharged engine now has the characteristics of the non-supercharged engine.

Fig. 211. This graph shows that less horsepower is required at higher than at lower altitudes to maintain equal air speed. The reason for the decrease in horsepower is that the density of the air is lower at higher altitudes and there is less resistance to be overcome, so that less power is required.

Fig. 212. The curve on this illustration shows the variation of fuel consumption per hour at different speeds. Notice in the "Power Required" curve that fuel consumption is greater at very low speeds. This is because the high angle of attack increases the drag to such an extent that more power is required to overcome it. For maximum rate of climb, your speed must be greater than the most economical speed; for maximum range—that is, to get the greatest mileage per gallon of gas—the speed of the plane must be increased above that for maximum rate of climb.

(You realize, of course, that this is only a general discussion and that exact information can be obtained only when the performance of a particular plane is being studied.)

If you study the "Power Available" curve, you will see that you cannot draw more power out of your engine than is shown between the points *A* and *B*.

To find out the maximum rate of climb for a given plane, curves must be drawn for the power required and the power available for that particular plane at various speeds. The maximum rate of climb occurs at the points where the gap between these two curves is widest. In Fig. 212 this gap is indicated by *C*.

Fig. 213. For maximum time in the air you can and must decrease the speed of your plane to conserve your fuel, as shown in this illustration. During a flight, if you find you must remain in the air as long as possible, continuously decrease the speed of your plane as it becomes lighter with the consumption of fuel. This is a general rule. For best results the performance of a particular plane must be analyzed to determine its most economical speeds for various loads.

The difference between good and poor
airmanship is that the first respects the
weather.

XXI

DEAD RECKONING

How to Get Where You're Going

DEAD reckoning consists in calculating—from the distance and the course you have already flown—your position at a given time. Flying by dead reckoning is wholly reliable only when you can check your position with reference to a fixed ground location. Suppose, for instance, that you are flying above the clouds and have lost sight of the ground. Your course has been plotted in accordance with information about wind direction and velocity obtained at the start of your flight. But while this information was correct at the time you plotted your course, if the winds aloft change their direction or velocity, or both, your calculations will be all messed up.

Formerly, whenever dead reckoning was used, the only way of checking the accuracy of your course was by identifying landmarks along the way (cities, rivers, etc.), the location of which was shown on your flight map. When it comes to flying in and through the overcast, dead reckoning is still your basic method of avigation, but now your check points are radio stations, radio beams and radio marker beacons.

Before we go into the subject of dead reckoning in detail, here are a few general points for you to remember:

Your compass wants to tell you the truth, but first you must know how far it is deviating from the true direction.

Your compass will deviate to the east or north according to your location in relation to the earth's surface—that is, according to your latitudinal and longitudinal position. Lines connecting points of identical variation are shown on your flight map.

Whenever the winds aloft do not blow parallel to your plotted course, your plane will drift to the left or right, depending upon the direction from which the wind blows. To maintain your course, you must fly a compass course corrected for wind velocity and direction. *The nose of your plane, therefore, will not always point directly toward your destination.*

Fɪɢ. 214. A crab angle is the angle between a line connecting your point of departure and your destination, and a line parallel to your plane's longitudinal axis. In this illustration you can see how the crab angle for a plane traveling at a given speed changes with variation in wind direction. (The crab angle also changes according to wind velocity.)

First, study the plane at *A*. Here we assume that the wind is blowing 30 miles an hour from true north; that you are flying true north at an indicated air speed of 150 m.p.h., at 10,000 feet; that your true air speed is 171 m.p.h., and your ground speed 141 m.p.h. Under these circumstances, your only problem is to correct for compass variation. If there is a 10° variation to the west, you must add 10° to your compass course in order to fly due north; if the variation is to the east, you must subtract 10°.

Now study the illustration at *B, C, D, E, F* and *G* and you will see how the crab angle changes with variation in wind direction. The velocity of the wind, in each instance, remains the same.

The crab angle is affected not only by wind direction and velocity, but also by the true air speed of your plane, which is obtained, you will remember, by means of the speed calculator shown in Fig. 119 or by the equation given on page 139, which takes into consideration both temperature and pressure at a given pressure altitude.

To the right in this illustration is shown a method for finding the true ground speed and crab angle when wind direction, velocity and the true air speed of your plane are known. First, establish the geographic direction of your plane; then plot the angle of wind direction and mark off the velocity by means of a linear scale. Lay off the true air speed as shown, and draw a diagonal as shown by the heavy black line. This line, measured by the same linear scale used for wind velocity and true air speed, gives you the ground speed of your plane. Notice that in this case the crab angle is 8°. If you study this illustration, you will find it easy to construct parallelograms of forces and to find the answers for different wind directions and velocities at different true air speeds.

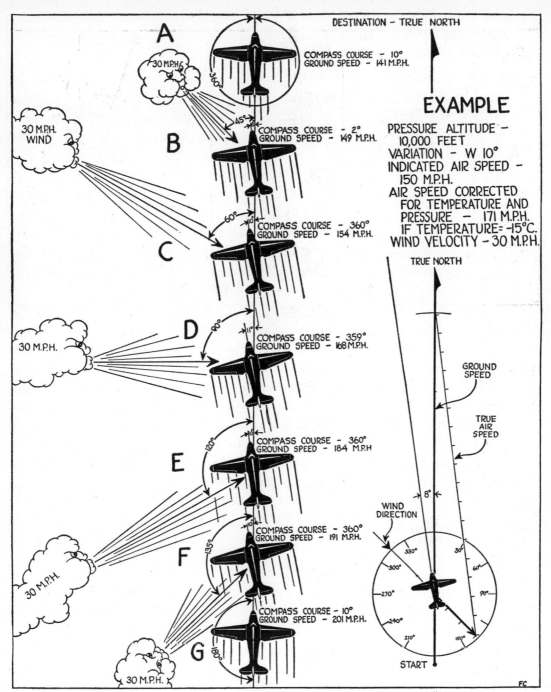

A COMPASS COURSE – 10°
GROUND SPEED – 141 M.P.H.

B COMPASS COURSE – 2°
GROUND SPEED – 149 M.P.H.

C COMPASS COURSE – 360°
GROUND SPEED – 154 M.P.H.

D COMPASS COURSE – 359°
GROUND SPEED – 168 M.P.H.

E COMPASS COURSE – 360°
GROUND SPEED – 184 M.P.H.

F COMPASS COURSE – 360°
GROUND SPEED – 191 M.P.H.

G COMPASS COURSE – 10°
GROUND SPEED – 201 M.P.H.

DESTINATION – TRUE NORTH

30 M.P.H. WIND

30 M.P.H.

30 M.P.H.

30 M.P.H.

EXAMPLE

PRESSURE ALTITUDE –
10,000 FEET
VARIATION – W 10°
INDICATED AIR SPEED –
150 M.P.H.
AIR SPEED CORRECTED
FOR TEMPERATURE AND
PRESSURE – 171 M.P.H.
IF TEMPERATURE = -15°C.
WIND VELOCITY – 30 M.P.H.

TRUE NORTH

GROUND SPEED

TRUE AIR SPEED

WIND DIRECTION

START

FIG. 214

243

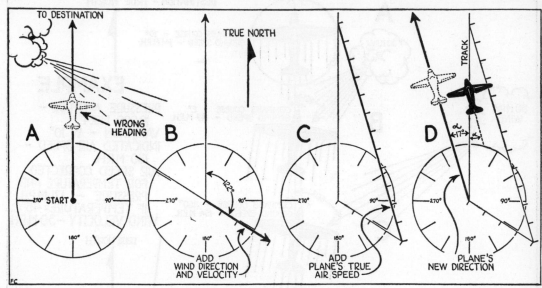

FIG. 215

FIG. 215. This shows you again, step by step, how to find your final compass heading by taking the crab angle into consideration. Start at *A*. If your destination and heading are true north, as shown, and if there is any wind blowing from the left, you will never get where you are going. But if you plot wind direction and velocity, as shown in *B*, and add your plane's true air speed, as shown in *C*, you will obtain the crab angle. Subtract this from what would have been your compass heading if no side wind had been blowing, and you will get the correct compass heading.

FIG. 216. Here the destination has been changed from true north. Following the same procedure given in Fig. 215, you can obtain the correct heading as shown in *D*.

WINDS ALOFT

The velocity of the wind aloft is not of great importance when you are flying short distances, as you will see later, but it is of considerable importance when you are flying long distances. On long trips wind aloft is one of the factors that determine the time required to fly from your point of departure to your destination. Time, however, is the last thing to be considered. First you must establish your minimum altitude in accordance with air

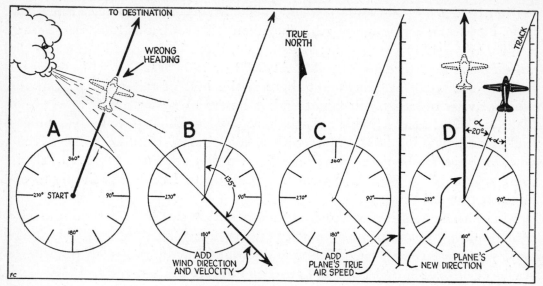

Fig. 216

regulations, the terrain over which you are flying, and prevailing weather conditions. Then you must decide whether the altitude selected is the best one for engine performance and for comfort. Then you are ready to consider winds aloft. If the velocity of the wind is greater than 10 per cent, approximately, of the high speed of your plane, you cannot overcome its retarding effect by pushing your engine or engines. Even if you could increase the cruising speed of your plane by 10 per cent, it would be impractical, since the engine or engines would have to be wide open. This would mean that your plane is flying approximately at its high speed, and such a procedure would not promote the well-being of your power plant.

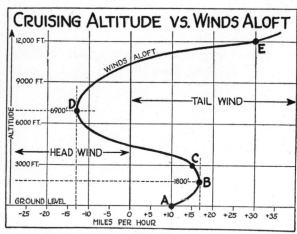

Fig. 217

Fig. 217. When everything else has been taken into consid-

245

eration, you must use your own judgment in selecting your cruising altitude. For instance, if you study this chart you will see that at 1800 feet there is a tail wind of 17 miles an hour; at 3000 feet, there is also a tail wind but the velocity has decreased to 15 miles. At 6000 or 7000 feet you will encounter head winds, while at 12,000 feet there is the best of tail winds. From the point of view of safety, you might find it better to fly against headwinds at 6000 or 7000 feet than with tail winds at 1800 or 3000 feet. Or you might find smoother flying at 3000 feet with a tail wind of 15 miles an hour than you would at 1800 where the velocity is 17 miles an hour. On a short trip there would be no advantage at all in going up to 12,000 feet simply to obtain a better tail wind.

I have been pointing out various factors which can influence your choice of flight level, but remember that if you are flying over an established airway, you must choose an odd-thousand-foot indicated pressure altitude above sea level on east-bound trips and an even number of thousand feet on a westbound trip.

Flying over a country that has run out of railroads.

XXII

POWER VS. TIME AND DISTANCE

KEEPING to schedule in flying is important not only in regular airline service, but also in connection with military operations. Cloudy Joe cannot conceive of the fact that military planes flying from different bases must frequently meet at the same time and at the same place *in the air*. But keeping ethereal appointments of this kind is one of the things a military flyer must be able to do with as much precision as though he had arranged to meet the gang on a familiar street corner.

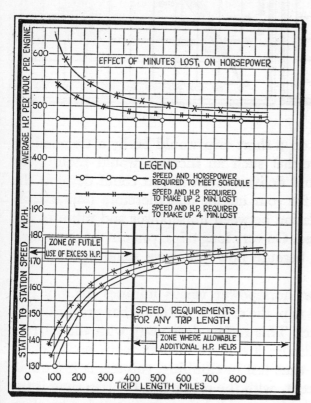

FIG. 218

FIG. 218. This illustration, which is applicable to any type of plane, shows important characteristics about time, distance and power. Put this information on mental file, for you may need to use it some time.

The lower curves demonstrate the futility of trying to make up for lost time, in transport or military operation, by using extra horsepower. This is especially true on very short trips. In other words, the speed of any airplane on a short trip is relatively unimportant because so much time is taken up during normal maneuvering on the ground. The only way you

247

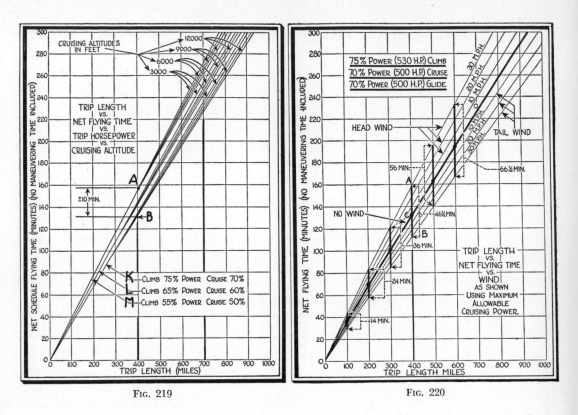

FIG. 219   FIG. 220

could save any appreciable time on a short trip would be by a tremendous increase in speed. The chances are that such an increase would require far more power than your engine could deliver. Even if you could develop the necessary speed, it would be bad for your engine and therefore impractical.

The upper curves show the relation between horsepower and minutes lost as the length of the trip is increased. On very long trips, you can make up for a reasonable amount of lost time because now you have some flexibility in power control.

FIG. 219. This illustration shows horsepower versus minutes for any trip length. Notice that on a 400-mile trip, the cruising altitude has practically no effect upon the number of minutes. This rather does away with the current conception that high cruising altitudes are more advantageous on block-to-block schedule performance. The time lost in climbing, you see, is just about offset by the time gained in descent, with the result that the trip time is the same regardless of the cruising altitude, provided there is no wind. The effect

248

of cruising altitude upon minutes saved is not appreciable until your trip gets into the seven or eight hundred mile class, or over.

The normal range of horsepower variation to accommodate flexibility in scheduled operation is between 50 and 70 per cent at the present time. This spread of available cruising power will probably continue as a normal operating range in airline service. Actually you are limited in the number of minutes you can gain or lose, through the use of horsepower, to about plus or minus ten minutes on a 400-mile trip. Even Cloudy Joe agrees with this.

Fig. 220. These curves show the minimum time in which a flight can be made by using the maximum allowable cruising power with any of the wind combinations noted. (You can develop these curves from those given in Fig. 219 by using a little simple arithmetic.) By comparing Figs. 219 and 220 you will discover that a careful analysis of wind-aloft variation is much more important than horsepower in determining the most efficient altitude at which to fly under a given set of conditions. By flying wind instead of power on a 400-mile trip such as we have been considering, you would gain a normal expectancy of about forty instead of ten minutes in scheduled time. In other words, you can do a more efficient job in maintaining your schedule on a given trip if you make an accurate analysis of the winds aloft and juggle your cruising power accordingly.

These last two illustrations will help you to make a logical flight plan for any trip length with any type of airplane, provided the data given in these illustrations fit your particular type of plane. You will know the length of your projected trip in miles, and by studying the wind-aloft information, you will be able to obtain the cruising component of the wind at various altitudes, and to select your cruising altitude according to the conditions existing at the time of your proposed flight. From Fig. 220 you can obtain the minimum time required to make the trip; or if you are not interested in minimum time but wish to keep to a particular schedule, Fig. 219 will give you just the power needed to maintain that schedule under existing conditions.

*Deliberate, cool and systematic procedure is
essential when flying on instruments.*

XXIII

ABOUT RADIO

WHENEVER I fly cross-country in soupy weather in a plane that has no radio receiver and transmitter, I feel as sure of my location as though I were lost on a desert. I don't mean that flights cannot be made without the aid of radio. They can—sometimes—but only in what used to be called "flyable" weather.

Fortunately the Bureau of Air Commerce (a part of the Department of Commerce) has installed radiobeacon stations from coast to coast. These light-houses of the air send out invisible beams that overlap, forming highways for "flying carriages" so that you can now fly all over the country guided solely by beacon stations. Naturally I don't have to point out that to take advantage of these aerial guides you must equip your plane, at the very least, with a radiobeacon receiver, or an aircraft radiocompass. If you add a transmitter to your equipment, then you have something to talk about!

What kind of information will you be able to pick out of the air during flight? First, there are the on-course signals that sound like a long dash, and the *A* and *N* sector code signals (dot-dash, and dash-dot). You can get complete weather reports covering actual conditions along the airway, including upper-air wind direction and velocity, and from some of the stations you will pick up news about the condition of flying fields that may be particularly valuable when you are coming down at an unfamiliar airport. From airport stations

250

equipped with traffic control transmitters you will also be able to obtain instructions for landings and take-offs which are particularly helpful when there is a large amount of air traffic or flying conditions are poor.

All stations keep a constant listening watch for planes equipped with transmitters and furnish, on request, additional data about the weather along the route, and any requested data about landing fields. Scheduled airlines maintain their own radio communication stations, which exchange airplane position reports, traffic schedules, weather en route and other information with their planes during flight. While these airline radio stations are intended only for the use of the line's own planes, you can arrange in advance, if you are an itinerant airman, to use these private facilities.

There is another type of radio guide to help you during flight, provided your plane is equipped with a radiocompass. I won't discuss this type of compass now, since it is described in detail later on, but with its left-right course indicator you can fly directly toward or away from an *entertainment* broadcasting station, as well as a beacon station. When I say "directly," I don't mean that your path will always be a straight line, for any drift caused by side wind will change your path from a straight line to a curve. The important thing to remember is that you will finally reach the station if you aim at it. Since entertainment broadcasting stations are on the air the greater part of a twenty-four-hour day, and beacon stations a full twenty-four hours, these stations are continually at your service.

It has taken years of research and painstaking effort in the laboratory to develop aircraft radio equipment, for, unlike the ordinary commercial sets, aircraft radio must be dependable *at all times*. Aircraft sets must be strongly built; yet they must also be as compact and light as possible. Receiver controls must be so simple to operate that there will be no difficulty in picking up beacon signals, weather reports, traffic control, entertainment, and other aircraft signals. Today, with such improvements as pre-selected frequency control (made possible through the use of quartz crystals) you can tune your receiver automatically by throwing a switch which establishes immediate contact between your plane, transport planes and their airline stations. Another recent development in aircraft radio is a special antenna to reduce rain-snow static to a minimum. Most important of all recent contributions to radio avigation is the radiocompass, which you can use as an ordinary receiver, as a guide toward or away from broadcasting and beacon stations, and as a means

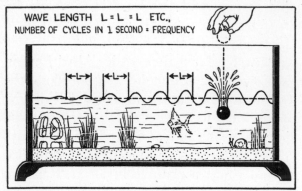

FIG. 221

WAVE LENGTH L = L = L ETC.,
NUMBER OF CYCLES IN 1 SECOND = FREQUENCY

of checking the relative position of your plane, by taking bearings for line of position, plotting the reciprocals of two or more stations, and thus obtaining a "fix."

FIG. 221. If you drop a pebble into a fish bowl, you will notice that the waves set up are all the *same length*. No matter how deep or how shallow the trough may be between the waves, the distance from wave to wave is always the same. You will also notice that, while the wave length remains the same, the strength or amplitude of the waves grows weaker as they travel away from the point where the pebble entered the water.

A radio transmitter sets up waves in the ether just the way a pebble does in a fish bowl. The length of these waves is constant, but the strength or amplitude decreases with distance from the transmitting station. The actual linear measurement of the wave (as shown by *L* in the aquarium) is known as the *wave length* and is given in *meters*. The completion of one wave length is a *cycle,* and the number of cycles set up in one second is called *frequency*. Radio waves travel with the speed of light (186,000 miles per second). Since radio frequencies mount up to the thousands and millions, they are expressed in kilocycles—that is, "thousands of cycles"—so that 3105 kilocycles stands for 3,105,000 cycles a second.

Flying through the overcast without radio is as safe as driving at night without headlights.

252

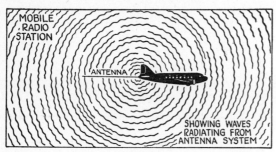

FIG. 222

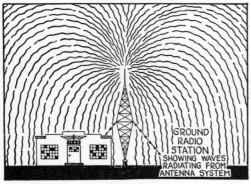

FIG. 223

FIG. 222. Here you see the wave pattern set up by a mobile radio transmitting station. Since the center of this wave pattern is constantly moving, signals from the plane grow weaker or stronger as the distance between the plane and the receiving station increases or decreases.

FIG. 223. A ground transmitting station emits waves in a fountain-like pattern. If there are high steel buildings near the station, the wave pattern is sometimes distorted. Most of the waves deflected by obstructions are not blotted out; they simply bend around the obstruction, reappearing on the far side, and eventually reach their normal penetrating distance.

This bending of radio waves by obstructions such as high buildings or mountains has an important bearing on your use of the radiocompass. Suppose, for instance, that you are flying on one side of a large city where there are high steel buildings, and that you have tuned your radiocompass on an entertainment broadcasting station located on the opposite side of town. The waves from the transmitting antenna of the station will reach the loop of your radiocompass after passing through, or over, a zone of high steel structures. As the waves pass through this zone, they are bent by the obstructions, with the result that the left-right indicator needle of your compass will fluctuate. Don't let this worry you. Simply use your radiocompass as reference, and guide your plane by the magnetic compass or by the Sperry directional gyro until the fluctuation stops. If, on the other hand, the waves from the transmitting station are unobstructed, and the needle of the radiocompass is centered, the nose of your plane is in line with the station to which you are tuned, and you will need no other guide than the radiocompass. Even under these conditions, as I said before, side winds may cause your plane to drift along a curved instead of a straight course.

253

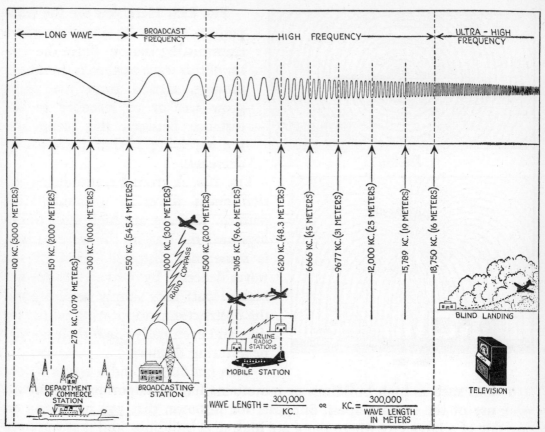

FIG. 224

FIG. 224. Department of Commerce airways stations operate in the long-wave band on frequencies between 200 kc. and 400 kc. Ships at sea transmit in the long-wave band on frequencies between 150 kc. and 300 kc. Broadcast stations, which you will use in connection with your radiocompass, transmit on frequencies between 550 kc. and 1500 kc. Amateur stations, and plane-to-plane transmissions or plane-to-ground-station transmissions, have been assigned to still higher frequencies, while the ultra high frequencies are reserved for such services as instrument landing of aircraft, and television. Some amateur stations also operate in the ultra high-frequency band.

At the bottom of this chart are two equations which give you the relationship between wave length in meters, and kilocycles.

254

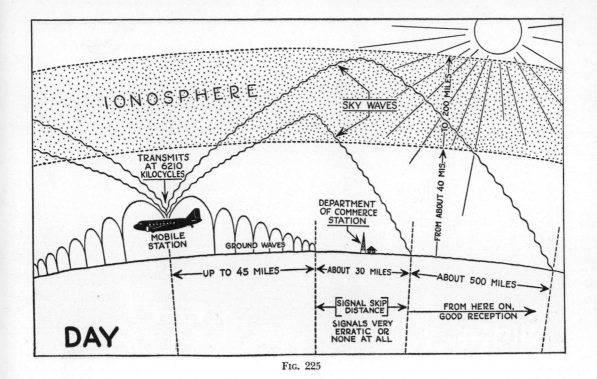

FIG. 225

FIG. 225. The antenna of a transmitting station emits two general types of waves—ground and sky. Ground waves follow the surface of the earth and are used primarily for radio communication on long waves, and for relatively short-distance work on the high frequencies. The sky waves go up as far as 40 to 200 miles and are reflected back to earth from the ionosphere. This ionized layer lies closer to the earth during the day, and its density varies with the seasons. The density of the ionosphere also varies from year to year, because of sun spots and other factors of which we know but little at the present time.

The mobile station shown in this illustration has a ground-wave range, during the day, of approximately 45 miles. From the point where the ground waves end to the point where the reflected sky waves strike the earth, there is a "skip" zone in which the signals are either very erratic or non-existent.

FIG. 226. At night, ground waves emitted by the mobile station shown in the preceding illustration extend over a radius of approximately 65 miles. The sky waves travel at a flatter angle than during the day, causing a skip

255

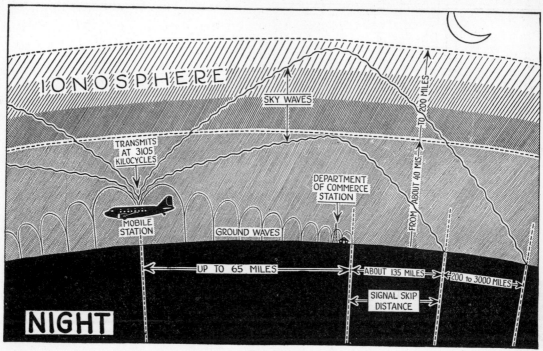

FIG. 226

distance of approximately 135 miles. Notice that the zone covered by the sky waves at night is about 3000 miles—a far greater distance than that reached by the same station during the day.

FIGS 227 TO 232. Different types of ground stations emit different types of waves, as you will see by studying these illustrations. For instance, while the old-type beacon station emits ground waves during the day, and ground and sky waves at night, the new-type beacon station emits ground waves only, day or night. Notice the difference in waves emitted during the day and during the night by a broadcasting station transmitting on 500-900 kc., and notice the difference between a broadcasting station operating on 500-900 kc. and 900-1500 kc.

FIG. 233. This will give you a still better picture of the wave pattern set up by a mobile radio station. You can readily see that the various ground stations shown in the illustration will be contacted or lost according to the wave zone in which they are located. Since the radio wave pattern moves with the speed of the plane, the wave zone constantly changes in relation to the ground.

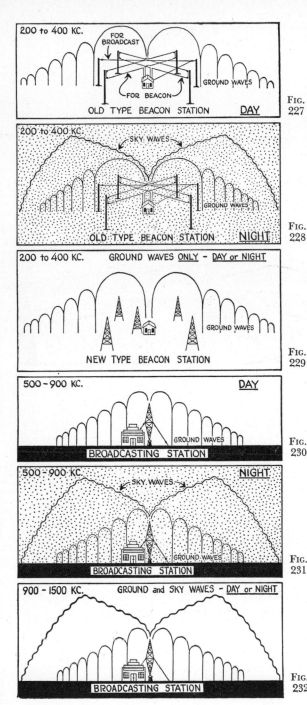

200 to 400 KC. — FOR BROADCAST — FOR BEACON — GROUND WAVES — OLD TYPE BEACON STATION — DAY

200 to 400 KC. — SKY WAVES — GROUND WAVES — OLD TYPE BEACON STATION — NIGHT

200 to 400 KC. — GROUND WAVES ONLY – DAY or NIGHT — GROUND WAVES — NEW TYPE BEACON STATION

500 – 900 KC. — DAY — GROUND WAVES — BROADCASTING STATION

500 – 900 KC. — NIGHT — SKY WAVES — GROUND WAVES — BROADCASTING STATION

900 – 1500 KC. — GROUND and SKY WAVES – DAY or NIGHT — BROADCASTING STATION

This accounts for the fact that you hear a station, then lose it, then hear it again as you fly. This temporary loss of contact always alarms our friend Cloudy Joe, for once he gets into the air he forgets all about radio-signal skip zones.

FIG. 234. The different frequencies assigned for radio communication between mobile stations, or between mobile stations and the various ground radio facilities, are shown in the illustration on page 259.

THE RECEIVER

Radio theory is far more complicated than the few points we have just been considering would indicate. The designing and construction of radio equipment call for the highest type of engineering knowledge and skill. But, fortunately for you, and especially for our friend Cloudy Joe, the operation of modern aircraft radio equipment is comparatively simple.

FIG. 235. This illustration shows the general arrangement and hook-up of an RCA aircraft receiver. Like most modern aircraft receivers, this unit covers all of your airway requirements through

257

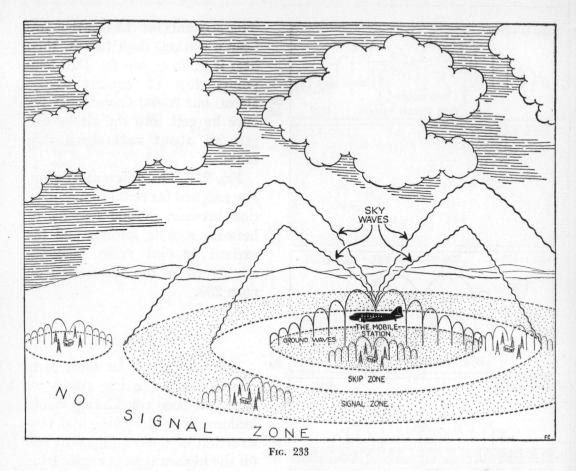

Fig. 233

the medium of three frequency bands—weather (X), broadcast (A), and aircraft communication (B). The principal operating points are:

(1) *Master Control Knob,* by which the receiver is turned on. Since it takes a little time for the receiver tubes to reach operating temperatures, the master control must always be turned on before you leave the ground and while your engines are still warming up. Turning your receiver on at this time also enables you to find out if it is functioning properly before you get into the air.

(2) *Limiter Switch,* used during adverse weather conditions only, when static is exceptionally heavy. At all other times the switch must be in the OFF position. As a general rule, the use of the limiter switch with volume control at full may enable you to "read" voice broadcast weather reports

258

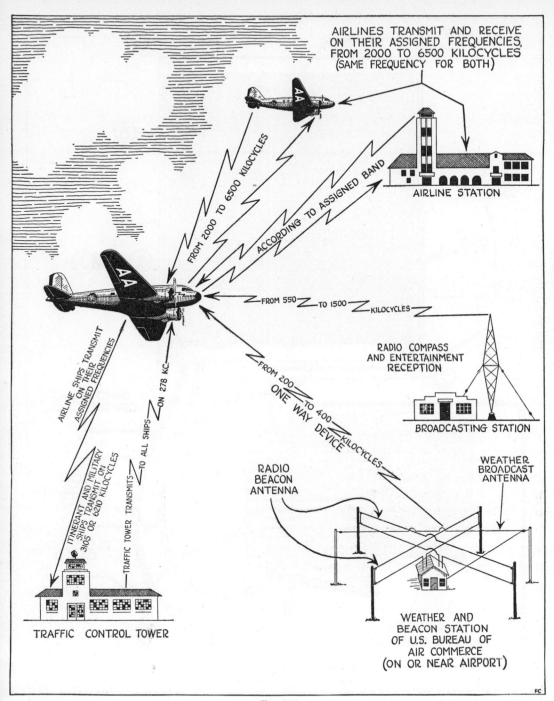

AIRLINES TRANSMIT AND RECEIVE
ON THEIR ASSIGNED FREQUENCIES,
FROM 2000 TO 6500 KILOCYCLES
(SAME FREQUENCY FOR BOTH)

FROM 2000 TO 6500 KILOCYCLES

ACCORDING TO ASSIGNED BAND

AIRLINE STATION

FROM 550 TO 1500 KILOCYCLES

RADIO COMPASS
AND ENTERTAINMENT
RECEPTION

FROM 200 TO 400 KILOCYCLES
ONE WAY DEVICE

BROADCASTING STATION

AIRLINE SHIPS TRANSMIT
ON THEIR
ASSIGNED FREQUENCIES

ON 278 KC.

TO ALL SHIPS

ITINERANT AND MILITARY
SHIPS TRANSMIT ON
3105 OR 6210 KILOCYCLES

TRAFFIC TOWER TRANSMITS

RADIO
BEACON
ANTENNA

WEATHER
BROADCAST
ANTENNA

TRAFFIC CONTROL TOWER

WEATHER AND
BEACON STATION
OF U.S. BUREAU OF
AIR COMMERCE
(ON OR NEAR AIRPORT)

FC

Fig. 234

259

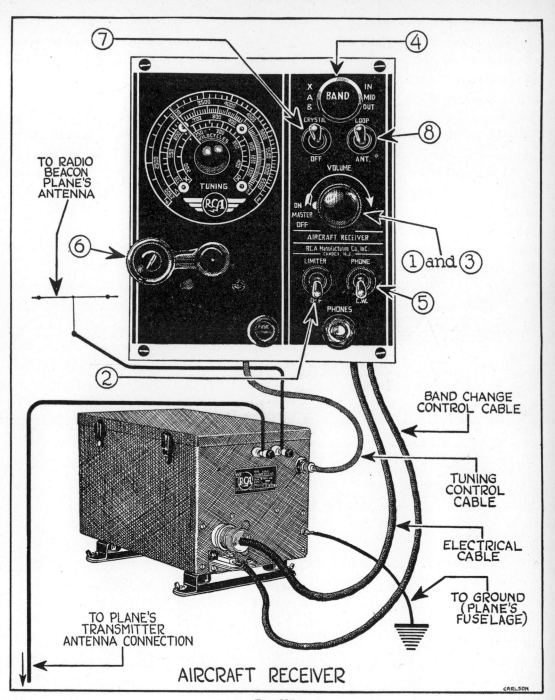

TO RADIO
BEACON
PLANE'S
ANTENNA

BAND CHANGE
CONTROL CABLE

TUNING
CONTROL
CABLE

ELECTRICAL
CABLE

TO GROUND
(PLANE'S
FUSELAGE)

TO PLANE'S
TRANSMITTER
ANTENNA CONNECTION

AIRCRAFT RECEIVER

CARLSON

FIG. 235

260

during adverse weather which you could not possibly receive otherwise.

(3) *Volume Control*. This has been combined with the master control so that you will have one gadget less to worry about.

(4) *Selector Knob*, with which the various bands are switched in. Cloudy Joe keeps this set at the broadcast band—at full volume—because he likes to be amused. The primary purpose of this band is to provide for an aural type of direction finding when a loop antenna is used with the receiver.

(5) *Phone-CW Switch (beat-frequency oscillator)*. This switch, which is not standard equipment on all receivers, enables you to receive continuous-wave telegraph signals and to read radiobeacon signals more easily and accurately than would otherwise be possible during poor atmospheric conditions. Keep this control in the OFF position whenever you wish to receive voice signals. If you don't, the voice will be garbled.

(6) *Tuning Knob*, connected with the frequency indicator dial above it by a set of gears, and with the receiver itself by a mechanical, flexible shaft. Since carelessly or improperly tuned receivers often result in improper course signals and erroneous cones of silence, there is only one safe thing to do—and that is, to learn how a receiver should be tuned. First set the volume control nearly at its full ON position, then rotate the tuning control until you pick up the right signal. Continue to rock the tuning control back and forth until you have it at exactly the *one* point where the signal is loudest and clearest. Once you have found this point, turn down your volume control. You will find that you will get the best results when you are following a radiobeacon if you can barely hear the signal. You can get changes of low intensity much more quickly with low volume than you can with high volume, in just the same way that you can hear the slightest sound in a very still room while you would be unable to hear a much louder noise in a noisy room. By keeping your headphone volume level carefully adjusted, you will be able to fly a much more accurate course with far less fatigue.

(7) *Crystal Control Switch*. This control makes it possible for you to "lock in" on two pre-selected high frequencies in the high-frequency (airline communications) band. The advantage of this feature is obvious, for with it you can listen in on reports exchanged between scheduled transport planes, or between these planes and their ground stations. These reports are especially valuable if you are an itinerant flyer using the same route as a transport, be-

cause they constitute a running weather report on the conditions you will encounter along the way.

In using the switch, set the selector-band switch to the airline-communications band, flip the crystal switch to ON, and rotate the tuning control to approximately the desired frequency. You will hear very little, if any, noise in your headphones as you turn the tuning knob until the receiver is tuned to approximately the prearranged frequency crystal. At this point you will get the conventional tube hiss and noise in the phones, and the crystal automatically locks. Your next and last step is to rock the tuning control back and forth very slightly, during the first transmission you pick up, until you find the point where the signals are clearest and loudest. (You will find that tuning which uses a crystal control is not as sharp as conventional tuning.) From then on, reception is automatic until you flip the switch back to its OFF position.

(8) *Loop Control Switch,* used with a rotatable, electrostatically shielded loop antenna. In addition to a fixed, non-directional antenna, you may equip your radio receiver with a rotatable loop antenna which can be used to reduce rain-snow static during instrument flight. When this switch is turned to the ON position, the receiver is automatically disconnected from the fixed antenna and connected to the loop antenna. The loop is rotated until it lies in the plane of flight (90° or 270° on the azimuth scale of the loop-rotating unit) and the receiver is then used in the usual way. The procedure which I have just described is followed when you are flying a radiobeacon course and wish to eliminate, or reduce, rain or snow static.

You can also take bearings on the station you are receiving by rotating the loop antenna until you locate the point where the signal fades out. Now read the azimuth scale of the loop-rotating unit, add or subtract this reading from the heading of your plane, and you will get the bearing of the station, which may be plotted on a chart. If you are not quite sure whether the station is ahead of, or behind you, set your ship on the bearing obtained, and with the loop antenna at 90° or 270° (on the azimuth scale) heading position, fly the course with the volume control set at minimum. Within a few minutes the signals will increase or decrease in volume, indicating the true bearing of the station. Be sure, during this procedure, not to touch the volume control once it has been set to the minimum point.

Aircraft Radiobeacon Receiver Antenna. There are two types of antenna

262

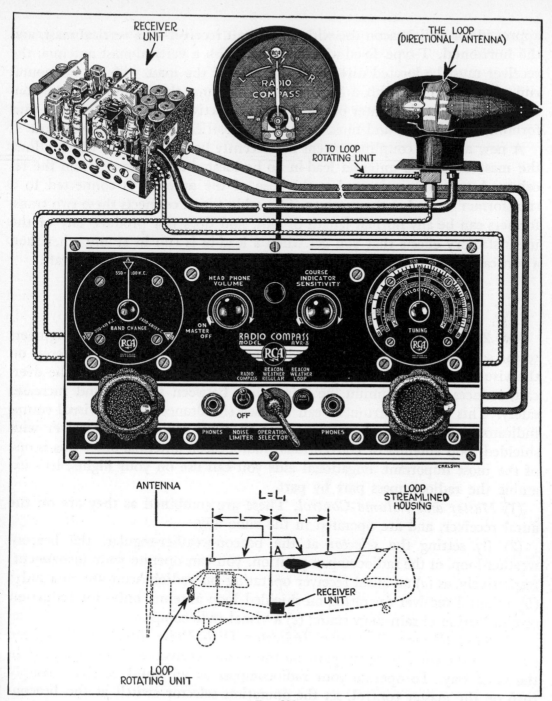

RECEIVER UNIT

THE LOOP (DIRECTIONAL ANTENNA)

TO LOOP ROTATING UNIT

550 - 1500 K.C.

HEAD PHONE VOLUME

COURSE INDICATOR SENSITIVITY

BAND CHANGE

KILOCYCLES

RCA

ON MASTER OFF

TUNING

RADIO COMPASS MODEL AVR-8

RCA

RADIO COMPASS   BEACON WEATHER REGULAR   BEACON WEATHER LOOP

OFF

PHONES   NOISE LIMITER   OPERATION SELECTOR   PHONES

ANTENNA

$L = L_1$

LOOP STREAMLINED HOUSING

L   L₁

A

RECEIVER UNIT

LOOP ROTATING UNIT

FIG. 236

263

approved for radiobeacon use with an aircraft receiver—the vertical mast, and the horizontal, T-type fixed-wire antenna. With a vertical-mast antenna, the receiver must be located directly at the base of the mast with no horizontal run of the lead-in. With a horizontal, T antenna, the lead-in must be connected exactly in the center of the electrically active, horizontal portion, thus forming a perfect T, and must drop or rise vertically to the receiver unit.

A new antenna coupling system has recently been developed which allows the mast or T-type antenna lead-in to be located at a distance from the receiver. A transformer located at the base of the antenna is connected to a transformer located at the receiver. The cable which connects these two transformers can be any normal length or run, and does not produce any of the unsatisfactory effects that you get when a lead-in is run in at any other than a vertical plane. This new system simplifies radio installations in aircraft.

The Radiocompass

Fig. 236. Probably the greatest contribution yet made by radio engineers to the science of avigation is the radiocompass. With its needle centered on the visual indicator, the compass acts as an efficient guide through the overcast, reduces to a minimum the flying time between stations, and increases safety. This single instrument can be used simultaneously as a visual course indicator and as an aural receiver, or as an aural radiobeacon receiver with shielded loop antenna or conventional radiobeacon antenna. Since this is one of the most important avigational aids you can use on your flights, let's examine the radiocompass part by part.

(1) *Master and Volume Control.* These are combined as they are on the aural receiver, and are operated in the same way.

(2) By setting the *selector* at the beacon-weather-regular, the beacon-weather-loop, or the radiocompass position, you can operate your instrument, respectively, as (a) an aural receiver operating on radiobeacon antenna only; (b) an aural receiver operating on shielded loop antenna only—for reduction or elimination of rain-snow static; (c) a visual radiocompass.

(3) *Band Change—Frequency Indicator Dial—Noise Limiter.* These are similar to the corresponding parts on the aural receiver and are operated in the same way. To operate your radiocompass as an aural receiver, simply turn on the master control, set the operation selector switch at the beacon-

weather-regular position, and follow the instructions given above for the receiver.

(4) *Indicator Sensitivity Control.* This control is used to adjust the needle on the face of the indicator to the most desirable sensitivity of movement. In operating this instrument as a radiocompass, turn on the master control while the engines are warming up, set the operation selector in the radiocompass position, carefully tune in your station, and set the indicator sensitivity control to about one-half its clockwise position. Then rotate the loop antenna until the visual indicator is centered, and note the loop azimuth control bearing. Next rotate the loop 30° off this bearing, either right or left, adjust the indicator sensitivity control until the needle of the indicator reads just (not more nor less than) full scale deflection, and reset the loop azimuth control to 0°. You are now ready to home on your station.

(5) *Visual Indicator.* Cloudy Joe thinks he knows all about this part of the radiocompass, which is located on the control panel of the plane. He says it is obvious that when the needle is centered, his plane is in line with the guiding station, and that when the needle is off center, the plane is out of line with the station. What Cloudy Joe does not know is that if you are headed *right* or *left* of a station AHEAD of you, the needle swings to the *right* or *left* respectively, but that if you are headed *right* or *left* of a station BEHIND you, the needle swings to the *left* or *right* respectively.

Another thing that Cloudy Joe does not know about the visual indicator is that, in homing on a station, you must first center the needle approximately, by swinging your plane to the proper heading, noting this heading by means of the magnetic compass, or gyro, and that you must then turn off the heading by 30° right or left (or rotate the loop, if it is the rotatable type). Hold the off-course heading until you have adjusted the course indicator sensitivity control so that the R-L indicator needle moves just off-scale. Then, and no sooner, you can bring your plane back to the proper heading by watching the R-L needle. Once you have adjusted the sensitivity of the needle, let your radiocompass controls alone until you change to some other station. The automatic volume control circuits will take care of any change in signal intensity as you approach and pass the station, and the needle will be smooth in operation and easy to follow.

(6) *Fixed Wire Radiobeacon Antenna.* The radiocompass, like any radiobeacon receiver, must have a fixed wire, non-directional antenna which may

be either a vertical mast or a horizontal T. Notice in the diagram that this particular radiocompass is equipped with a horizontal T-type antenna, and that the lead-in, rising vertically from the receiver, divides the horizontal wire at A so that L equals L_1.

(7) *Directional (Loop) Antenna.* A radiocompass is equipped with a directional loop antenna, which may be fixed or (like the one in the illustration) rotatable. This loop is encased in a streamlined housing. Since a loop cannot pick up signals approaching from right angles to the plane of the loop, all fixed loops must be mounted with the plane of the loop at right angles to the line of flight.

While the fixed-loop antenna is more commonly used than the rotatable type, you can see that the latter has certain definite advantages. It can be rotated through 360° without changing the heading of the plane. The only way you can take a bearing on a station off the line of flight with a fixed-loop-antenna type radiocompass is to swing the heading of your plane until the loop is in the proper position. With the rotatable loop, all you have to do is to turn the loop itself, holding in the meantime to whatever course you wish to fly. The fixed-loop antenna is also at a disadvantage during rain-snow static. To reduce the effect of this type of static with a fixed type of loop, you must switch the operation selector to the beacon-weather-loop position, and then fly a zigzag course 20° or more off heading from the radio station in order to get sufficient pick-up for usable aural signals.

Whenever the operation selector is set at the radiocompass position, the equipment utilizes both its loop and fixed-wire antenna. This selection cuts in a very high speed, wide amplitude, automatic volume-control circuit which makes it impossible to fly an aural radiobeacon course with this setting. You can receive radiobeacon signals aurally while you are using your visual indicator, but these signals should not be followed. You can, however, receive usable voice signals, such as weather reports and entertainment broadcasts, through your headphones, when you are using the visual indicator.

Whenever the operation selector is set in the beacon-weather-regular position, you automatically disconnect both the loop antenna and the visual indicator, thereby converting your set into a receiver operating on a fixed wire antenna *without* automatic volume control. If you are using a fixed wire antenna of the symmetrical T, or of the vertical mast type, your set will now function as a perfect radiobeacon receiver.

266

Whenever the operation selector is set in the beacon-weather-loop position, you automatically disconnect and ground the fixed wire antenna and disconnect the visual indicator with its associated circuits, so that the receiver portion of your set now operates on the loop antenna only. If the loop is in the proper position with respect to the station you wish to receive, your instrument will function satisfactorily as an aural radiobeacon receiver and will help to reduce rain-snow static.

(8) *Loop Rotating Unit.* This unit, like the visual indicator, is located on the control panel of the plane. It contains an azimuth scale, a pointer, and a train of gears, and is connected to the loop by means of a flexible control cable.

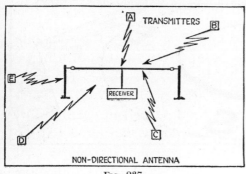

FIG. 237

FIG. 237. The non-directional antenna shown in this illustration is of the horizontal T-type. The horizontal antenna is the most practical, as a general rule, for aircraft radio. Remember that the T must be perfectly symmetrical, with the lead-in bisecting the horizontal wire and rising vertically from the receiver.

A good rule to remember in installing your radio equipment is this: *A receiver is no better than its ears.* Cloudy Joe says that the best antenna installer he knows is his brother, who has a good supply of wire and whose prices are rock-bottom. Yet Cloudy Joe cannot figure out why he gets such poor results from good radio equipment. I don't need to tell you that the installation of even the simplest fixed-wire antenna should be done by a specialist in the installation and maintenance of *aircraft* radio. Another thing—be sure to check your antenna installation and receiver carefully during contact flights for course width, course ambiguities, cones of silence, etc., before you try flying on instruments.

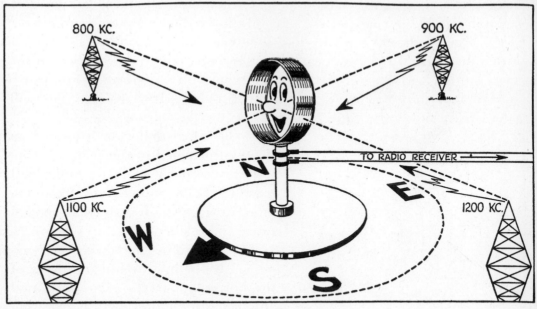

FIG. 238

FIG. 238. As you already know, one of the characteristics of a loop antenna is that it cannot receive signals approaching from right angles to the plane of the loop. The loop shown here cannot in its present position pick up signals from the 900 kc. or 1100 kc. transmitting stations, even though the receiver is tuned to these stations. To get the stations, the loop must be swung into their plane—either by turning the loop, if it is of the rotating type, or by changing the heading of the plane, if the loop is fixed. Signals from a transmitting station will be heard with diminishing intensity as soon as the plane of the loop deviates from a right-angle position in relation to the station; signals will be heard with maximum intensity when the plane of the loop lies in the plane of the station. In this illustration, signals from the 800 kc. and the 1200 kc. stations will be received at maximum intensity if the loop is connected with a receiver tuned to the proper frequencies.

FIG. 239. As I mentioned before, your plane is heading toward the station to which your radiocompass is tuned when the needle of the visual indicator is centered. But it takes detective work to find out whether the station is ahead of you or behind you. If the needle comes to center position when you tune your radiocompass on a homing station, give your plane right rudder.

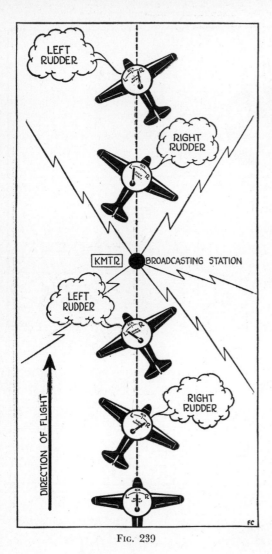

FIG. 239

The needle will swing to the right if the station lies AHEAD; to the left if the station lies BEHIND. Or, if you give the plane left rudder, the needle will swing to the left if the station lies AHEAD, and to the right if the station lies BEHIND.

If the needle is already off center to the left, right rudder will bring it back toward center if the station lies AHEAD, and still further to the left if the station lies BEHIND.

If the needle is already off center to the right, left rudder will bring it back toward center if the station lies AHEAD, or still further to the left if the station lies BEHIND.

Aircraft receivers and radio compasses are sensitive instruments and you must not expect them to maintain their adjustment indefinitely. Give them periodic check-ups and inspections, preferably at the same time you are having your engine checked or overhauled. Have this work done by some one who is thoroughly experienced in aircraft radio work, and particularly in the type of apparatus you own. Aircraft radio service stations are established all over the country, and you are sure to find one at almost any major airport. It costs comparatively little to have an efficient check-up of your radio apparatus, and this precaution pays big dividends in safety. Don't wait until something in your set breaks while you are in the overcast before you think about having this work done.

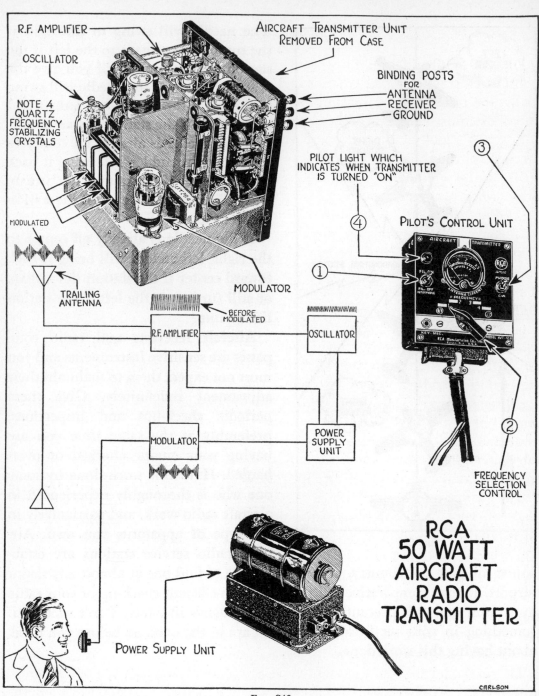

R.F. AMPLIFIER

OSCILLATOR

NOTE 4 QUARTZ FREQUENCY STABILIZING CRYSTALS

MODULATED

TRAILING ANTENNA

AIRCRAFT TRANSMITTER UNIT REMOVED FROM CASE

BINDING POSTS FOR
ANTENNA
RECEIVER
GROUND

PILOT LIGHT WHICH INDICATES WHEN TRANSMITTER IS TURNED "ON"

Pilot's Control Unit

MODULATOR

R.F. AMPLIFIER

BEFORE MODULATED

OSCILLATOR

MODULATOR

POWER SUPPLY UNIT

FREQUENCY SELECTION CONTROL

POWER SUPPLY UNIT

RCA 50 WATT AIRCRAFT RADIO TRANSMITTER

CARLSON

FIG. 240

FIG. 240. Offhand, this illustration will probably give you the idea that a transmitter is much more complicated than a receiver or radiocompass. Actually, the transmitter is the simplest of the three instruments to operate; it only looks more complicated here because I have taken you behind the scenes.

First, let's look at the various parts shown on the pilot's control unit at the right of the illustration:

(1) *Master Filament Control Switch.* This should be turned to the ON position when you start your engines, and left on until you stop your engines.

(2) *Frequency Selector Switch.* After turning the transmitter on, set the frequency selector switch at the frequency you wish to use and press the microphone control button whenever you wish to talk.

(3) *Emission Control Switch.* If your transmitter is equipped for telegraph transmission, throw the emission switch to the CW position before you use the telegraph key.

(4) *Pilot Lamp.* All transmitters are equipped with pilot lamps which light when the master filament control switch is on, just so that Cloudy Joe won't forget to turn the transmitter off before cutting his engine or try to send out messages, either by voice or key, while the instrument is off.

Antenna Current Indicator. On the final flight tuning of your transmitter, watch this indicator to see what current your transmitter puts out on each frequency, and make a note of this information. Whenever you notice on subsequent flights that your transmitter shows less than its normal output on any of its frequencies, have your equipment serviced by a reliable agency.

The power-supply unit shown at the bottom of the illustration supplies power to the oscillator, modulator and amplifier. When you speak into a microphone, the sound waves you set up are first amplified, then superimposed in the oscillator circuit on the radio frequency energy. This energy is then further amplified and placed on the radiating system.

Aircraft Transmitter Antennae. The whole subject of aircraft transmitter antennae is so highly technical that a detailed discussion would leave Cloudy Joe completely bewildered. But there are a few facts about antennae which even he should know, and here they are:

The most practical and efficient type for general purposes is a retractable, unweighted, trailing antenna with one-quarter or three-quarter wave length

271

for the frequency or frequencies being used. A flexible wire antenna, about 100 feet long, is coiled around a reel built of insulated materials, and located inside the aircraft. This wire, on the end of which is a linen or rubber sock, reels in and out of the plane through an insulated fairlead projecting through the plane's skin. As the wire unreels, the sock provides enough drag to pull the wire out and to keep it straight astern during flight. The length of wire ejected depends upon the frequency used and the initial tuning of the transmitter. The wire is never ejected except in flight.

On some reel antennae, the reel is located in the extreme tail of the plane, and is connected by a mechanical shaft to a control unit in the cockpit. Other reel antennae have the reel mounted in the cockpit within arm's reach of the operator. This type is much less expensive, but more difficult to install, since the wire must first be run up and out through a fairlead located in the top skin, then back to the stern through an insulated bushing on top of the rudder hinge post. The sock, of course, is fastened to the wire beyond the stern fitting. Regardless of the type of transmitter antenna you use, you will need a T or mast antenna for radiobeacon receiver operation. If you have a reel antenna, you can probably arrange to have a remote, electrically operated switch and load coils installed so that when your plane is on the ground with the trailing antenna reeled in, you can switch your transmitter over to the receiver T antenna. This allows you to get the maximum of transmitter efficiency both on the ground and in the air.

Each aircraft has its own peculiar problems in transmitter and receiver antenna installations. Don't try to solve these problems yourself, and don't let Cloudy Joe's brother handle the installations for you. First, read the manufacturer's instruction book and find out what type of antenna he recommends for your particular set. Then—follow his instructions, but turn the actual installation over to a radio installation agency. Another point to remember: The range of your transmitter depends upon the electrical efficiency of the antenna, and a small difference in required length may make the difference between a twenty-to-thirty-mile and a hundred to two-hundred-mile range. Be sure to keep a record of the exact number of turns it takes to unreel the amount of wire needed for each of your operating frequencies.

An unweighted, trailing antenna of the tiller-rope type is also commonly used on aircraft transmitters but is less efficient than the type I have just de-

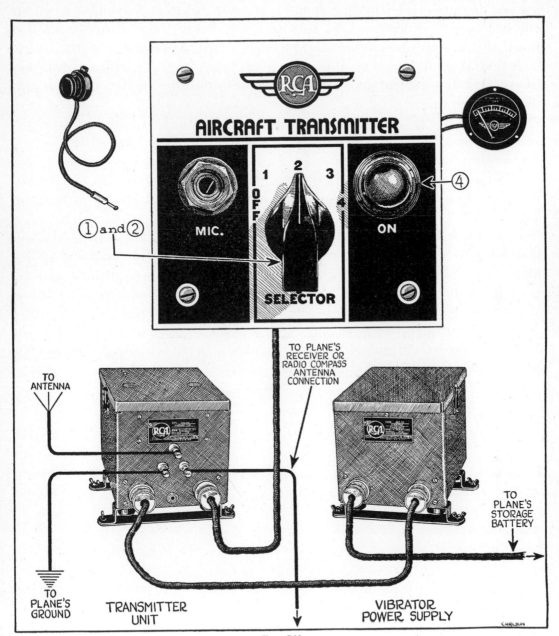

FIG. 241

273

scribed because of its limited length. If your plane is equipped with the tiller-rope type of antenna, be sure to check before every flight to see that none of the length was lost on the preceding trip. Any change in the length of this kind of antenna is critical and will seriously interfere with the efficiency of your set. If you want good results, be sure to install a good, retractable reel antenna system.

Before it can give satisfactory results, your transmitter must be carefully tuned when it is installed on your plane for the first time. Some of this tuning can be done on the ground, but the final tuning must always be done in the air. No matter how fine a transmitter you have, you cannot get full output nor the results the designer built into it unless the final tuning is made in flight.

FIG. 241. A 20-watt transmitter such as the one shown here has its filament control switch (1) and selector switch (2) combined, and is operated in the same way as the 50-watt transmitter except that it is not equipped with an emission control switch (No. 3 in Fig. 240) for telegraphic-key operation. There is very little difference in the range of a 20-watt and the range of a 50-watt transmitter when both are operated on an efficient antenna, but the increased power output of the latter makes it more reliable during adverse weather conditions.

*A good radio carelessly installed is like
a fine violin poorly tuned.*

274

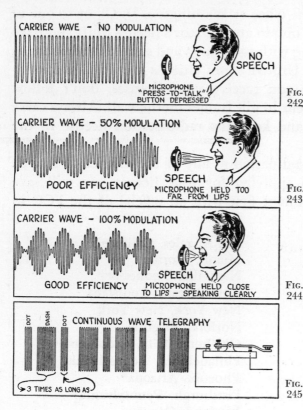

CARRIER WAVE - NO MODULATION

MICROPHONE "PRESS-TO-TALK" BUTTON DEPRESSED

NO SPEECH

FIG. 242

CARRIER WAVE - 50% MODULATION

POOR EFFICIENCY

SPEECH

MICROPHONE HELD TOO FAR FROM LIPS

FIG. 243

CARRIER WAVE - 100% MODULATION

GOOD EFFICIENCY

SPEECH

MICROPHONE HELD CLOSE TO LIPS - SPEAKING CLEARLY

FIG. 244

DOT DASH DOT CONTINUOUS WAVE TELEGRAPHY

3 TIMES AS LONG AS

FIG. 245

FIGS. 242 TO 245. As soon as your microphone "press to talk" button is depressed, your transmitter starts sending out unmodulated carrier waves. These waves are modulated, as shown in Figs. 243 and 244, as soon as you start to speak. Waves emitted by a telegraph key are unmodulated, as shown in Fig. 245.

A receiver, you will remember, is no better than its (or your) ears. A transmitter is no better than the voice that goes into it. Aircraft anti-noise microphones modulate carrier waves only when the diaphragm of the microphone is subject to certain voice pressures. Be sure to hold an aircraft microphone *within one-half inch or less of your lips.* Speak in a normal tone (don't shout) and *speak directly into the microphone,* not across or sidewise to it. One more hint: Don't tip the microphone; hold it in an upright position. Cloudy Joe thinks that the louder he yells into the mike, the farther his voice will carry. That is why no one on the receiving end can ever tell what Cloudy Joe is talking about.

While you may operate a radio receiver or a radiocompass without a Federal license, as soon as you convert your plane into a mobile radio station by installing a transmitter, you will need both a Federal operator's license and a radio station license. To obtain the latter, send in a written application on a special form provided by the Federal Communications Commission at Washington, D. C. This application must include full details—technical data, etc.—about the transmitter you intend to use. (The technical information is usually furnished with your set.) After your application has been reviewed and accepted, you will receive a radio station license for your plane.

You must also apply to the FCC for your *operator's license,* submitting your application either to the main office at Washington, D. C., or to one of the branch offices. But you cannot obtain an operator's license until you have passed a written examination dealing with radio laws and simple fundamentals of radio theory. (Incidentally, only United States citizens are eligible for station and operator licenses.) Once you receive your licenses, don't follow Cloudy Joe's example and hang them in gilt frames on the wall. Always carry your operator's license with you, and keep the radio station license in the plane itself.

You can take your operator's examination at any of the district or branch offices of the FCC listed below. In applying for your license you will save time by making a definite appointment first with an official of the FCC in the office nearest you.

Albuquerque, New Mexico*	Los Angeles, California
Atlanta, Georgia	Miami, Florida
Baltimore, Maryland	Nashville, Tennessee†
Billings, Montana*	New Orleans, Louisiana
Bismarck, North Dakota*	New York, New York
Boise, Idaho*	Norfolk, Virginia
Boston, Massachusetts	Oklahoma City, Oklahoma†
Buffalo, New York	Philadelphia, Pennsylvania
Butte, Montana*	Phoenix, Arizona*
Chicago, Illinois	Pittsburgh, Pennsylvania†
Cincinnati, Ohio†	Portland, Oregon
Cleveland, Ohio†	St. Louis, Missouri†
Columbus, Ohio†	St. Paul, Minnesota
Dallas, Texas	Salt Lake City, Utah*
Denver, Colorado	San Antonio, Texas†
Des Moines, Iowa†	San Francsico, California
Detroit, Michigan	San Juan, Puerto Rico
Galveston, Texas	Schenectady, New York†
Honolulu, Territory of Hawaii	Seattle, Washington
Jacksonville, Florida*	Spokane, Washington*
Kansas City, Missouri	Winston-Salem, North Carolina†
Little Rock, Arkansas*	

Never operate a transmitter unless you hold a qualified Federal radio operator's license; and before you apply for your operator's license, be sure to get a copy of the FCC Rules and Regulations from the Superintendent of

* Examinations held not oftener than twice a year.
† Examinations held quarterly.

276

Documents, United States Government Printing Office, Washington, D. C. Study these regulations until you are thoroughly familiar with them, and keep them for reference. You will find that they answer a number of difficult questions, and that they can save you money and trouble. There is a $10,000 fine, a jail term of not over two years, or both, for violating the provisions of the Communications Act of 1934—and these penalties apply to each offense. Not only that, but the operator's license is subject to suspension for two years, and the station license can be revoked. For violating any of the regulations of the FCC, there is a fine of not over $500 for each day on which the offense is committed.

Your operator's license gives you the right to operate any aircraft radio station within the class of your license. For all practical purposes, you will find that a third-class telephone license is all you need. Fortunately this type of license is so easy to get that Cloudy Joe already has his.

Flying the radio beams without dead reckoning may turn out to be like driving into a dead-end street.

XXIV

AIRWAY RADIO FLYING AND ORIENTATION

WHEN you fly along or across Federal airways, or use the facilities of a controlled airport in other than the best of weather, you are almost as rigidly bound by traffic regulations as the engineer of a train. You cannot take off until your flight plan has been approved by a Federal Airways traffic-control office. Both at the airport and within a 30-mile radius of your point of departure, or destination, you are under the jurisdiction of the traffic-control officer for a controlled airport.

Your obligations to the authorities begin before you taxi out onto the field. If your plane is equipped with a transmitter, call the traffic-control office and give him your flight plan, your name, the make and type of plane you are flying, and its cruising speed. Tell him the hangar where you are warming up, the time you wish to leave, your destination, the altitude at which you wish to fly, and the time (expressed in local standard time on the 24 hour scale) you expect to arrive at your destination. The airport control officer will relay your flight plan to a Federal Airways traffic-control officer, get his approval or instructions, and give you full taxi-ing and take-off instructions.

Before you call the traffic control officer, be sure to:

(1) Turn on the master controls of the receiver and transmitter when you start warming up your engines.

(2) Set the receiver in the beacon-weather-band position; check to see that the noise limiter switch is in the OFF position; adjust the headphone volume control to one-half or three-quarters of its total movement; plug in the headphones and tune the receiver to 278 kc. If, after a reasonable time, you have not heard the traffic-control signals, rotate the tuning control slightly to each side of the 278 kc. position. Your receiver dial calibration may be slightly off, and in this way you can pick up the traffic station as it operates for other aircraft.

(3) Check your transmitter, if it is of the multiple-frequency type, to see that

the frequency selector is in the proper position. If your transmitter is of the telephone-telegraph type, also check to see that the emission selector switch is in the TELEPHONE position, and that the microphone is plugged in. Now press the microphone button and call the traffic-control officer— "Cloudy Joe—NC1900, calling WREE, NEWARK."

If you are operating a plane equipped only with a receiver, your procedure, of course, is different. Notify the traffic-control officer in advance (in person or by telephone) of your flight plan and get it approved. Then follow the instructions in (1) and (2) above, and taxi slowly onto the field. (If you are using a radiocompass instead of a receiver, set the operation selector switch in its beacon-weather-regular position and follow the usual procedure for a receiver.)

As you taxi onto the field, listen for the traffic-control signals, and be ready to readjust your volume control so that you don't miss instructions. The traffic officer will call you by the make or type of your plane—"Hello, 'Cub,' " (or Fairchild, Stinson, etc.) If you hear me, wiggle your rudder." As soon as you have complied, you will receive full take-off instructions. Here again be ready to readjust your volume control so that you won't miss what is being said to you. Since you are under the traffic-control officer's supervision within a 30-mile radius of the airport, keep your receiver tuned to 278 kc. until you have passed beyond that distance or until the traffic officer is satisfied that you are clear of all traffic in his area and has signed you off.

From now on, until you are within 30 miles of your landing field, you are under the eye of the Federal Government. Not only has the Federal traffic-control officer verified the safety of your flight plan, but he has sent out a teletype message advising all points along your route of your flight plan. This "movement report," commonly called a PX, is entered on the records of each station, is compared with all other current PX reports for possible conflict in safety of movement, and is finally cleared upon your arrival at your destination. During the course of your flight, you must keep these stations advised— if you have a transmitter—of the progress you are making, so that accurate record can be kept of your ground speed.

Every plane equipped with a transmitter and flying over an established airway is also required to report when cruising altitude is reached or left. (You can see for yourself how important this is when weather conditions are poor or when you are flying on instruments.) Suppose, for example, that you are flying from Newark to Washington at a cruising altitude of 6000 feet, and that you reach this altitude and level off within 30 miles of your home field. Call the field at once, giving the place and the time at which you have leveled off. (In all messages including time, use the 0000-2400 scale and standard time.) As soon as you are within communicating distance of the Washington airport, call the airport and ask for permission to let down from 6000 feet, giving time and place, preparatory to landing at Washington. After the safety of this movement has been verified by the Washington airport, you will be given permission to let down. When you are near enough to the Washington airport for the traffic-control officer to see you, he will give you detailed landing instructions. Incidentally, be sure to keep your kollsman altimeter set or adjusted to sea-level reference and to report indicated sea-level altitudes only.

The control officer continues to give you taxi-ing instructions until you reach the hangar. He then files a message with the Federal Airways traffic-control officer, telling him of your safe arrival at a given time. The message is relayed back along the route to Newark by teletype, and your PX is cleared from the records, officially completing your flight.

If you are flying without a transmitter, you must immediately report your arrival personally to the Federal Airways traffic control officer in order to have your PX cleared. If you don't, all sorts of telegrams and telephone calls may be sent out in an effort to find you. This is not only embarrassing and expensive for you, but it also gets you into disfavor with the authorities. Cloudy Joe, who invariably forgets to show his mug at the end of a trip, is always in disgrace, and broke from paying for telegrams and telephone calls made at his expense.

In flying a plane equipped with a transmitter over established airways, communicate with the stations along the route, and keep them fully advised of your progress, your altitude, and your destination. These messages will be acknowledged and relayed by teletype to the other stations along the route. In this way an accurate check is kept of your ground speed and calculations about your flight progress can be corrected if necessary.

If your plane is not equipped with a transmitter, the stations along the route will keep an eye out for you, and report your passage over the airport if you are seen.

Be sure to know the Civil Air Regulations before you fly the Federal Air-

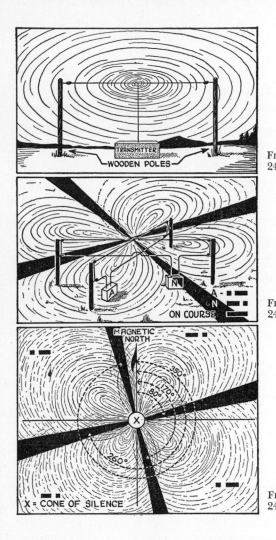

FIG. 246

FIG. 247

FIG. 248

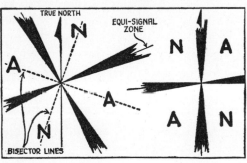

FIG. 249

ways in any except CAVU (ceiling and visibility unlimited) weather. These regulations require two-way radio—a receiver or radiocompass, and a transmitter—on practically every kind of flight except those made in good weather. From these same regulations you will also be able to get the details of the required radio operation as well as of flight procedures.

FIG. 246. The antenna which most broadcasting stations and some marker beacon stations use is non-directional and emits waves in a circular pattern.

FIG. 247. Radio range stations—the stations which pave the airways with radio beams—use two intersecting, loop, or equivalent antennae which set up a wave pattern as shown in the illustration. Over one of these antennae, the code letter $A(.—)$ interrupted about every half minute by a station-identification letter, is sent out by a mechanical arrangement; over the other is broadcast the code letter N (—.), also interrupted by station identification.

As a result of the wave pattern set up by the loop antennae, the letter A predominates in two diagonally opposite sectors, and the letter N in the other two. In four definite sectors, extending outward from the station like beams of light, the two code letters merge into a steady monotone or hum,

281

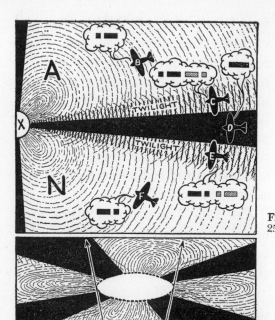

Fig. 250

Fig. 251

interrupted every half minute by *two station identification signals of equal intensity*. This steady hum, or long dash, is the "on-course" signal.

Fig. 248. The angles at which radio beams cross each other depend upon the nature of the terrain and the routes to be covered. These angles are determined by radio engineers at the time the beacon station is constructed. Whatever the geographical location of the beams, all sectional charts give the bearing of the beams *toward* the station and with reference to the *magnetic* north. The beams shown here have magnetic bearings of 80°, 170°, 260°, and 350° respectively. The reciprocals of these beams, found by adding 180°, are 260°, 350°, 80° and 170°. It is the reciprocals which are shown on aeronautical charts.

Notice that at the center of the beams, directly over the transmitting station, there is a *cone of silence* where no signals are heard. If the radio waves sent out by a station did not form a fountain-like pattern (remember Fig. 223?), this cone of silence would not exist and Cloudy Joe would never know when he was passing over the station.

Fig. 249. Whenever two adjacent radio beams extend to the east and west of the true north, the sector between them—and its diagonally opposite sector—are *N* quadrants. If one of the beams lies in line with the true north, the sector to the west—and its diagonally opposite sector—are always *N* quadrants. This arrangement, as you will see later, is a great help when it comes to finding yourself in the air, and in steering a path to the nearest radio beam. The dotted lines which bisect the angles between the beams are also important when it comes to finding your way through the overcast.

Fig. 250. Along the edges of each radio beam lies a twilight zone in which the *A* and *N* signals are heard alternately, but with unequal strength. When the twilight zone lies next to an *A* quadrant, the *A* and its station identification signal predominate, as shown by the airplane *C*. When the zone lies next to an *N* quadrant, the *N* and its station identification letter predominate, as shown by the airplane *E*. Now suppose you are flying in a twilight zone. You hear both the *A* and *N* signals and two station identification signals, one louder than the other. If the weaker of these two station signals begins to grow stronger, it is a sure indication that you are headed toward the nearest on-course beam where both station signals are heard with equal intensity. If the weaker of the two signals continues to grow weaker, then you know you are headed away from the on-course. By the time he tries to blaze a path through the overcast, Cloudy Joe will have forgotten this point, but, as you will find for yourself, it is a help when it comes to figuring out where you are going.

In the illustration, notice that planes *B* and *F* have left the twilight zone and are now receiving just one set of signals—the *A* and *N* (with their station identification) respectively.

Fig. 251. The cone of silence extends vertically above the transmitting station, its area increasing with altitude. Just before you enter this zone, the signals definitely increase in volume. As you leave the zone, the signals reappear, again in a sudden burst of volume, and then gradually diminish as you leave the station behind. Be sure to keep your receiver volume at minimum, and to keep exactly on-course as you approach the station; otherwise the signals will not fade out completely.

In flying, expecting the unexpected
sometimes saves you a lot of worry.

283

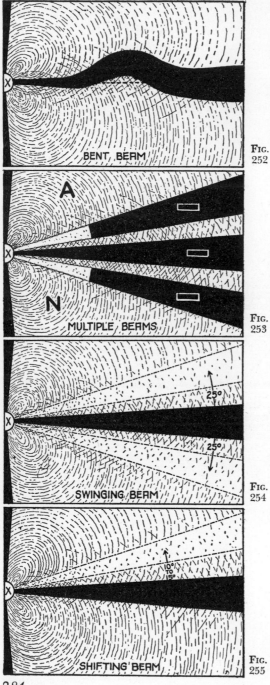

FIG. 252

FIG. 253

FIG. 254

FIG. 255

BENT BEAM

MULTIPLE BEAMS

SWINGING BEAM

SHIFTING BEAM

FIGS. 252 TO 255. Radio beams are approximately 50 feet wide near the station, and seven miles wide a hundred miles from the station, where the signals finally disappear. To cover this range you must have the proper antenna installation. Theoretically, these beams are straight, single, undeviating paths, but just so that flying through the overcast won't be too easy for you, the beams occasionally act up. Mountains, large bodies of water or mineral deposits can bend a beam or break it up into several beams. You can detect a multiple beam, as you fly across it, by the fact that you go from an on-course zone into an *A* or *N* sector, back into an on-course, then into the *N* or *A* sector, without passing through any twilight zones. At sunrise or sunset, a beam may occasionally start to oscillate; or it may shift its position by 10° to 15°, hold its new position for awhile, and then return to its original position. Bends are generally small, but in mountainous country you may find it necessary to change your compass heading as much as 45° to stay on course.

Nothing makes Cloudy Joe more panicky than to lose a radio beam even for a minute. He forgets all about his magnetic compass and his gyro, but I expect you to hold your course by these instruments long enough to find out whether you have

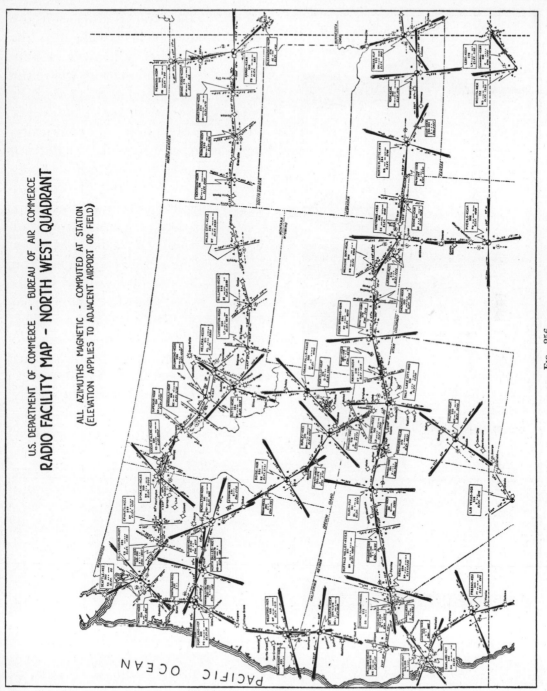

U.S. DEPARTMENT OF COMMERCE - BUREAU OF AIR COMMERCE

RADIO FACILITY MAP - NORTH WEST QUADRANT

ALL AZIMUTHS MAGNETIC - COMPUTED AT STATION
(ELEVATION APPLIES TO ADJACENT AIRPORT OR FIELD)

PACIFIC OCEAN

Fig. 256

285

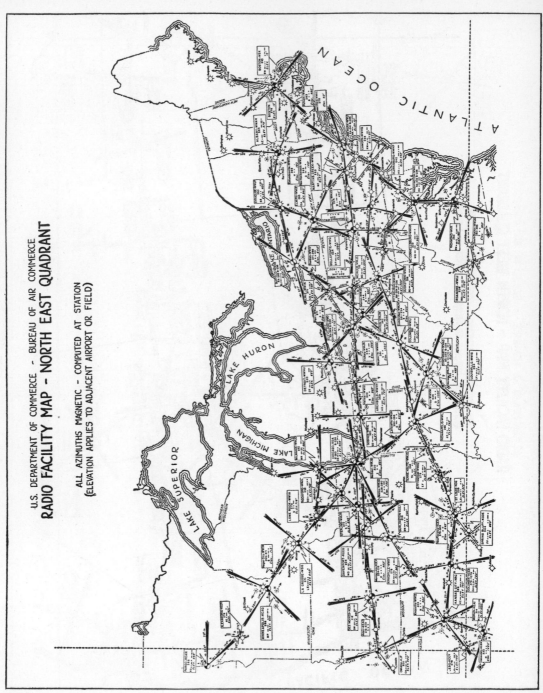

U.S. DEPARTMENT OF COMMERCE - BUREAU OF AIR COMMERCE
RADIO FACILITY MAP - NORTH EAST QUADRANT

ALL AZIMUTHS MAGNETIC - COMPUTED AT STATION
(ELEVATION APPLIES TO ADJACENT AIRPORT OR FIELD)

Fig. 257

286

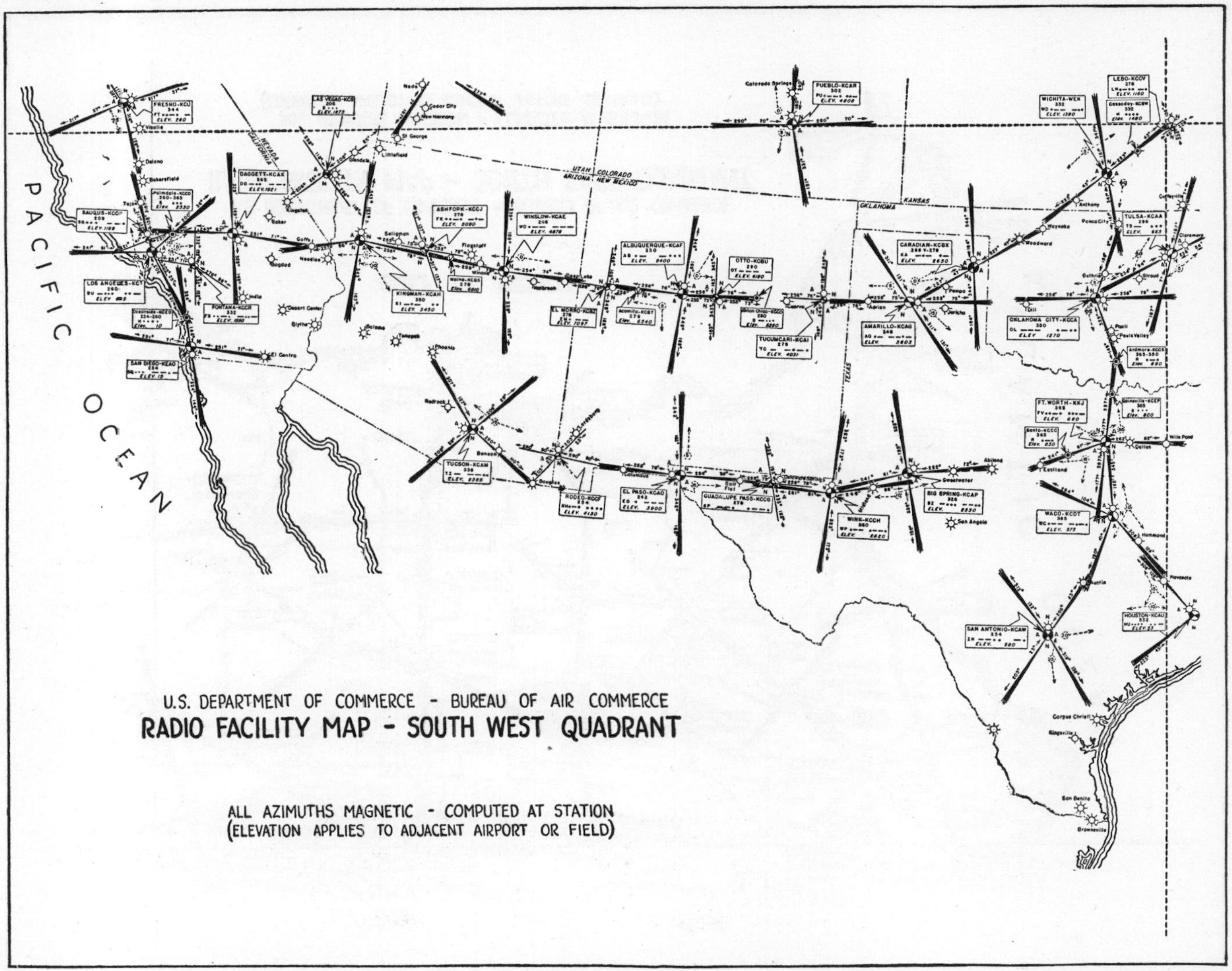
U.S. DEPARTMENT OF COMMERCE - BUREAU OF AIR COMMERCE
RADIO FACILITY MAP - SOUTH WEST QUADRANT
ALL AZIMUTHS MAGNETIC - COMPUTED AT STATION
(ELEVATION APPLIES TO ADJACENT AIRPORT OR FIELD)
PACIFIC OCEAN
UTAH COLORADO
ARIZONA NEW MEXICO
OKLAHOMA
KANSAS
TEXAS

FIG. 258

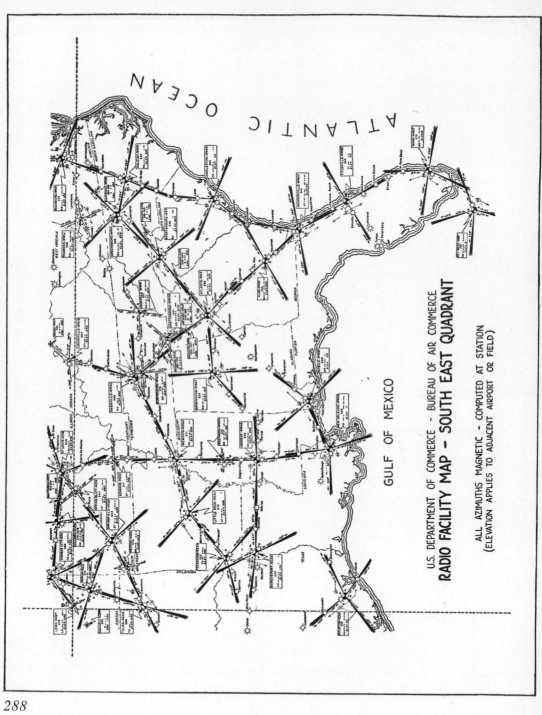

GULF OF MEXICO

U.S. DEPARTMENT OF COMMERCE - BUREAU OF AIR COMMERCE
RADIO FACILITY MAP - SOUTH EAST QUADRANT

ALL AZIMUTHS MAGNETIC - COMPUTED AT STATION
(ELEVATION APPLIES TO ADJACENT AIRPORT OR FIELD)

Fig. 259

really lost the beam, or whether the beam itself has merely gone off on a temporary spree. I expect you to do even more—to sit down before you start on a trip, and study the characteristics of the beams you are going to use. Find out all their peculiarities while you are still on the ground, or during contact flight in good weather.

FIGS. 256 TO 259. These maps show how completely the United States is covered with radio-beam highways. In addition to the main radio range stations, there are also marker beacon stations located at the intersection of two radio ranges, or at prominent landmarks. These stations send out a code letter about every 10 seconds when the ceiling is limited and visibility is under two miles.

The marker beacons, which have a limited range (three to ten miles) broadcast on the same frequencies as the adjacent radio range stations. As you approach the limits of one range, you automatically pick up the signal of the marker beacon without retuning and, unless you are like Cloudy Joe and ignore its warning, you tune at once to the next radio range. This type of radio marker beacon serves as an additional means of checking your position in the same way that a visual object on the ground serves as a check during contact flight.

Cloudy Joe is working out a way to hang green lights and install bell buoys along radio beams, but until he gets his invention patented, I am afraid you will have to depend upon some other method, when you fly radio beams, to keep from getting lost or to find yourself once you are lost.

Precautions against getting lost begin on the ground. *Plot your course, first for dead reckoning; never* plan to depend solely upon radio beams to get you anywhere. Something may happen to the transmitting apparatus of the range station. Something may happen to your own receiver equipment. Heavy static may make it impossible to receive beacon signals. First and last, radio beams are an aid to, never a substitute for, dead reckoning. After you have plotted your course by dead reckoning, study the air map of the territory over which you are going to fly. Learn everything there is to learn about the habits—good or bad—of the beams you intend to use, *before you leave the ground.* Make up problems in orientation and solve them on paper by the methods shown later. Then practise the maneuvers in contact flying, and train your ear to detect slight variations in the volume of signals. The more you practise downstairs on paper, and the more you practise upstairs in good

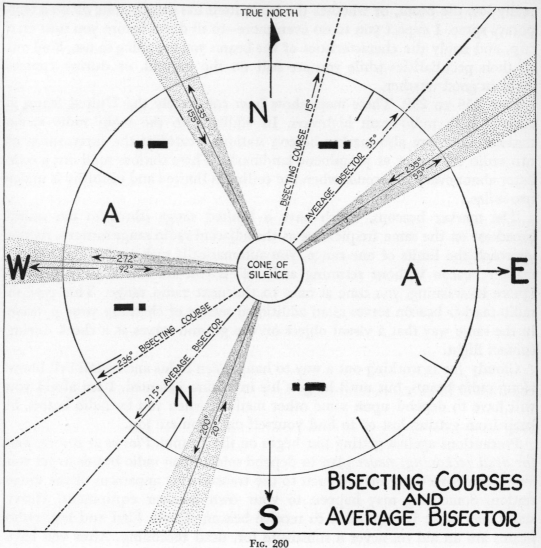

FIG. 260

BISECTING COURSES
AND
AVERAGE BISECTOR

weather, the more accurately will you be able to fly the radio beams in bad weather.

FIG. 260. *Bisecting Course and Average Bisector*. Not only must you take every precaution against getting lost, before you leave the ground, but you must also provide for finding yourself if you should get lost. This is done by establishing, in advance, a definite reference line for each quadrant of each radio range you plan to use.

Let's begin by finding this reference line for the N quadrants of the radio range shown in Fig. 260. If these two quadrants were equal you could establish this line merely by bisecting the two angles. But since the angles are unequal, you must find a reference line which can be used in either quadrant. First bisect each of the quadrants. Then take 15°, the bisecting course of the north N quadrant; add 56° (the reciprocal of the 236° bisecting course), and divide by two. The answer is 35½°, or, for our purpose, 35°. Now measure off 35°, and its reciprocal, 215°, from the true north. The two courses established at these points are the average bisectors of the N quadrants. You can also establish these *average* bisectors, once you have bisected the angles, by laying a straight-edge across the map and using a compass rose. Average bisectors for the A quadrants are found in the same way.

In locating the average bisectors there are several points to remember: (1) If both of the A quadrants and both of the N quadrants are equal, the bisecting courses and the average bisectors will fall on the same line; if the beams are laid out in such a way that the various quadrants are unequal, then the bisecting courses and the average bisectors will not lie along the same line. (2) Average bisectors are figured to the nearest 5°, with 31½° becoming 30°, and 33° becoming 35°. (3) Average bisectors must be determined in advance for the radio ranges you are going to fly. (4) The more you practise establishing these reference lines, the more proficient you will become.

A shoemaker who has sewed thousands of shoes is not necessarily a craftsman, neither is a flyer an airman who has flown a lot only around his home town.

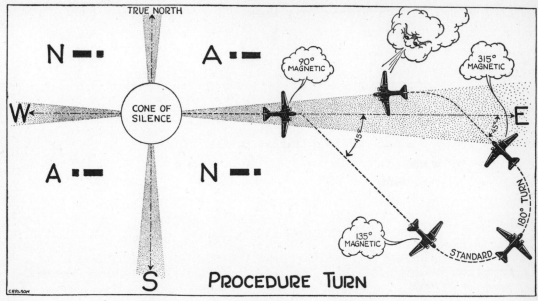

FIG. 261

FIG. 261. This diagram of a procedure turn—the kind of turn you will need to make in radio beam flying—almost explains itself. The first part of the turn is usually executed at 45° from your original heading (in this case 90°). After flying the new heading for a minute and a half, make a 180° standard turn which, in this case, brings you to a 315° heading and across the beam at a 45° angle. Fly to the far edge of the beam, then turn and fly along the edge of the beam. The procedure used in making these turns is always the same, regardless of your original magnetic heading.

FIG. 262. *The 90° Method of Orientation.* Let's assume that you are flying a radio range where the beams cross at right angles, and that you are receiving both the *A* and the *N* signals, the latter more faintly than the former. While you know that you are in a twilight zone bordering on an *A* quadrant, and you know the identity of the radio range, you are, nevertheless, lost. And lost you will stay until you have identified the radio range station and determined which of the two *A* quadrants you are in, and until you have picked up an on-course signal.

Your one reference is the average bisector for the *A* quadrants, which you have already established at 107° and its reciprocal, 287°. By adopting a head-

292

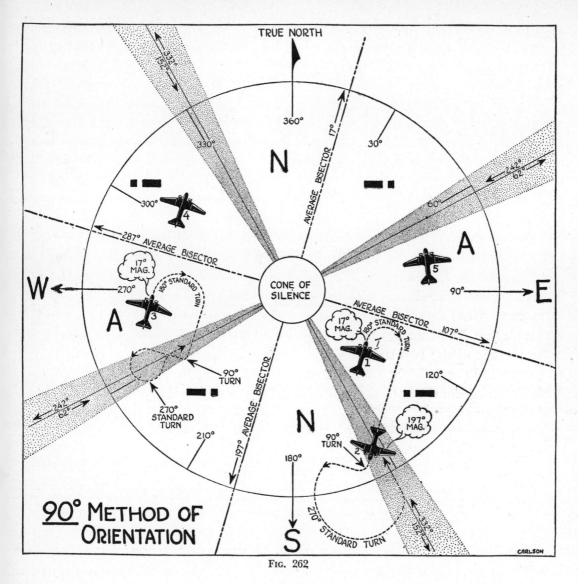

TRUE NORTH

332°
152°

360°

17°
AVERAGE BISECTOR

30°

242°
62°

N

60°

300°

4

A

287° AVERAGE BISECTOR

5

17°
MAG.

W

270°

180° STANDARD TURN

CONE OF
SILENCE

90°

E

AVERAGE BISECTOR

107°

A

3

17°
MAG.

180° STANDARD TURN

90°
TURN

1

120°

270°
STANDARD
TURN

242°
62°

210°

197° AVERAGE BISECTOR

197°
MAG.

N

90°
TURN

2

180°

270° STANDARD TURN

332°
152°

S

90° METHOD OF ORIENTATION

CARLSON

FIG. 262

ing of 17° magnetic—that is, a heading perpendicular to the bisector, you
know at once that you are flying away from the southeast or southwest radio
beam. (Study the illustration, and you will see why.) Fly the 17° heading
for several minutes, without adjusting your volume control in any way, listening carefully to the relative intensity of the two station signals. If the weak
signal continues to grow weaker, you know you are flying away from the

293

nearest on-course zone. Your next step, then, is to make a 180° standard turn, following your new course until you reach and cross the radio beam. As soon as you hear the *N* signal on the other side of the beam, make a 90° right turn and then, at last, you will know which beam you have crossed. How? If the turn takes you back into the beam, you are in the southwest leg. If it takes you still further into the *N* sector, you are near the southeast beam. If the turn has taken you back into the beam, hold your course until you have again crossed the beam and heard the *A* signal. Then make a standard 270° turn back to the far edge of the beam, complete the turn, and follow the beam to the station. In other words, maneuver your plane as shown by the dotted line for the No. 3 plane in the illustration.

If, however, your 90° turn takes you into the *N* sector, hold the course a few seconds, then make your standard 270° turn back into the beam and straighten out for the range station.

The procedure I have just described applies when you find yourself flying away from the nearest radio beam. If, as shown by the No. 4 and No. 5 planes, you find that you are flying toward the nearest radio beam—that is, if the weaker of the two station signals grows stronger—or if you find that you are outside the twilight zone, set your course at right angles to the average bisector and continue to fly until you cross one of the beams. At the far side of the beam, make your 90° turn to the right. Again, the turn will either bring you back into the beam or take you into the *N* quadrant, and you complete the maneuver as shown by the No. 3 or No. 2 plane.

This method, known as the 90° orientation method, gives you a relative position with reference to two beams as soon as you fly at right angles to the average bisector, and gives you a relative position with reference to a definite beam as soon as the beam is crossed and the 90° turn is made.

Now that I have shown you the basis for the 90° method of orientation, get out your pencil and practise orienting yourself from various positions in the *N* quadrants.

FIG. 263. *Fade-out Method of Orientation.* The 90° method of finding yourself is more practical in some cases, particularly when the beams cross at—or nearly at—right angles, than it is in other cases such as the one shown here. You can see for yourself that if you were well out in the east *A* quadrant, you would have to fly a great distance before picking up one of the beams

294

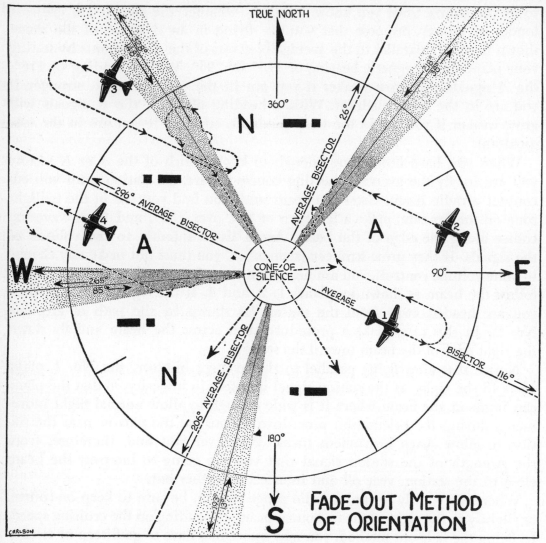

FIG. 263

and even then might not pick one up at all. So let's figure out another way for getting your bearings.

Begin by flying the average bisector, or a course parallel to it, and listen carefully to the volume of the *A* or *N* signal. Set the volume down as low as you can without losing the signal, so that you can detect the slightest variation in volume—and *then do not touch the volume control again.* Continue to fly the course until you know definitely whether the signals are growing louder or fainter. Suppose that you are flying in an *A* sector of the range shown here. Fly parallel to the average bisectors of the *A* quadrants by setting your plane on a magnetic bearing of 116° or 296°. With a heading of 116°, the *A* signals will grow weaker if you are in the east quadrant, stronger if you are in the west quadrant. With a heading of 296°, the *A* signals will grow weaker if you are in the west quadrant, stronger if you are in the east quadrant.

When you have flown long enough to know which of the *A* or *N* sectors you are in, fly the average bisecting course toward the station until you encounter a radio beam. Cross the beam until you find yourself in the twilight zone on the far side, make a left turn of not over 180°, and fly a wavering course along the edge of the beam. Again listen intently to the volume of the signals. If they grow stronger (remember, you must not make any change in your volume control), you are headed in toward the station, and you simply follow the beam as shown by planes 1, 2, and 4. If the signals grow weaker, you are headed away from the station (as shown by the path of airplane No. 3). In this case, make a procedure turn across the beam and fly down the right edge of the beam toward the station.

Notice that after flying parallel to the average bisector, the No. 1 plane veers to the right, as the station signal increases in intensity, so that the plane can intersect the beam where it is wide enough to allow normal flight movements during the orientation procedure. Beams are too narrow near the station to allow sharp instrument turns. Whenever you find, therefore, from the strength of the station signal that you are going to intersect the beam close to the station, veer off and intersect it further out.

Whenever you fly toward a radio range station, be sure to keep on-course, or slightly to the right of the on-course beam, depending on the cruising speed. In flying the fade-out method, you may sometimes have to go fifteen or twenty minutes in one direction before you know definitely whether the signals are growing stronger or weaker.

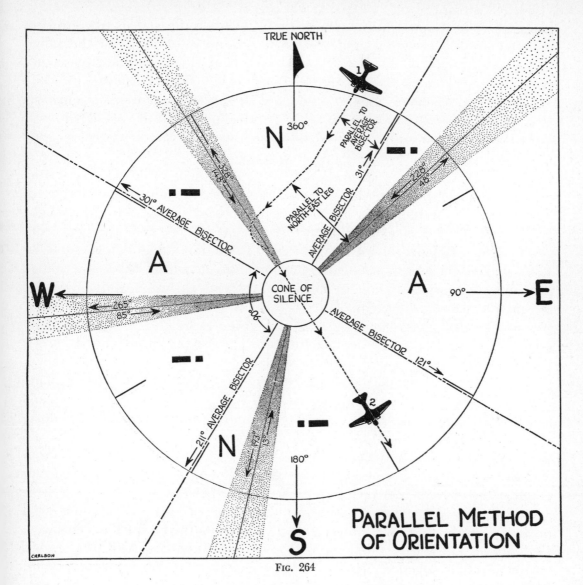

FIG. 264

FIG. 264. *Parallel Method.* When you wish to approach a station along a definite beam, use the parallel method of orientation. Simply fly parallel to the average bisector until you find out in which direction and in which quadrant you are flying, as explained in the previous illustration. Decide which of the two beams bounding this quadrant you wish to use; then change your course until it is parallel to the *other* of the two beams. This

297

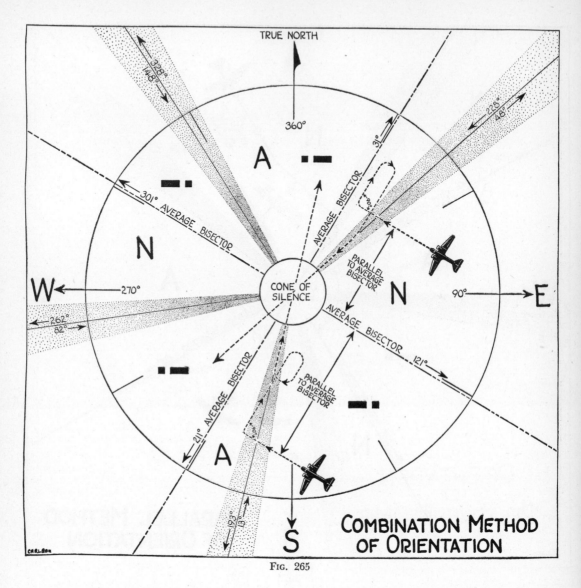

FIG. 265

course will bring you to the beam you wish to use, as shown by the dotted line. Fly across the beam until you reach the twilight zone on the other side, turn back into the beam in the usual way, and fly along it toward the station. Notice that in this example the plane emerges from the cone of silence and finds itself in the *A* quadrant.

FIG. 265. *Combination Method.* Sometimes, when you know in which quad-

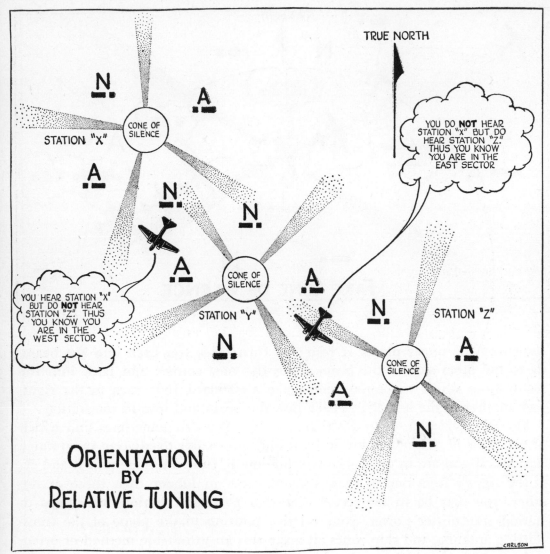

FIG. 266

rant you are flying, you combine two methods of orientation. Start by flying parallel to the average bisector until you cross a radio beam, and make a 90° turn to the right. If the turn takes you further into the twilight zone, or definitely into the opposite quadrant, hold your course for a few seconds, make a standard 180° turn, and fly back until you again enter the beam, as

299

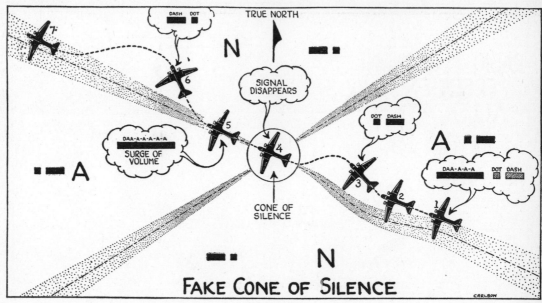

FIG. 267

shown by the upper plane. If your 90° turn takes you back into the beam, fly to the other side of the beam along the new course, and back into the sector from which you came, then make a standard 180° turn to the right, and another to the left, flying back into the beam and toward the station.

FIG. 266. *Orientation by Relative Tuning.* You can sometimes find which of two *A* or *N* sectors you are in by tuning alternately to adjacent radio range stations. If you are in an *A* sector of Station *Y*, tune alternately to *Z* and *X*. If the signals from one of these stations come in louder than those of the other, you may be in the sector near that particular station. Variations in station transmitter power, your relative position to the plane of the transmitting antenna, and skip zones all make this an unreliable method of orientation which should never be depended upon unless there is confirmatory evidence.

FIG. 267. A true cone of silence can be detected in two ways: First, there is a *definite* increase in volume just *before you enter* and *just after you leave* the cone. Second, the quadrant to your right after emerging from a true cone of silence is not the same quadrant that lay to your right before you entered the cone.

300

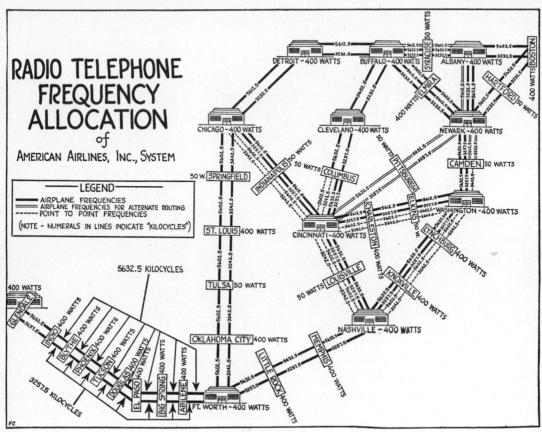

FIG. 268

Radio beams, as you know, frequently play tricks. A bent beam, for instance, may occasionally create a fake cone of silence. There is no definite increase in volume, however, just before you enter or just after you leave a fake cone, and the quadrants to the right do not change.

In Fig. 267, the plane flies on-course with an occasional swing to the right where it picks up the *A* signal as shown at *1*. At *2* it enters an area where, because of the bend in the beam, there are no signals. At *3*, the plane again swings to the right and again picks up the *A* signal, proving that the area of silence was not the actual cone of silence. At *4*, the signals again disappear; there is a surge of volume at *5*, and at *6* a turn to the right brings in the *N* signal, proving that the second area of silence was authentic. At *7* the plane has swung back into the beam again to fly a course away from the station.

301

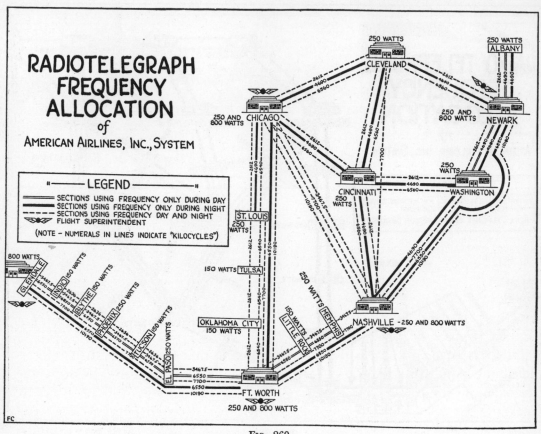

FIG. 269

FIGS. 268 AND 269. Besides depending upon radio range stations and marker beacons, established airlines have their own private radio station facilities for the use of their transports. You will get an idea of how completely radio communication has been provided for in airline operation by examining these two illustrations. Whenever possible, make arrangements in advance to use these private radio facilities on your own flights.

A thrilling aerobatic performance in itself does not prove true airmanship.

XXV

INSTRUMENT TECHNIQUE
and
How Not To Be Confused

THERE is no such thing as flying half-and-half—that is, flying on instruments and at the same time trying to keep in contact with the ground. Cloudy Joe cannot understand why one may not fly on instruments and occasionally check the accuracy of his flight by coming down through soupy weather and looking at the ground. He does not realize that it is exactly this sort of flying that leads to serious trouble. In fact, you can almost tell in advance that a flight carried out in this way will be the last one made by the man at the controls. If both the ceiling and visibility are good, you fly contact; otherwise you fly on instruments, not half-and-half, but wholeheartedly.

In our previous discussions I have told you all I could, within the space available, about the weather, and how to deal with it; also about instruments, engine power, and other allied subjects, for this is the kind of knowledge you must have before you begin to fly on instruments. But such knowledge alone will not equip you to fly through the overcast; you must first go through a period of thorough instrument training on the ground. You can get facts by reading books, but judgment is acquired only through long experience, and technique only by constant practice.

Cloudy Joe has had more than one cousin who never acquired this judgment because their promising careers were cut short by lack of practice in the early days of instrument flying.

During those pioneering days there was continual conflict between the airplane, the weather, the instruments, and the airman's own senses. Since very little was known about any of these factors, many had to pay dearly for the experience gained. I remember a case where one of Cloudy Joe's cousins flew over a stretch of nice, level ground. As he approached the hills, the weather became thicker, the ceiling dropped, and fog formed close to the ground. The man had instruments in his plane, but he used them half-heartedly, hoping for the fog to rise. The fog didn't rise, however, and he began to lose confidence in his instruments. Poking his head out of the plane, he came down through the overcast to look at the ground. Well, he got just one glimpse of the good earth—his last.

Cloudy Joe's cousin is not an isolated example. Similar cases occurred frequently back in the early flying days and still do occur, but I am counting on you to follow the golden rules upon which safe flying is based; to fly contact when you can, and to practise on the ground and during good weather until you are proficient enough and confident enough of your ability to fly through the overcast on instruments without trying to see what you are flying over. In actual instrument flight through the overcast, remember that you know, from dead reckoning and other avigational aids, what you are flying over. If your calculations are right, you don't need to see what is below you; if your calculations are wrong, coming down to take a look at the terrain will only add to your troubles.

Another thing that caused trouble in the early days was that very few airmen believed their instruments, for the simple reason that they had no idea how to interpret them. They tried to guide themselves through the overcast by the "feel" of the controls which they had acquired during contact flying. "Feel" is a reliable guide, however, *only* during contact flying; in the overcast it merely confuses the airman and has brought many a plane and its pilot to grief. But time, experience and study have gradually taught us what was wrong, and we have finally learned the right way to fly on instruments.

Since the airplane and its instruments behave in the same way in or out of the overcast, it does not much matter where and when the plane is flown. What does matter is that your sensation of balance and direction varies according to whether you can or cannot see the horizon, and that you, yourself,

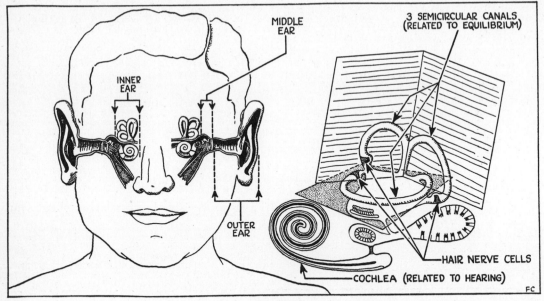

MIDDLE EAR

INNER EAR

3 SEMICIRCULAR CANALS (RELATED TO EQUILIBRIUM)

OUTER EAR

HAIR NERVE CELLS

COCHLEA (RELATED TO HEARING)

FC

Fig. 270

can be the chief—or the least—cause of trouble when you are flying through the overcast. When your eyes are open and you have visual contact with the ground, you will, under normal conditions, maintain your balance. But when you lose visual contact, your balance and your sense of direction become thoroughly mixed up. Try walking along the street blindfolded, and you will see how quickly loss of visual contact confuses your sense of balance. Try sitting blindfolded in a revolving chair and being spun around, and you will see how quickly you lose your sense of direction. If you are being spun to the left, you will find, when the rotation stops, that you continue to spin—or so your senses say—to the right. This spinning sensation, whether you want to call it by its high-hat name of vertigo, or its plain name, dizziness, causes conflicting sensations and false impressions of the rate and direction of rotation. On flights made without flight instruments, the human mechanism, confused by dizziness, tends to react incorrectly and to move the controls in the wrong direction.

FIG. 270. The human ear consists of three main parts—the outer, the middle, and the inner ear. It has been found that it is the inner ear, with its three semicircular canals, that has so much to do with balance. The structure of the inner ear is shown at the right of the illustration. Notice that the three

305

semicircular canals lie in three distinct planes, and that toward the end of each canal is an expanded portion. This section of the canal contains hair cells. The semicircular canals, and the utricle, the membranous sac into which the canals open, are filled with a liquid. Any motion of this liquid moves the hair cells, which in turn stimulate certain nerves, conveying the sensation of motion to the brain. Because each of the canals has its own distinct plane, the liquid in one canal can be set in motion while the liquid in the other two canals is inactive. If you spin around in your chair, for example, the liquid in the horizontal canal is set in motion and you get a sensation of horizontal movement. If you move in a vertical plane, liquid in one or both of the vertical canals is set in motion.

There are all sorts of theories and explanations for the way in which the inner ear and the brain react to motion, but these theories are not important for our purpose. What is important is this: You cannot depend upon the evidence of your inner ear when you have no visual reference. In flying through the overcast, therefore, you must disregard your own sensations of motion and depend *solely upon your instruments.*

YOUR BASIC FLIGHT INSTRUMENTS

The turn and bank indicator, the air speed indicator, and the vertical speed indicator are the basic reference instruments for maintaining and controlling your plane in the desired attitude relative to the earth. Each of these instruments gives you its own separate indication, but you must learn to use them together, and in a definite order.

Contact flying needs a good head. Instrument flying needs a better one.

306

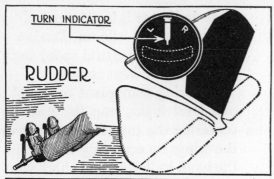

TURN INDICATOR

RUDDER

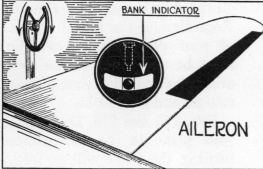

BANK INDICATOR

AILERON

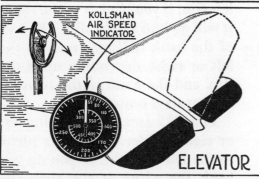

KOLLSMAN AIR SPEED INDICATOR

ELEVATOR

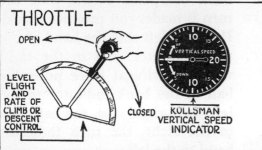

THROTTLE

OPEN

LEVEL FLIGHT AND RATE OF CLIMB OR DESCENT CONTROL

CLOSED

KOLLSMAN VERTICAL SPEED INDICATOR

FIG. 271. The turn indicator reacts to any application on the rudder that causes a turn, and registers the rate and direction of the turn. The turn indicator and the rudder, therefore, are closely related.

Fig. 271

FIG. 272. The bank indicator shows whether the wings of the plane are level, or at an angle with the horizon, and reacts to the aileron control. The turn and bank indicators have been combined into one instrument, and together show whether your plane is being turned correctly or not, as you will see later.

Fig. 272

FIG. 273. The air speed indicator registers an increased or decreased rate of speed in accordance with the position of the elevator.

FIG. 274. The vertical speed indicator shows whether you are maintaining level flight, or indicates the rate of ascent or descent, in accordance with the amount of power being drawn from your engine or engines above that required for a given air speed.

Fig. 273

In making a turn, first apply the rudder, then follow instantly with the aileron to keep the bank indicator ball centered. Remember, the turn indicator is kept in the right position by your feet, which control the rudder, while the ball of the

Fig. 274

LEFT BANK
NO TURN

LEFT SLIP

FIG.
275

RIGHT BANK
NO TURN

RIGHT SLIP

FIG.
276

LEFT RUDDER

NO BANK

—— RIGHT SKID —→

FIG.
277

RIGHT RUDDER

NO BANK

←— LEFT SKID —

FIG.
278

STRAIGHT AND LEVEL FLIGHT

FC

FIG.
279

bank indicator is kept centered by controlling the aileron. During a level turn, the vertical speed indicator must be kept at zero.

To bring your plane to straight and level flight, stop the turn by centering the turn indicator, level the wings by centering the ball of the bank indicator, and check your air speed by means of the elevator. Regardless of the initial position of your plane, these operations must be performed in the exact order given to bring your plane to straight and level flight.

FIGS. 275 AND 276. If you bank your plane to the left without turning, the plane will go into a left slip; if you bank it to the right, it will go into a right slip. The ball of the bank indicator rolls to the left or right, depending upon the slip, and the hand of the turn indicator stays centered.

FIGS. 277 AND 278. Applying left or right rudder turns your plane to the left or right. If you do not bank the plane at the time the turn is made, you produce a skid. During a left skid the hand of the turn indicator goes to the right while centrifugal force pulls the ball of the bank indicator to the left. In a right skid, the ball goes to the right, the turn indicator hand to the left.

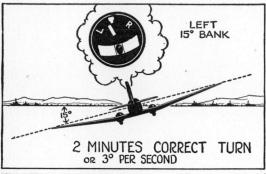

LEFT 15° BANK

15°

2 MINUTES CORRECT TURN
or 3° PER SECOND

FIG. 280

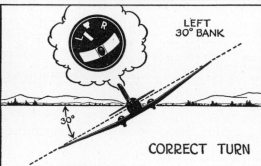

LEFT 30° BANK

30°

CORRECT TURN

FIG. 281

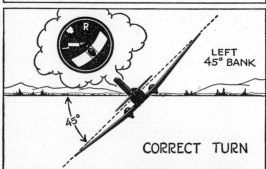

LEFT 45° BANK

45°

CORRECT TURN

FIG. 282

STOP TURN BY CENTERING TURN INDICATOR

SPERRY DIRECTIONAL GYRO

FC

FIG. 283

FIG. 279. During straight and level flight, the hand of the turn indicator and the ball of the bank indicator are both centered. Regardless of the position of your plane—that is, whether the plane is in straight or level flight, or turning—remember that the ball of the bank indicator should be kept centered.

FIG. 280. If a shallow, 15° bank left turn is made correctly, the ball of the bank indicator remains centered while the turn indicator swings to the left. In learning to make turns, start practising on the 15°, which is the easiest to execute. Then try 180° (one minute) turns, stopping the turn within plus or minus 10°. As you become more proficient, this error will be reduced. Time your turns from the instant you first apply the rudder until the instant you finally apply the rudder at the end of the turn.

FIG. 281. As the rate of turn increases, the pointer of the turn indicator is deflected still further from the center. The ball of the bank indicator must be kept centered. When you come out of a steep bank (30° or more), coordinate the controls so that the plane will roll out smoothly. Another thing—air speed drops during a steep bank, and continues to drop as you come out of the turn because the nose of the plane tends to go up. In coming out of a turn, therefore, use the rudder first, then follow with the ailerons, checking your air speed, and observing the vertical speed indication. The vertical speed indicator, you will remember, is always a few seconds slow and shows what is happening only after it has happened.

FIG. 282. As the rate of turn continues to increase, you must bank your plane still more steeply to keep the ball of the bank indicator centered. During a turn at 45° bank, the elevator lies nearer the vertical plane, and the rudder nearer the horizontal, so that the work of these controls is partially reversed. When the nose of your plane drops during a steep bank, you bring it up again by using the top rudder instead of the elevator. Remembering the position of your rudder and elevator in relation to the earth will help you coordinate your controls during banks of 45° or more.

On steep banks, be careful not to tighten the turn. When this happens, your turn indicator shows a greater rate of turn. Steep turns require more accurate coordination of controls than shallow turns, but you will find that control coordination is merely a matter of practice.

FIG. 283. During a precision turn, a standard two-minute turn (3° per second at 15° bank) or a faster turn (6° per second), guide yourself by using your directional gyro. But stop the turn by centering the pointer of the turn indicator, not by using the directional gyro. In regulating the attitude of your plane during a turn, use your turn and bank indicator only, and keep your vertical speed indicator at zero, thus maintaining your altitude.

It is a good thing to remember that instruments never shout. They *whisper* their information to you. Watch them carefully so that you will not miss a thing they say—and always try to act a little ahead of them rather than behind them.

Doing one thing at a time is one of the
secrets of instrument flying.

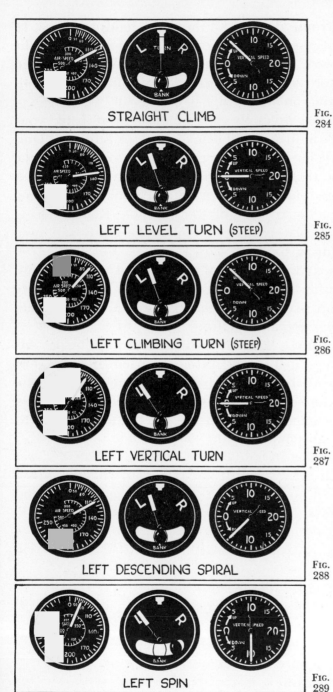

STRAIGHT CLIMB

LEFT LEVEL TURN (STEEP)

LEFT CLIMBING TURN (STEEP)

LEFT VERTICAL TURN

LEFT DESCENDING SPIRAL

LEFT SPIN

FIG. 284

FIG. 285

FIG. 286

FIG. 287

FIG. 288

FIG. 289

FIG. 284. As long as you climb in a straight line, the turn indicator and the ball of the bank indicator will be centered. The air speed indicator must be made to show the desired air speed for your plane, while the rate at which you ascend is shown by the vertical speed indicator and depends upon the excess power of your engine above that required for the indicated air speed.

FIG. 285. To execute a correct left level turn, you must manipulate your plane in such a way that the air speed indicator will show the necessary air speed for your particular plane; the turn indicator will swing to the left; the ball of the bank indicator will remain centered, and the vertical speed indicator must register zero.

FIG. 286. During a left climbing turn, your instruments should show approximately the indications given here. The air speed indication will fall off, if you do not increase the power, and the vertical speed indicator will register the rate of climb.

FIG. 287. If you make a left vertical turn from a level

311

flight position without changing your engine power output, the turn indicator will show the rate of turn. The air-speed indication will, of course, drop.

Fig. 288. By reducing the power and causing a left descending spiral, you will find that your instruments react approximately as shown.

Fig. 289. If, on the other hand, you fall into a left spin, the wings of the plane will strike the air at such a high angle of attack that the air speed will be reduced, the ball of the bank indicator will be off center, toward the right, and the turn indicator will be deflected according to how tight and fast the spin is. The vertical speed indication will largely depend upon the type of plane you are flying, its wing loading, and the general overall drag characteristics.

The illustrations I have just explained apply to left turns; right turns produce exactly the opposite effect upon your turn and bank indicator, while you will get approximately the same indications from your air and vertical speed indicators as shown in Figs. 285 through 289.

Notice that in explaining the reactions of your instruments during various maneuvers, I have used the words "approximately as shown." The reaction of your air speed and your vertical speed indicators will vary according to the characteristics of the plane you are flying, and these, you will remember, include cruising and stalling speeds, climbing ability (dependent upon the power output of the engine or engines), and type of propeller used. The turn and bank indicator, on the other hand, always reacts exactly as shown in these illustrations, regardless of the characteristics of the plane.

Out of Stall and Spin by Instruments

Now that you know how to make normal flight maneuvers on instruments, you should also know how to recover from unintentional maneuvers like stalls and spins. It is bad enough to make mistakes in the air, but it is even worse if you do not know how to correct them.

When your plane goes into a stall, through loss of forward speed, push the nose of your plane down. As soon as your air speed indicator starts to show an increase, ease back slightly on the controls. Be careful, however, to bring the nose of your plane up before the air speed indicator shows the normal, desired speed. Act ahead of the air speed indicator, bringing the nose of the plane up slowly while you avoid gaining excess speed. When you reach the desired normal speed, check on your rate of climb, making sure that the pointer of the vertical speed indicator is at zero. During this stage of the recovery, also make sure that the pointer and the ball of the turn and bank indicator are centered.

If your plane goes into a left spin, as shown by the instruments in Fig. 289, depress the elevator and, by applying right rudder, bring the pointer of the turn indicator to center. As the rotation of the plane stops, you will find yourself in a straight, forward-diving position, with the ball of the bank indicator centered. Now that you have pulled yourself out of the spin, continue to recover as from a stall. In recovering from a spin, remember the usual procedure—that you must (1) stop the turn; (2) center the ball of the bank indicator; (3) check your air speed, by using the rudder, the aileron, and the elevator, in the order named.

No one—not even Cloudy Joe—can expect to fly successfully on instruments without thorough practice in the use of each individual instrument. Fortunately for Cloudy Joe, this training is given on the ground in a Link trainer unit, where the simple mistakes that he has such a genius for making will not end in disaster.

Only when you have mastered your instrument board with the same skill with which a pianist masters his keyboard, can you fly successfully through the overcast.

313

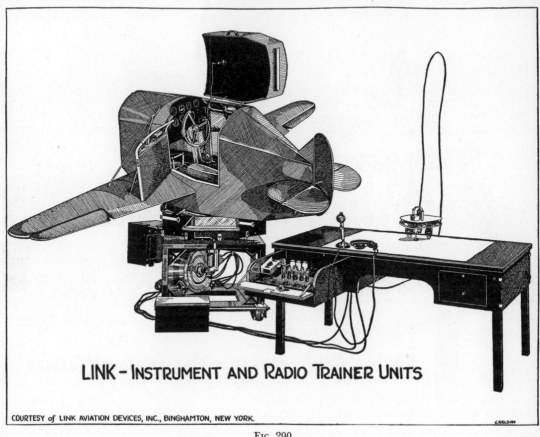

LINK - Instrument and Radio Trainer Units

CARLSON

Fig. 290

Fig. 290. The Link unit consists of a dummy airplane, complete with wings and control surfaces, and an instructor's table equipped with radio, telephone, and a charting device that keeps an accurate record of your "flight." The dummy plane is mounted on a turntable, and this, in turn, is mounted on a stationary base.

Don't make the mistake of thinking that this "dummy" plane is easy to manage. It pitches, rolls, turns, simulates dives and climbs, and can spin so rapidly that you will get the same sensations of vertigo that you would in the overcast. Bumps can be turned on to give you all the practice you need in rough air. In fact, the trainer is far less stable and much more sensitive to control than a regular plane, for the simple reason that you can get much

314

LINK – Instrument and Radio Trainer
(Instructor's Table)

Fig. 291

better training in a hypersensitive plane than you can in a slower and more stable machine.

The training unit is connected both by radio and by phone to the instructor's table. Over the telephone he gives you various commands and instructions; over the radio come radio-beam signals to give you thorough experience in flying the airways while you are still safe on the ground.

Your training begins with the simplest of operations—making constant-rate turns to the right and left. You make these turns first with the hood up, later with the hood down. An important part of your training at this stage is learning to make accurately timed turns without the aid of a clock by *counting* the required number of seconds.

The Link trainer is equipped with all the various instruments which have been explained in the preceding pages, and before you complete your training you will have to prove yourself proficient in the handling of each instrument in rough as well as smooth weather, and in flying with the aid of radio beams and dead reckoning.

Fig. 291. On top of the desk which Cloudy Joe's instructor uses is, at the beginning of each lesson, a blank sheet of paper. Every maneuver Cloudy Joe makes, every mistake he commits, is recorded on this chart by an automatic writing device. This motor-driven apparatus travels less than an inch a minute, and when it finishes its work, Cloudy Joe's record—for better or worse—is down in black and white.

Lessons in the trainer usually last about 30 minutes, and a normal instrument training course usually requires about 25 hours of hard work.

CLIMBING, TRIMMING, DESCENDING

Flight through the overcast begins before you leave the ground. You are already familiar with various adjustments that must be made on your radio and other equipment before you take off, but I cannot overemphasize the fact that upon the precision with which these adjustments are made depends to a large extent the success or failure of your flight.

On the engine alone there are at least sixteen operations that must be performed before the take-off, and after fuel and oil have been carefully checked. These operations include nine engine-control settings, priming, starting and warming-up, and do not take into account the adjustments that must be made to meet special weather conditions. So that Cloudy Joe won't have to depend too much upon his remarkable memory, here is a list of the engine-control settings:

(1) Fuel supply cock—ON. (Remember to turn on the *right* octane rating fuel tank for take-off. In most cases you will need a higher octane rating fuel for take-off than you will later at cruising speed.)
(2) Ignition switch—OFF. (Cloudy Joe will forget this, sooner or later.)
(3) Throttle—at 700 to 800 r.p.m.
(4) Two-position-pitch propeller—LOW PITCH.
(5) Constant-speed propeller—TAKE-OFF.
(6) Carburetor air heater—COLD.
(7) Manifold pressure regulator—at take-off pressure.
(8) Oil-cooler shutter—CLOSED.
(9) Exhaust-gas analyzer—ON.

316

Here are a few other hints to be followed before you take off: Always check to see that the combustion chambers are clear by turning your propeller around three times before you turn on the ignition switch. Be careful not to overprime your engine. If you should overprime it, open the throttle and turn your engine over with the starter until it clears out. Then return the throttle to 700-800 r.p.m. (Your ignition switch must be off, of course, during this operation.) In warming up, run your engine at 1200 r.p.m. until the temperature of the oil reaches 60° F., and keep the throttle open to specified cruising manifold pressure and r.p.m. until you have checked each magneto and your fuel and oil pressures. Never start to take off if the cylinder-head temperature has gone over 400° F. or below 250°.

I don't need to tell you that your plane should be headed into the wind for take-off, but since the weather sometimes refuses to cooperate with the airport, you may be hampered by a cross-wind. If you are flying a multi-engine plane, decrease the power output of the engine on the far side so that the excess thrust of the propellers on the near side will compensate for the effect of the cross-wind on the tail of your plane. This is particularly important during slow ground speed before you have reached your maximum take-off acceleration. Cloudy Joe tries to solve cross-wind take-off problems by putting on the brakes and opening the engine to full speed in the hope that the bigger the noise, the faster he will take off. His technique, however, is just about as effective as if he tried to start an automobile in sandy soil by putting on full speed ahead, instead of by applying power gradually.

If you think there is any chance of running into icing conditions, be sure to adjust your carburetor air heater to give a maximum mixture temperature of 35° F., or, with certain types of carburetor, a maximum intake air temperature of 90° F.

Since your airplane will accelerate more rapidly when it is in the air, do not keep it rolling on the ground any longer than is absolutely necessary. After taking off, you will find that a higher speed is more useful than a high altitude, so try to gain as much excess speed as possible before you start climbing. This precaution will come in handy if an engine fails during take-off, for you will be able to maintain forward flight even though one of your engines is out of commission.

During climb, adjust the manifold pressure to the specified rated power for your particular engine and adjust the r.p.m. to the manifold pressure. You

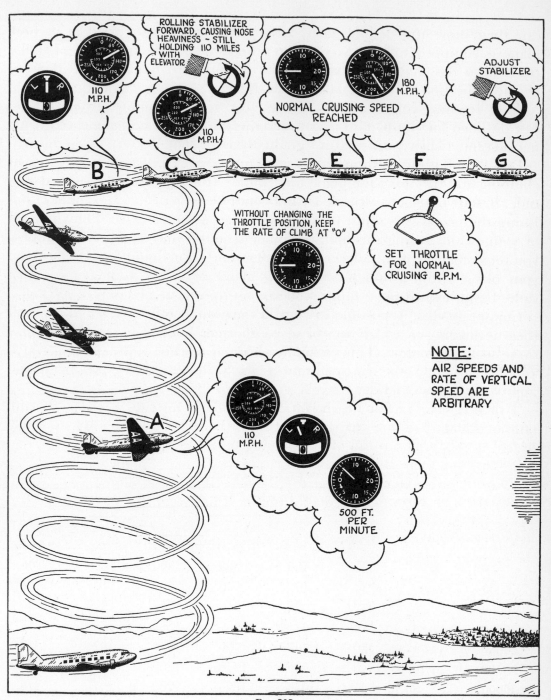

FIG. 292

can then draw the desired rated horsepower from your engine. If your plane is equipped with a two-position propeller, keep the propeller set at low pitch until the engine has exceeded the rated r.p.m. Regulate the mixture by the indication on the exhaust gas analyzer.

After reaching your cruising altitude, follow the procedure which I have just outlined for climb, adjusting your power output to cruising speed. During descent, richen your mixture gradually as altitude is lost.

FIG. 292. This illustration shows the instrument procedure followed in climbing and trimming the plane to altitude. After reaching the desired altitude, B, start to trim to altitude C, and continue as shown at D, E, and F, finishing the process by adjusting your stabilizer as shown at G. The air speed of your plane, during this and any other stage of your flight, is controlled, you remember, by manipulation of the elevator. To maintain level flight, keep your plane within a hundred-foot limit above or below your cruising altitude. If you exceed these limits, you are no longer in precisely level flight.

Coming as close as possible to your destination before you let down, and then descending at a high rate of speed shortens your flying time but may cause some discomfort. This discomfort is the result not of the speed at which you descend but of the increased rate of change in atmospheric pressure as you approach the lower levels.

TABLE II. The rate at which you must climb or descend, in order to maintain a constant pressure change, is given in the following table up to 30,000 feet.

TABLE II

VARIATION OF RATE OF CLIMB OR DESCENT FOR CONSTANT PRESSURE CHANGE

Altitude (ft)	Standard Pressure (" Hg)	Rate (ft/min)	Rate (ft/min)	Rate (ft/min)	Rate (ft/min)	Rate (ft/min)	Rate (ft/min)
0	29.92	200	400	600	800	1000	1200
5000	24.89	230	465	700	935	1165	1400
10000	20.58	262	538	810	1085	1350	1630
15000	16.88	315	643	957	1283	1660	2033
20000	13.74	380	767	1150	1533	1920	2320
25000	11.10	440	900	1340	1800	2275	2740
30000	8.880	525	1075	1625	2200	2675	3270

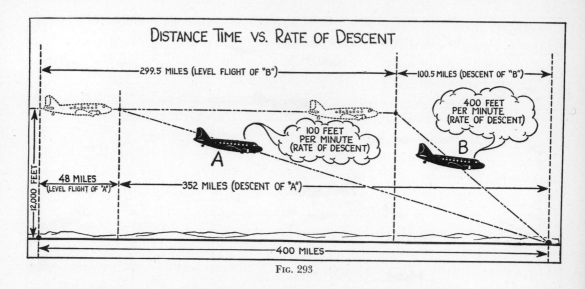

Fig. 293

From the figures in Table II you can readily see that to maintain constant atmospheric pressure during descent, you start coming down at a higher rate of vertical speed and gradually decrease this speed as you approach your landing point.

Fig. 293. This illustration shows the effect upon the air speed of the kinetic energy—in terms of additional horsepower—produced by the weight of the plane during various rates of descent. The weight of the plane contributes much less toward the potential horsepower than does the rate of descent. The greater the rate of descent, the greater the added horsepower, and therefore the greater the forward speed of your plane.

In the illustration, two planes, A and B, are shown descending from 12,000 feet during a 400-mile flight. A starts to come down at 100 feet per minute after it has traveled 48 miles in level flight. B starts to come down at the rate of 400 feet per minute after making a level flight of 299½ miles. A will take much longer to travel the total distance of 400 miles than B. (Both planes are transport, twin-engine planes with a gross weight of 24,000 lbs., and 550 hp. output per engine throughout the flight.) The descent problem on page 324 will give you a comparison of horsepower, speed, and time, for the two planes.

In catching a ball, you act ahead of the ball; in instrument
flying, you act ahead of the instruments.

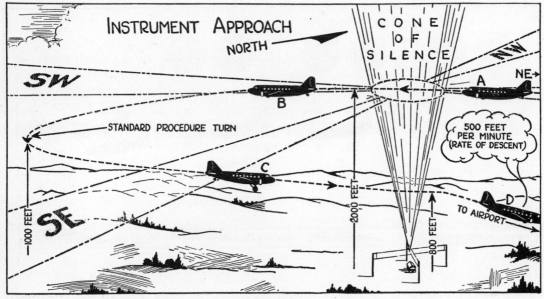

FIG. 294

LANDING OUT OF THE OVERCAST ON INSTRUMENTS

Before you try to land on instruments through the overcast, you must be sure that there is an adequate ceiling at the airport which you are planning to use. If the ceiling is the minimum allowed by air regulations, your approach will have to be low, and will have to be made with the help of radio beams, which you already know how to use from our previous discussion. The approach to different landing fields varies according to the surrounding terrain and local conditions, and you must be thoroughly familiar with the characteristics and limitations of the field before you try to come down—information which can be obtained from your airway maps and by radio during flight. (All planes flying on instruments are required at the very least to have a radio receiver on board.)

FIG. 294. Let's assume that you are landing at an airport which requires you to cross the cone of silence at 2000 feet (indicated), and later, during the final approach, at 800 feet. Your first concern as you come in on the radio beam is the proper trimming of your plane so that it will be comparatively easy to handle in rough air, thus allowing you more time to concentrate on direction and altitude.

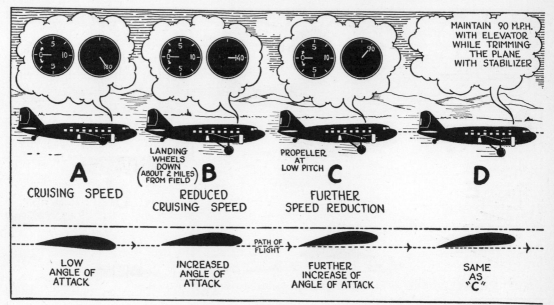

FIG. 295

You are coming in, in this illustration, on the northeast leg of the range, maintaining a 2000-foot indicated altitude. As you cross the cone of silence (identified, you remember, by a sudden build-up of signal, followed by silence, then by a second, even more marked, surge of sound), you begin to lose altitude at the rate, say, of 500 feet per minute until you reach 1000 feet. At this point you make a procedure turn (Fig. 261) and decrease your rate of descent, trimming the plane for an almost "hands off" condition. Cross the cone of silence at 800 feet, then decrease the power of your engines at once, and again start descending at the rate of 500 feet per minute, heading for the airport. At this stage of the approach, you are concerned with air speed and your actual altitude above the ground. If, after reaching the minimum allowable altitude, you do not see the ground, you must climb and await instructions over the radio. If, however, conditions are favorable for landing, continue to lose altitude and make your final approach into the wind.

FIGS. 295 AND 296. The various stages in your final approach are shown in these illustrations. First decrease your speed to reduce cruising speed, still maintaining level flight. Then set the propeller at low pitch or at the rated r.p.m., depending upon the type, and lower the landing gear as shown at B.

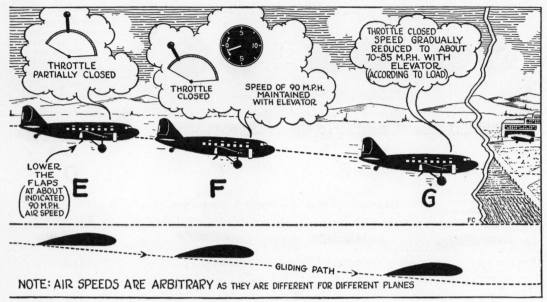

Fig. 296

Continue to reduce your air speed to, let us say, about 90 miles an hour; maintain this speed with the elevator, and trim the plane (*C* and *D*). You have now established your direction and properly trimmed and balanced your plane. If your plane is equipped with flaps, partially close the throttle, lower the flaps at the permissible indicated air speed (*E*), reduce the power still further (*F*) while maintaining the correct air speed for your particular plane, and start to lose altitude gradually. During the final stage of the approach (*G*), maintain speed with the elevator and come in for a landing. The amount of speed required at this stage of the approach depends upon the load of your plane.

Upon your skill in letting down
through depends the likelihood of
your taking another flight.

DESCENT PROBLEM

550 H.P. CRUISING; GROSS WEIGHT—24,000 LBS.

	Plane A.	Plane B
Rate of descent	100 ft/min.	400 ft/min.
Potential horsepower	73 hp.	291 hp.

$$= \frac{\text{Rate of descent (ft./min.)} \times 24000 \text{ (Gross weight)}}{33000}$$

	Plane A.	Plane B
Theoretical horsepower (no propeller loss)	92 hp.	365 hp.

$$= \frac{\text{Potential hp.}}{.80}$$

	Plane A.	Plane B
Total level brake horsepower delivered by engines	1100	1100
Total descent, theoretical brake horsepower	1192	1465
Percentage of increase in speed during descent (1)	104.1%	111.52%

$$= \sqrt[3]{\frac{1192 + 1100}{1100}}$$

	Plane A.	Plane B
Speed level at 12000 ft. with 1100 hp.	182	182
Speed level at 6000 ft. with 1100 hp. (2)	174	174
Average speed during descent = (1) x (2)	181 m.p.h	194.0 m.p.h
Time during descent (3)	120 min.	30 min.
Distance during descent	352 miles	100.5 miles
Miles level = (400 — descent distance)	48 miles	299.5 miles
Time level at 182 m.p.h. (4)	16 min.	99.0 min.
Time for 400 miles = (3) plus (4)	136 min.	129.0 min.

The following formulas will enable you to find the ground speed, the ground distance, and the minutes needed to cover a given distance:

$$\text{Ground speed (miles per hour)} = \frac{\text{Distance flown} \times 60}{\text{Minutes}}$$

$$\text{Ground distance (miles)} = \frac{\text{Airplane ground speed m.p.h} \times \text{min.}}{60}$$

$$\text{Minutes (for given distance)} = \frac{\text{Distance} \times 60}{\text{Ground speed in miles}}$$

XXVI

CELESTIAL NAVIGATION

WITH the increase in the flying range and cruising altitudes of the modern plane which will soon enable it to fly at substratosphere levels, the importance of celestial navigation is becoming more and more widely recognized as a check to dead reckoning. Radio beams, marker beacons and landmarks will continue to contribute their share, but I believe it will not be long before celestial navigation will be considered as necessary to the safety of the airman as it has been for centuries to the safety of the mariner. Since celestial navigation may soon be a compulsory tool during long-range flights, I am going to introduce you and Cloudy Joe to the fundamentals upon which this system is based.

Celestial navigation consists in establishing lines of position and obtaining a fix by observing two or more celestial bodies, or by taking two or more observations of the same celestial body—that is, of the sun during the day, or the moon on nights when its brilliance makes it difficult to use the stars or planets. Cloudy Joe says he doesn't believe it is possible to find the position of an airplane traveling two hundred miles an hour by fooling around with something a couple of million miles out in space. But once again Cloudy Joe is wrong. The position of a plane can be determined within an average accuracy of six miles by taking bearings on objects many billions of miles away. With practice, dead reckoning positions can be checked in about three minutes by use of celestial objects.

To obtain your line of position from a celestial body, you make certain observations from your actual position, compute certain values for the body from an assumed position, and compare and combine the results of these two operations. Among the values which you must determine for the celestial body are *altitude* (angular distance above the horizon) ; *declination* (angu-

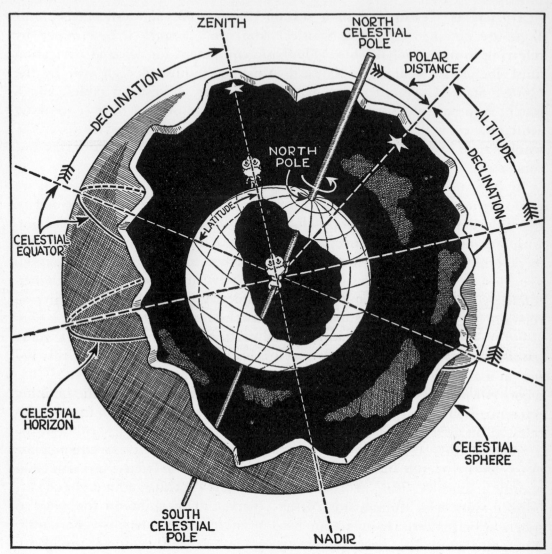

FIG. 297

lar distance from the celestial equator); *hour angle* (angular distance along the celestial equator between the meridian of the object and the meridian of the observer), and *azimuth* (angular distance, measured generally from the north along the celestial horizon, between the meridian of the observer and a vertical circle containing the object).

326

Altitude is measured with a sextant. *Declination* and *Greenwich hour angle* are obtained from the Nautical Almanac. *Azimuth* is determined by referring to navigational tables. The basic equipment for celestial navigation must include a sextant, a Nautical Almanac, published each year by the United States Government, navigational, or line of position tables, and a watch. As a part of your mental equipment, you must also have a speaking acquaintance with twenty or more conspicuous stars, selected to cover the whole range of the sky, and a knowledge of certain astronomical terms and concepts.

In comparison with the universe, the earth is only a point in space. If we could reduce the sun to a globe two feet in diameter and reduce the rest of the universe in proportion, our globe would be about the size of a small pea, with a diameter of 0.22", and the nearest star would be 8000 miles away. Yet to determine your position in relation to the earth by celestial navigation, you must first find the celestial equivalent of latitude and longitude for an infinitely remote object, and then determine the position of that object in relation not to the microscopic earth, but to the even more microscopic *you*.

FIG. 297. From whatever point on the earth's surface you see it, the sky looks like half a huge sphere, so that it is easy to conceive of ourselves as living on a globe within a globe on the inner surface of which are the stars, sun, moon and planets. Like our own earth, this outer globe has certain invisible reference points and lines used in establishing the location of the various celestial bodies.

Some of these references—the celestial poles and the celestial equator, for example—are merely projected to the celestial sphere from the earth, and occupy a fixed position in the heavens. Others—zenith, nadir and celestial horizon—vary with the position of the observer. The point on the celestial sphere which is directly over your head at any given moment is your zenith. The point which lies directly under your feet on the other side of the sphere is the nadir, and a line connecting these two points passes through the center of the earth. Circling the sphere halfway between the zenith and the nadir is the celestial horizon, the plane of which is always at right angles to the zenith-nadir line.

With these various references, you can begin to establish certain facts about the location of a celestial object. You can determine its altitude—its angular distance above the celestial horizon, and its zenith distance—its angular distance below the zenith. The altitude and zenith distances cannot be determined in advance, since the zenith and the celestial horizon change their position on the celestial sphere every time you change your position on the terrestial globe. But since the plane of the celestial horizon is at right angles to the zenith-nadir line, the altitude of a celestial body always equals 90° minus the zenith distance, and conversely, the zenith distance always equals 90° minus the altitude.

By using the celestial equator and the poles for reference, you can determine the polar distance of a star—its angular distance below the pole, and its declination—its angular distance above the celestial equator. Since the positions of the poles and the celestial equator are fixed and do not change with the observer's position, both the polar distance and the declination of a celestial object at any given time can be determined in advance. You will find the declination of the sun, moon, stars and planets listed by date and hour in the Nautical Almanac. Since declination plus polar distance equals 90°, polar distance is obtained by subtracting declination from 90°. As you will notice from the illustration, declination on the celestial sphere corresponds to latitude on the surface of the earth.

The point on the surface of the earth which lies directly beneath the celestial object is its "sub" point, or geographical position. If you stand on the substellar point of a star, the star will be in your zenith, and a line drawn from the star at the zenith to the center of the earth would intersect the substellar point. At nine o'clock at night the substellar point of a certain star might be New York. A few hours later the substellar point of the same star would be farther west, but in the same latitude as New York.

Projections of the earth's meridians of longitude are also used as reference lines on the celestial sphere, but these celestial meridians rotate with the rotation of the earth while the celestial sphere remains motionless. Imagine for the moment that you are looking at the celestial sphere from the center of a glass globe representing the earth, and marked with the parallels of latitude and longitude. As the globe rotates on its axis you will see the meridians, projected against the celestial sphere, traveling eastward. If you were to clock two successive crossings of the sun by one of these meridians, you would find, of course, that the crossings were 24 hours apart. But if you were to clock two successive crossings of one star by the same meridian, you would find that the crossings were 23 hours, 56 minutes and 3.33 seconds apart. The difference

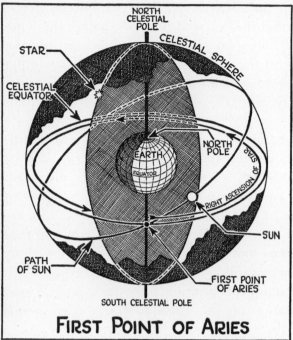

FIG. 298

STAR

CELESTIAL EQUATOR

NORTH CELESTIAL POLE

CELESTIAL SPHERE

EARTH

EQUATOR

NORTH POLE

RIGHT ASCENSION OF STAR

SUN

PATH OF SUN

FIRST POINT OF ARIES

SOUTH CELESTIAL POLE

FIRST POINT OF ARIES

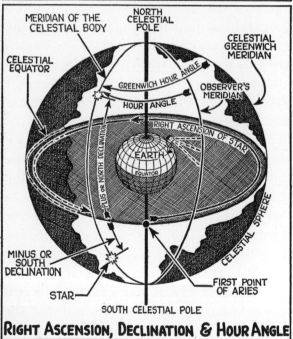

FIG. 299

MERIDIAN OF THE CELESTIAL BODY

NORTH CELESTIAL POLE

CELESTIAL GREENWICH MERIDIAN

CELESTIAL EQUATOR

GREENWICH HOUR ANGLE

OBSERVER'S MERIDIAN

HOUR ANGLE

RIGHT ASCENSION OF STAR

EARTH

EQUATOR

PLUS or NORTH DECLINATION

CELESTIAL SPHERE

MINUS OR SOUTH DECLINATION

STAR

SOUTH CELESTIAL POLE

FIRST POINT OF ARIES

RIGHT ASCENSION, DECLINATION & HOUR ANGLE

in time between two successive crossings of the sun and of a star by the same meridian is caused by the fact that the earth not only rotates on its axis but also revolves in an orbit around the sun. Because of the earth's trip around the sun, you see the stars once more often every year than you do the sun.

FIG. 298. If you could maintain your position at the center of the glass globe for a year, you would find that the sun appears to travel a definite course around the celestial sphere, and that twice a year—once at the beginning of spring and once at the beginning of fall— the path of the sun crosses the equator. The path of the sun through the heavens is called the ecliptic, and the point at which the sun crosses the equator in spring is known as the vernal equinox, or the First Point of Aries.

The First Point of Aries is used to determine the right ascension of a celestial object, a value which, combined with declination, establishes the position of the object in the heavens in the same way that longitude, combined with lati-

329

tude, establishes the position of a place on the earth's surface. Right ascension is the angular distance of a celestial body measured east along the equator from the First Point of Aries. Like declination, right ascension of a celestial body at any given time can be determined in advance and is listed for sun, moon, stars and planets in the Nautical Almanac. Instead of being given in degrees, minutes and seconds like declination, right ascension is measured in hours, minutes and seconds, one hour of arc being equal to 15°.

FIG. 299. There are four celestial meridians which you will need to use in celestial navigation. These are the Greenwich celestial meridian; the meridian passing through the First Point of Aries; the meridian passing through the celestial object, and your own meridian—that is, the meridian containing your zenith. These and the other meridians are divided into two branches—the upper extending above the celestial horizon, and the lower extending below the celestial horizon.

A civil day, as you know, consists of 24 hours and is reckoned from the time the mean sun crosses the lower branch of the Greenwich meridian. Because the earth travels around the sun at a varying speed, the sun appears to revolve around the earth at a varying speed. Since it is impossible to synchronize a timepiece with the irregular, apparent motion of the sun, civil time is based on the motion of an imaginary mean sun around the earth. Apparent time is reckoned from the instant the center of the real sun crosses the lower branch of the Greenwich meridian. In calculations in celestial navigation, civil time—the time to which your clock or watch is set—must frequently be converted into apparent solar time with the help of the Nautical Almanac.

A sidereal day is 23 hours, 56 minutes and 3 seconds long and is reckoned from the moment the First Point of Aries crosses the upper branch of the Greenwich meridian. Before you can solve a problem in celestial navigation by use of a star, you must know the Greenwich sidereal time (how many hours the meridian of the First Point of Aries is from the upper branch of the Greenwich meridian); the Greenwich hour angle (how many sidereal hours the star is from the Greenwich meridian), and the hour angle, or how many hours the star is from the meridian of your own (assumed) position.

Greenwich sidereal time is shown on a sidereal timepiece. The Greenwich hour angle (GHA) is obtained by subtracting the right ascension of the star (RA) from Greenwich sidereal time (GST). If the Greenwich sidereal time

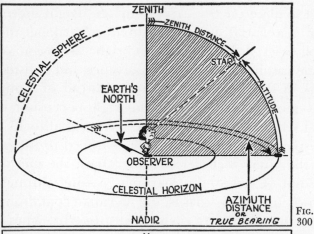

FIG. 300

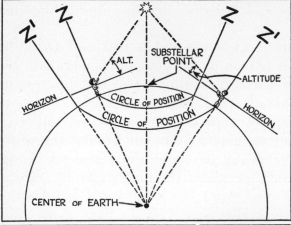

FIG. 301

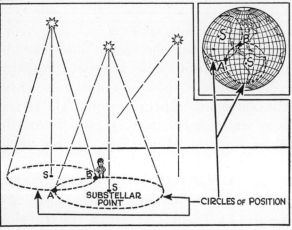

FIG. 302

is smaller than the right ascension, twenty-four hours are added to it before subtracting the RA. Hour angle (HA) is obtained by adding the east longitude of your position, expressed in hours, to the Greenwich hour angle, or by subtracting the west longitude. Since one of the things you are trying to find out with celestial navigation is your longitude, it is obvious that you cannot find out the hour angle of a celestial body for your actual position. An hour angle can only be ascertained for an assumed position, as explained later.

FIG. 300. One of the coordinates of a celestial object which is used in celestial navigation is azimuth. Azimuth is the angle at the zenith between a circle containing zenith, celestial object and nadir, and the observer's meridian. Azimuth is measured east or west from the north point of the horizon through 180° along the arc of the celestial horizon, and is expressed as N 45° E, N 32° E, N 165° W, N 59° W, etc.

FIG. 301. The "sub" or geographical position of a celestial body, you will remember, is the point on the earth's surface which is directly underneath the object at a given time. Since the altitude of a celestial body is its angular distance above the horizon, the altitude of a star at its substellar point is always 90°. If you move away from the substellar point so far that the star is on your horizon, its altitude will be zero. Seen from anywhere between these two points, the star will have an altitude greater than zero and less than 90°. Since it takes one nautical mile to bring about a change of one minute in altitude, the altitude of the star would decrease one degree for every sixty miles between you and its substellar point, provided the earth were a perfect sphere. If you stood 120 miles away, to the north, east, south or west, the altitude of the star would be 88°. If you were 2700 miles from the substellar point, the altitude of the star would be 45°. At 5400 miles, the star would appear on your horizon, and at more than 5400 miles from the substellar point, the star would be below your horizon.

If you know the geographical position of a celestial object, and observe its altitude, you can establish a circle of position on the globe, somewhere along which you must be. Simply put the point of a drawing compass on the substellar point, take a radius equal to the 90° minus the observed altitude converted into nautical miles and reduced to the scale of your globe, and draw a circle. From anywhere along this circle, your star will have the altitude which you have already observed. From any place nearer the substellar point, the star will have a higher altitude; from any place farther away, a lower altitude.

Fig. 302. By taking observations on two celestial objects, the substellar points of which are known, you can obtain not only a circle of position, but two definite points, one of which represents your location at the time of the observations. Your procedure in this case consists of choosing two celestial objects some degrees apart, observing their altitudes, and drawing a circle of position for each. These two circles will intersect at two points, *A* and *B,* as shown on the illustration. You know that from anywhere along one of the circles you will see one of the stars at its observed altitude. You also know that from any point on the second circle you will see the second star at its observed altitude. But only at two points—*A* and *B*— will you be able to see both stars at the observed altitudes. At the time of your observations, therefore, you must be either at point *A* or *B*. Now look at the map, and see where these points fall in our particular case. One is on the coast of the

Gulf of Mexico, the other in the South Pacific. No one, not even Cloudy Joe, could be so confused about his location that he wouldn't know which of these two points represented his true position.

Finding your position on the surface of the earth by drawing two circles of position would be a simple matter if it were not for one difficulty. Since it takes sixty nautical miles to bring about one degree of latitude change on the surface of the earth, and since your two stars might be many degrees apart, you would have to plot your circles of position on a map showing most of the earth. If you were working with two stars, one with an altitude of 88° and one with an altitude of 58°, you would have to describe circles having a scale radius of 120 nautical miles and 1920 miles respectively. The intersection of these circles would show you where you were in relation to the entire surface of the earth, but they would not show you your position in relation to an obscure point like Hohokus, New Jersey, or Huntsville, Texas.

To get around this difficulty, you have to obtain your position by using only a small arc of the circle of position. A small arc of a large circle can, of course, be drawn as a straight line, so that instead of using circles of position, you use lines of position in obtaining a fix. These lines of position can be obtained only by solving the "astronomical triangle." "Solving a triangle," in case Cloudy Joe has forgotten, means finding the values of all its sides and angles when the values of some of the parts are known.

The astronomical triangle runs from the pole to the zenith (the observer's position projected onto the celestial sphere) to the celestial object. One side equals the zenith distance (90° minus the altitude of the star); one side equals the polar distance (90° minus the declination), and one side equals 90° (the distance from the equator to the pole) minus the terrestrial latitude of the observer. The two angles of the triangle with which you will be concerned are the angle at the zenith, in other words the azimuth, and the angle at the pole, which equals the hour angle (the angular distance in hours between the celestial meridian of the object and the observer's meridian).

From your actual position you can determine two sides of the triangle—the zenith distance and the polar distance. The first is obtained by measuring the altitude of the star with the sextant and subtracting it from 90°. The second is obtained by looking up the declination of the star in the Nautical Almanac and subtracting it from 90°. You cannot obtain the third side of the triangle because you do not know your latitude. You cannot obtain the

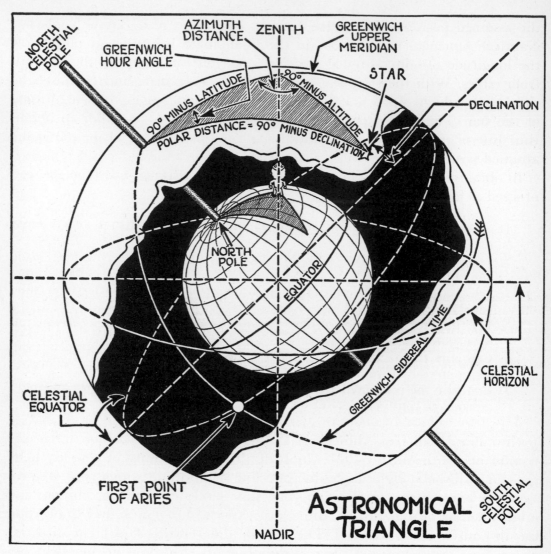

FIG. 303

hour angle because you do not know your longitude, and you cannot obtain the azimuth of the star because no way has yet been developed to measure the azimuth from a fast-moving airplane. From your actual position the triangle is undefinable.

Now let's see what happens if you assume a position. You can obtain the "90° minus latitude" side of the triangle because you know the latitude of

334

the assumed position. The polar distance side you already know from your Nautical Almanac. You can obtain the hour angle because you now know the longitude of your assumed position, and you can compute the azimuth from tables. With these values you can solve the triangle and compute the third side, which, since it equals 90° minus altitude, gives you the altitude of the star. The two important values which you need in order to obtain your line of position are the azimuth angle and the altitude of the star at the assumed position.

In obtaining a line of position by means of the astronomical triangle, you proceed as follows:

1. Take your bubble sextant (Fig. 304) and measure the altitude of a celestial object.
2. Look at your watch and note the exact civil time at which you have made your observation.
3. Select a geographical position on your map which you believe to be in your general vicinity.
4. For the Greenwich time of observation, find the hour angle and declination from the Nautical Almanac.
5. Compute the azimuth of the star for the assumed position.
6. Compute the altitude of the star for the assumed position.
7. Compare the computed altitude at the assumed position with the observed altitude at your actual position.

Now draw a line on your chart through the assumed position in the direction of the azimuth of the object. This line, the radius of your circle of position, will lie at right angles to your line of position, which, you will remember, represents a small portion of your circle of position. On the azimuth line, lay off the altitude difference expressed in miles, and draw your line of position at right angles. The altitude difference is laid off toward the object from the assumed position if the observed altitude is greater than the computed; away from the object, if the observed altitude is less than the computed.

By repeating the operation for a second celestial body, you can establish a second line of position, and from the intersection of the two lines obtain a fix.

FIG. 304. It has been found by experience that a bubble sextant, such as the Bausch and Lomb instrument shown here, is the most practical for aircraft use. Bausch and Lomb sextants have been used by Lindbergh, Gatty,

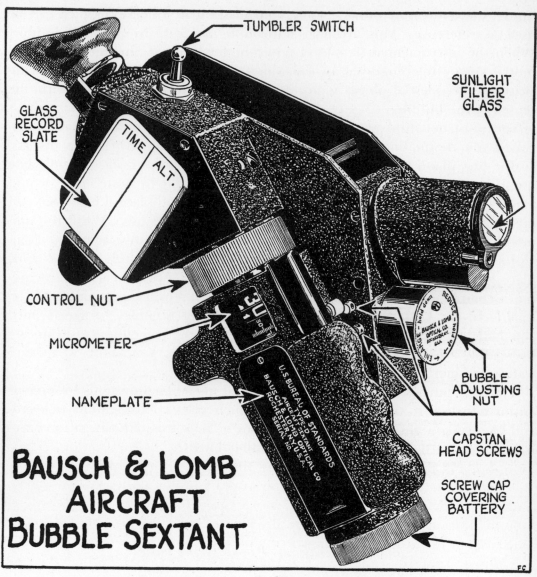

TUMBLER SWITCH

SUNLIGHT
FILTER
GLASS

GLASS
RECORD
SLATE

TIME ALT.

CONTROL NUT

MICROMETER

NAMEPLATE

U.S. BUREAU OF STANDARDS
ARMY TYPE SEXTANT
BAUSCH & LOMB OPTICAL CO
ROCHESTER, N.Y. U.S.A.
SERIAL No.

ENLARGE — hold down — REDUCE
BAUSCH & LOMB
OPTICAL CO.
ROCHESTER
U.S.A.

BUBBLE
ADJUSTING
NUT

CAPSTAN
HEAD SCREWS

SCREW CAP
COVERING
BATTERY

BAUSCH & LOMB AIRCRAFT BUBBLE SEXTANT

FIG. 304

Lincoln Ellsworth, Howard Hughes on his round-the-world flight, and many others.

Altitude is measured from the horizon, but because of haze, darkness, etc., a visual horizon is not always available when you want to make your computa-

336

tions. A sextant must provide some kind of simulated horizon which can be used as reference. This artificial horizon is provided by a round bubble. When the instrument is in a level position, the edge of the bubble is concentric to a circle engraved in the center of the sextant field. In measuring altitude, the celestial object is brought into a position coinciding with the center of the bubble.

You must not think that by studying this brief discussion of celestial navigation you are qualified to go out and navigate your plane by celestial objects. In the first place, this outline gives only the highlights of the system. The question of civil and sidereal time, and their relation to hour angle would make a long chapter if taken up in detail. In the second place, I have confined myself to telling you something about how the stars are used. While the sun, moon and planets are used in the same general way, you must adapt the principles I have outlined to meet their individual eccentricities. In the third place, even if I had given you every detail about celestial navigation, including a complete analysis of the sextant and how it works, you would still be unable to check your position with any degree of accuracy or speed until you had had considerable practice. Learning all the principles of swimming by reading a book of instructions doesn't qualify you, you know, as a deep-water swimmer!

The sole purpose of this chapter, as I said in the beginning, is to serve as an introduction to the fundamentals on which celestial navigation is based, and to give you and Cloudy Joe some idea of how this old navigational aid is being converted into a valuable avigational asset.

Hitherto, the tonnage displacement has had much to say as to Who's Who among the nations. Presently the wing area multiplied by the wing loading will have a marked bearing on a nation's standing.

XXVII

AS I THINK OF IT

MOST flying takes place in the thick of the weather at levels ranging approximately from 2000 to 14,000 feet. The reasons for this low altitude flying are the physical discomfort from lack of oxygen experienced at higher levels and the fact that at present most planes and engines perform best within these limits. But the day is coming when non-stop flights of over 3000 miles will be common, and when cruising altitudes will be raised to substratosphere or even stratosphere levels—say, about 35,000 feet.

This increase in flight levels is being made possible not only through improved airplane design but also through the use of engines, such as the Cyclone engine, which are equipped with more than one speed supercharger. The first, 7.14 to 1 blower-gear ratio of the Wright Cyclone brings its critical altitude to about 6000 feet; the second gear ratio of 10 to 1 carries the critical altitude, during the second stage, to 15,200 feet. As time goes on, further improvements will be made that will bring about still higher critical altitudes.

Another improvement that is of tremendous value to you is the development of a carburetor that is immune to icing, heretofore one of the most serious problems confronting the airman on flights through the overcast.

For flights at substratosphere levels, a more thorough investigation of the upper air levels, and long-range weather forecasting are essential. In the preparation of weather maps, upper air soundings until now have been obtained by sending up a plane equipped with an aerometeorograph. The data which the plane brings down serve as a basis for analyzing and forecasting weather. But these upper air soundings do not extend above 17,000 to 20,000 feet, so that we cannot fingerprint higher atmospheric levels by this method. These higher levels, however, provide extremely valuable data for more accurate forecasting of the weather. The more upper air sounding stations we have, within limits, over a given area, the more samples of the atmosphere we can obtain. Hence there will be more data for the meteorologist to work with.

338

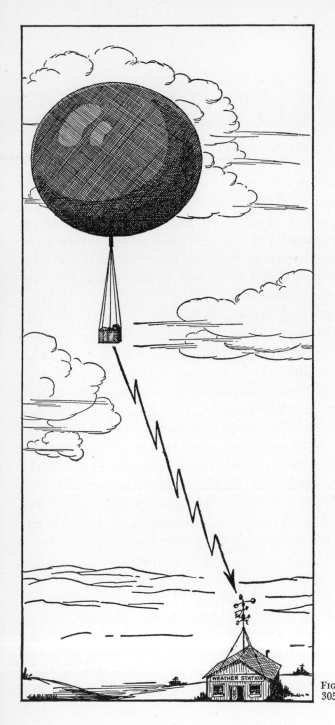

FIG. 305. One of the newest instruments for procuring upper air data is the radio meteorograph developed by the Bureau of Standards in cooperation with Julien P. Friez and Sons. Until recently radio meteorographs were not entirely satisfactory because of high cost, errors in calibration which crept in during shipment, and failure of, or trouble with, various mechanical parts. This new radio meteorograph eliminates these difficulties. It is a miniature radio transmitter which is sent up by balloon from the weather observation station, and, being entirely radio, does not contain clock movements or timing devices which are subject to inaccuracy under low temperatures. As the apparatus passes through various atmospheric levels it automatically radios barometric pressure, air temperature and humidity, and can also be made to record the height and thickness of clouds. In other words, the little radio transmitter and its component parts send back all the information necessary with the same accuracy with which these facts would be obtained by an air-

FIG. 305

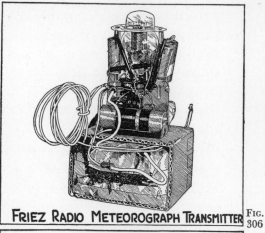

FRIEZ RADIO METEOROGRAPH TRANSMITTER FIG. 306

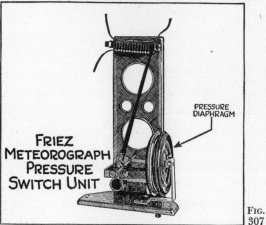

PRESSURE DIAPHRAGM

FRIEZ METEOROGRAPH PRESSURE SWITCH UNIT

FIG. 307

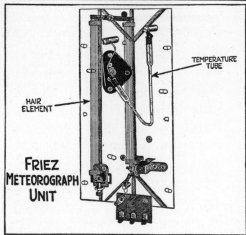

TEMPERATURE TUBE

HAIR ELEMENT

FRIEZ METEOROGRAPH UNIT

FIG. 308

plane equipped for upper air soundings. It has been found that the present accuracy of this method of upper air investigation is within one per cent. This is sufficiently close for any practical application.

Figs. 306 to 310. Various component parts enter into the radio meteorograph. The miniature transmitter (Fig. 306) operates on a dry-cell battery giving continuous radio emission. This transmitter is connected with what we might call the "nervous system" of the radio meteorograph—the pressure switch unit (Fig. 307). The meteorograph (Fig. 308) carries the hair element, which senses the changes in humidity, and the capillary temperature tube. The complete assembly of the meteorograph is shown in Fig. 309 (side view) and Fig. 310. The whole apparatus is enclosed in a corrugated box which is attached to the balloon.

In order to receive the information sent by the transmitter, a special receiving apparatus is required which is tuned to the frequency of the transmitter. This receiver is located at the meteorological observation station, where all the data are automatically recorded on special charts as they are received.

Regardless of how accurate a weather forecast may be, it is utterly impossible for the meteorologist to know the intensity of the vertical air

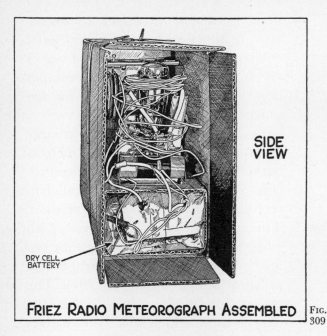

SIDE
VIEW

DRY CELL
BATTERY

FRIEZ RADIO METEOROGRAPH ASSEMBLED

FIG.
309

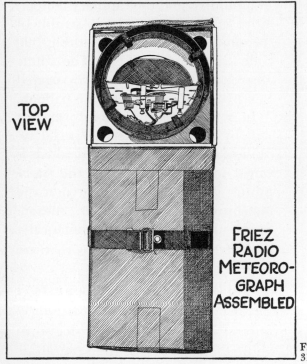

TOP
VIEW

FRIEZ
RADIO
METEORO-
GRAPH
ASSEMBLED

FIG.
310

currents which you will encounter in flight through the overcast or in more or less stormy areas. It has been found by experience that during a flight through a severe storm the plane can be lifted by vertical air currents or lowered several thousand feet within a very short time. This not only causes considerable physical discomfort but produces a severe strain upon the structure of the plane.

While you cannot always avoid passing through stormy areas, you can minimize the roughness of the ride by reducing the cruising speed of your plane. When you are lifted upward, it means that the mass of air surrounding your plane has a vertical motion. If you are quick enough to reduce your relative rate of climb by descending within the lifted air mass, you will find on emerging from the vertical current that your plane will strike the surrounding air with less violence. On the other hand, if the air mass has a downward motion, causing your plane to lose altitude, climb through the vertically moving air mass by using more engine power.

341

KOLLSMAN ACCELEROMETER

FIG. 311

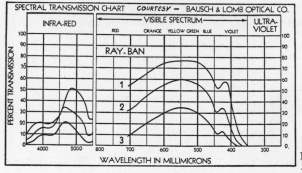

FIG. 312

FIG. 311. The accelerometer shows you the violence of the vertical motions of your plane and gives you constant positive and negative acceleration as well as maximum acceleration reached during flight. This information is valuable after, as well as during a flight, since it shows you whether your plane has been subjected to any unusual stresses. If it has, more careful inspection of the plane's structure should be made.

Whether you are flying in or out of the overcast, the intensity of the light which reaches your eyes is apt to produce eye strain. This trouble can be caused both by direct light and by the light reflected from the upper surface of the clouds, and results in nervous strain and fatigue. It is a good idea, therefore, to protect your eyes during flight with some sort of goggles which give maximum vision and at the same time absorb the violet and also the ultra-violet rays.

FIG. 312. This chart shows how the violet rays are reduced and the ultra-violet rays eliminated by the generally accepted Ray-Ban glasses which seem to give satisfactory results for flight purposes.

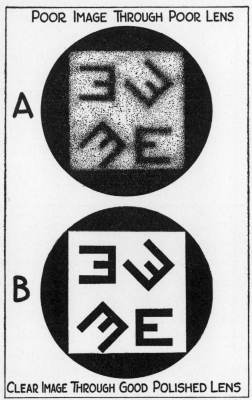

POOR IMAGE THROUGH POOR LENS

A

B

CLEAR IMAGE THROUGH GOOD POLISHED LENS

FIG. 313

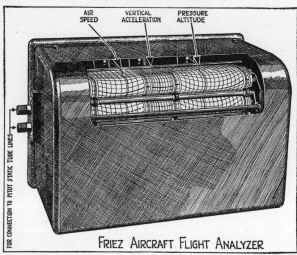

AIR SPEED · VERTICAL ACCELERATION · PRESSURE ALTITUDE

FOR CONNECTION TO PITOT STATIC TUBE LINES

FRIEZ AIRCRAFT FLIGHT ANALYZER

FIG. 314

FIG. 313. While it is important to protect your eyes from unnecessary light strain, be sure that the goggles you wear do not distort or cloud your vision as shown at *A*. Your eyes are among your most important flight instruments, and you need all the information they can give you. Whatever kind of glare-eliminating glasses you wear, their lenses should be of the ground and polished type for the best results.

FIG. 314. A flight analyzer of the type shown here keeps a record of air speed, vertical acceleration and altitudes during a flight. This instrument is particularly helpful if you are concerned with the operation of more than one plane, for you can then study and compare, at the end of simultaneous flights, their respective smoothness of operation at different altitudes. In addition to its altitude, acceleration and airspeed recording pens, the flight analyzer can be equipped with pens for recording other operations of the plane, such as the use of the gyropilot or radio, so that its record becomes a photographic report of the entire journey.

The commercial plane is the outgrowth of the military plane developed during the World War and of the severe testing which it received. The first time the airplane was used for mili-

343

COCKPIT OF THE CURTISS HAWK 75

FIG. 315

CURTISS HAWK 75 PURSUIT AIRPLANE

Courtesy of CURTISS AEROPLANE DIVISION • CURTISS-WRIGHT CORPORATION

FIG. 316

FUSELAGE GUN INSTALLATION - CURTISS HAWK 75

FIG. 317

tary purposes was in 1912 during the Balkan War. It did not prove a deadly weapon, but the eyes of the various nations were opened to its warfare possibilities, if and when sufficient improvements could be made to warrant its use. By the time the World War started, the airplane had become a definite part of the armed forces of all the principal countries.

It is interesting to see how great an improvement has taken place in war planes since those days. There has not been much change in the method of operation, but the effectiveness of the modern war plane is no longer limited by weather conditions and the lack of suitable flight instruments. The flying range of military planes has increased many fold, and their speed today is better than double that of their predecessors.

FIGS. 315 TO 319. The cockpit of a modern pursuit plane differs from that

345

WING GUN INSTALLATION

FIG. 318

of a transport plane in the general arrangement of its instrument board and accessories, owing to special military requirements. The modern pursuit plane provides for two or more machine guns to be placed in front of the occupant where the earlier planes provided space for only one, or at the most, two. Some of the modern pursuit planes also carry additional machine guns in the wings.

During the World War, 30-caliber guns installed on pursuit planes carried 600 rounds of ammunition and fired at the rate of 400-600 shots a minute in full automatic fire. When these guns were synchronized with the propeller, however, they were capable of discharging only 300-450 shots per minute. Present-day pursuit planes such as shown in the previous illustrations carry 30-caliber guns in the fuselage which fire from 600 to 900 shots a minute when they are synchronized with the propeller. Guns installed in the wings usually carry about 500 rounds of ammunition and fire at the rate of 1200 shots a minute. Whenever 50-caliber fuselage guns are used in the modern pursuit plane, they carry approximately 200 rounds or more of ammunition, and the rate of fire is about 450 shots a minute when synchronized with the propeller. When this type of gun is used in the wings, the rate of fire is 600 shots a minute.

While there have been many changes in pursuit planes since the World War, one factor has not changed—the man who mans the airplane. In itself, the modern war plane is a more deadly weapon than the earlier type, but the final effectiveness of any war plane, whether as an offensive or defensive weapon, depends in the same proportion as before upon the skill, ability and intelligence of the airman who flies it. The air tactics which proved effective in the old days still hold good. The best attack is still the one that takes the enemy by surprise. Approaching the enemy from the sun, or out of a cloud bank, is as good strategy as it ever was. The safest place to fly is still very high —or close to the ground even when it means flying over an unfriendly lawn. Last, but not least, it is always a good thing to remember that the other fellow

346

YESTERDAY

......and TO-DAY

Fig. 319

is many times just as scared as you are. If I had only known that during my war days, I would have run home less often!

It is not simply the machine and its fighting qualities that give the advantage to an airman, but understanding human psychology. You must know everything you can find out about your opponent's plane and its performance, but in the final analysis you can outwit your opponent only when you know your opponent. Different nations have their own systems of air strategy and air tactics which they carry out in their own way. But man is the same the world over, and that is the fellow the successful military airman must know just as well as he does his own machine.

While both war and commercial planes have changed considerably and man has not, it is surprising to see how this unchanging man has adapted himself to the changes brought about between yesterday and today. Flights that were inconceivable undertakings yesterday are common practice today, and the immense changes that have taken place in the past few years make it all the easier to visualize the possibilities which the air ocean offers mankind of tomorrow.

INDEX

INDEX

354

DATE DUE

23 FEB '87			
GAYLORD			PRINTED IN U.S.A